Howard Smith
90 Icknield Rd Luton
Beds

March 1943.

BRITAIN'S MODERN ARMY

ILLUSTRATED

*An authoritative account of the daily life of a
modern soldier and of the work, weapons
and machines of the Army*

ODHAMS PRESS LIMITED, LONG ACRE, LONDON, W.C.2

BRITISH TANKS IN THE DESERT

Tanks form the spearhead of a modern army in attack. These Matildas are advancing across the Libyan desert with Army Co-operation and bomber aircraft flying overhead

CONTENTS

COASTAL GUN AT PRACTICE

Around the shores of Britain the coastal guns are ever on guard against invaders. Practice
is an important matter and this crew is hard at work improving the accuracy of its fire.
When the gun is in action, rather than at practice, there would be fewer men in the gun-pit

INTRODUCTION

For the first time this book tells the story of what Britain's modern Army does and how it does it. In simple terms, yet with a full and accurate description of technical details, the functions of all the various branches of the Service are described.

The waging of modern land warfare is a difficult art. Within living memory, science and industry have changed the pattern and form of fighting power. Though it has become a matter of machines, the proper use of modern machines and weapons demands the finest type of man the country can produce. The more mechanized the Army becomes, the less mechanical must its members be. Alertness of mind, power of leadership and sound judgment are more essential than ever before. It is well, therefore, to realize that only the highest technical training can produce the first-class soldiers necessary.

These trained men will fight better and be more efficient soldiers if to a precise knowledge of their own particular branch of the Army is added an appreciation of the work done by other arms. Moreover, to the many thousand junior officers who are daily instructing their troops, this book will provide much useful material for talks. The whole organization of the Army today is a complex one; it is also closely linked in action with the other fighting Services. A fuller understanding by each Service of the part played by the others is an essential step towards closer co-operation.

Much land fighting has taken place; much more is certain to follow. It is the Army which has to hold the bases from which the Royal Navy and the Royal Air Force operate. Only the highest standards of military efficiency and discipline will bring victory. In modern warfare, co-operation is invaluable. Just as the three fighting Services are learning to work together and to appreciate each other, so the public, too, should strive to understand their work. In this way, instead of remaining uninformed critics and onlookers, we shall all become more intelligent and actively useful cogs in the total war machine.

GETTING TO CLOSE QUARTERS

The whole of the training of Britain's modern Army cultivates initiative and the offensive spirit. Even in a war of machines, the use of the bayonet is still of very great importance

CHAPTER 1

The Daily Life of a Soldier

Recruits join up. An old soldier's advice. The issue of kit. Hut cleaning and bed making. Army food. Unarmed combat. Drill. Weapon training. Recreation. Punishment and fatigues. Tattoo. Lights out

SOMEBODY says "Recruits." Old sweats about the barracks—seasoned, sand-blasted men, all legs and backbone, who have in their time played some grim games with short bayonets against long odds in hottish corners of the Empire—turn their hard-bitten faces and look.

There is the inevitable mutter of un-complimentary comment. "What is the Army coming to? . . . Are these men or mice?—Or what are they? . . . Thank God we've got a Navy . . ." It is perfectly true that we don't look particularly mili-tary. We come in at a very civilian walk—a strangely assorted bunch in all kinds of clothes, with fibre boxes or tin cans con-taining respirators slung over our shoul-ders and little parcels of personal kit in our hands. A veteran, whose bosom is as colourful with medal ribbons as a victory celebration, says: "If 'Itler could see them recruits, I bet 'e'd sign a peace by Wednesday—'e'd be frightened out of 'is life." Another, with a complete fruit salad of decorations, adds: "So why should Britain tremble, eh, Bert?"

THE ARRIVAL

We are shown into a dim, vast room, clean and terrifying as an operating theatre. Another scared group of new-comers that arrived an hour or so before, is waiting, killing time, sitting on the edges of long forms and worrying about the disposal of cigarette ends.

There is one man here who is obviously no stranger to the place. All the other beds are cold-looking, and temporary. His looks used. It has a kitbag at its foot, and his open locker contains something made of khaki cloth. A greatcoat hangs on one of his pegs. His eye is severe but calm. His right hand, which is tattooed with a complicated blue snake, toys with a tobacco pouch. He says:

SOUND ADVICE

"Find yourselves a place. Put your things down. You all look as if you were going to be shot at dawn. Maybe you are going to be. But stop looking like it. Come round here. Come on, come round here. I won't bite you. I wouldn't bite you if you paid me—and I've bit some pretty terrible stuff in my time . . .

"That's the stuff. Come right round me. Now listen. You all look horrible. You look like little boys just arriving at Borstal. You look frightened. Well, that's only natural. I daresay when I first came here twenty years ago I looked a bit frightened, too—but I hope I never looked anything like you bunch. Well, you'll get used to it. You'll even get to like it, after a time. You've come here to be soldiers. That's right, isn't it? And if there wasn't a war on, most of you would never have dreamt of coming into the Army. Eh? All right. Now you're here, you've got to muck in and make the best of it, and put your heart and soul into it, and beat Jerry from hell to breakfast. It'll take plenty of hard work. Then you can all go back to Civvy Street.

CULTIVATING THE OFFENSIVE SPIRIT

A British soldier is trained to attack. This party of men is practising the crossing of a stream behind a smoke-screen. Automatics and bayonets are both used in modern assaults

"But while you're here, you've got to forget Civvy Street. You've got to forget your way of living in Civvy Street, and get hold of the Army way of living. You've got to forget your civvy way of doing things, and do things the Army way. The Army's got its own ways and manners: you've got to pick them up and get them by heart. Do just what you're told, and you'll have nothing on earth to worry about. We don't handle men rough any more: that's a thing o' the past. Ride with the Army machine, and you're okay. Go against it, and you're fighting a steam roller. The first week is always the toughest in anything new. I'll tell you what happens, so you won't get lost."

The old soldier rolls a cigarette and continues with the voice of experience:

"The British soldier is a funny creature. You can't mass-produce him like you can the Jerry. He comes out of Civvy Street with no more notion of soldiering than of flying. And after a bit of training he'll fight like a stag. He pretends he doesn't take kindly to discipline, but he does—to the kind of discipline we dish out, anyway. Your instructor will tell you all about that, though. I'll just give you a rough idea of what you have to do.

"CIVVY" BECOMES SOLDIER

"First of all they cut your hair. Soldiers have all got to look alike, more or less, so it'll be cut off short, that being the quickest and smartest way. Then you'll be inoculated against tetanus, and all that. Then you'll go and draw your kit, and put on battle-dress and ammunition boots, and send your civvy clothes home and forget about 'em.

"Then you start to be soldiers. Some of you are smart. Some of you are thick. Some of you are reliable. Some of you ain't. It takes all sorts to make an army. We take it for granted that you're all absolutely ignorant of things, and for the first go off you're treated like children. Don't mind that. You won't go anywhere alone. You'll have no initiative, at first. You'll be marched along to your bath and watched while you have it. You'll be told in advance every little thing you've to do. That's until you get the hang of things, so don't be impatient about it.

"For the first few weeks you'll be hammered into shape with a lot of drill. It isn't the actual hard work that might get you down, so much as being yelled at all the time by your sergeant. Learn to take it. When you do your movements properly you won't get chased. You have to learn to react—pst! Just like this match lighting!—to the voice of the man in command. That makes for efficiency—

and anyway, if you don't like it, you can lump it. See? Again: grub. A lot of you'll find the food is lousy, at first—not what you get at home. Well, all soldiers are fed the same. A certain sum of money per man per day is allotted for food: you get fed to the extent of that; no more, no less. Much as fellers grumble, most of 'em put on weight when they join the Army; and those that lose weight, lose only fat.

AIRING GRIEVANCES

"If you've got any legitimate grumble coming, you can go and grumble to the officers if you want to. Any man can see his company commander and air a grievance. You'll find things are severe, but absolutely fair in this Army. It's just a matter of getting the routine.

"You've got to live to the bugle. That's your clock, from now on. It'll wake you

PRACTISING THE CROSSING OF WIRE OBSTACLES

Wire is still an effective weapon of defence. If it is not broken by gunfire or other means, infantry have to improvise their own way of crossing it. Here ladders and mats are being used

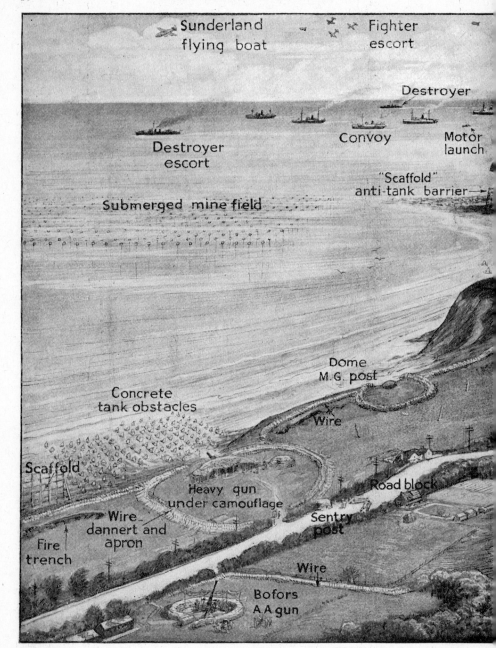

Sunderland flying boat

Fighter escort

Destroyer

Destroyer escort

Convoy

Motor launch

"Scaffold" anti-tank barrier—

Submerged mine field

Dome M.G. post

Concrete tank obstacles

Wire

Scaffold

Road block

Heavy gun under camouflage

Sentry post

Wire dannert and apron

Fire trench

Wire

Bofors A.A. gun

AN IMAGINARY AREA OF BRITAIN'S COAST

One of the objects for which a British soldier trains is the defence of his home country.
Here are seen, in imaginative manner, some of the defence methods employed. The sea is
mined, the beaches are protected against tanks, and the shore is defended by guns and

AND VARIOUS METHODS OF DEFENDING IT

machine guns. Roads inland are mined and there are numerous A.A. guns, searchlights and barrage balloons to hinder enemy air attack. Off the coast steams a convoy under its own aerial and naval escort. The strongest defences are near ports essential to an invading enemy

up at about six. It'll call you to breakfast, and warn you a quarter of an hour before each parade. It'll tell you when your dinner-time begins and ends, and when you're finished for the day. It'll warn you of air raids, and give you the All Clear when they're over. If you've got to see the company commander or the commanding officer, it'll call you out for Orders. It'll tell you when you've got to switch the lights out. Do just what that bugle says, when it says. You'll be doing right.

THE DAY'S WORK

"You'll be On Parade from about eight in the morning to around half-past four in the afternoon. After that, you're free, except for your cleaning. You're expected to keep yourself and your kit in apple-pie order. In fact, you've *got* to. You won't have a great deal of time to be homesick in. Personally, I like the Army: you do your job and you know where you stand, and you can't get the sack, and you're sure of your grub and your holidays. In peace time, that is. But there's a war on now. No time must be lost. They've got you here to make soldiers out of you as quickly as possible.

"You've got to mould yourself to the everyday life of the soldier. They make it as easy for you as they can, but it's mostly up to you. Remember that. In a few minutes you'll be taken out for your first Army haircut. But bear in mind what I've said. *You've got to mould yourselves to the Army day.* Do that and you'll be all right."

THE QUARTERMASTER'S STORE

The old soldier puts on his blouse. He is a lance-corporal. He rises. He says: "Now come and be soldiers." We follow him to the barber's shop.

With the clippings of his first haircut, a recruit leaves behind him all that is left of the civilian. From the receiving station he goes to the medical officer for inoculation, and to the quartermaster's store.

It isn't in the least like the quartermaster's store in the song. There is no confusion here, but a severe and cold efficiency that comes of perpetual checking, double-checking and book balancing. We pass through; are each given a dark kitbag, into which goes item after item of the kit with which we are issued. We receive a greatcoat, two suits of battledress, two pairs of boots, a pair of rubbersoled slippers, three shirts, three pairs of socks, two pairs of underpants, a pair of gym shorts, two gym vests, a woollen stocking hat for use as a cold weather head protector or as a general utility bag for little articles, two caps, a suit of denim overalls for dirty work, a canvas holdall for brushes and razor, a knife, fork and spoon, a housewife containing needles and thread and spare buttons, two towels. Later, the company quartermaster's store will issue us with rifle, bayonet, water bottle, brushes for boots and shaving, a razor with an unusable blade.

FULL EQUIPMENT

Then comes equipment—a big pack, a small pack, two ammunition pouches, a frog to hold the bayonet, an arrangement of straps for the water bottle, the braces which link everything with everything else, and the belt which constitutes the foundation and the anchor of all the rest.

The N.C.O.s and men concerned with the distribution of equipment move with a rough, but deadly accuracy and thoroughness. We are fitted with respirators before we have time to think of what is happening. Later on, having been instructed in the use of these respirators, we will be led into a murky, smoky little chamber, gas-masked and unrecognizable; and there we will be told to breathe. We'll smell nothing. Then the sergeant in charge will order us to take our respirators off. Instantly something will bite at our eyes and nostrils: tear gas. This will be ultimate proof that the protection afforded by the service respirator is really perfect.

Meanwhile, back in our hut, we are at once instructed in the daily procedure of the private soldier.

The hut is big and bleak. It contains a stove, some cleaning utensils, a coal box, and thirty beds. A bed, we observe, is made of three planks on two trestles and a straw mattress. Old soldiers prefer the firm resilience of the planks to the gentler pressure of springs. But one inevitable fact remains: we are to like it—or lump it.

the last note has sounded. Fifty yards away stands a washhouse, with about sixty basins. Many more than sixty men will want to wash and shave there before breakfast. Some men get up ten minutes before reveille, so as to perform their toilets in comfort. By ten past six that washhouse will be packed. Men will be washing and shaving at high pressure, while others wait beside their basins. There is no time to waste. Everybody must wash and shave before cookhouse

A RECRUIT'S ISSUE OF KIT

This recruit is being issued, in the open air, with the many articles of his Army kit. A soldier is personally responsible for always having them at any later kit inspection

"Forget Civvy Street. Here, you're your own washer woman and maid-of-all-work," says the corporal. He has a hard face but a kind eye like most old soldiers. Sitting cross-legged on a bed, he tells us what we will have to do.

The bugle will call us at six in the morning. We are to be out of bed before

sounds. Then beds are to be "made up."

The mattress — or the "biscuit" — is folded in two, with the bent edge outwards. One blanket is folded into a long rectangle. The other three are folded, one by one, to about an eighth of their size, placed on the oblong, and slapped down tight. The long piece is wrapped round, the ends are tucked out of sight, the pillow is tamped into the odd few inches of space behind; and so the bed becomes a hard, compact parcel. Then the hut has to be swept and dusted. "Swabbing jobs" are distributed and taken in turn. Every man sweeps his own bed area. Two others sweep the scattered piles of dust into one heap, which one man takes to the incinerator. Others polish the fire-buckets, coal tub and stove; pull all beds into line, arrange kit-bags in their prescribed positions, dust ledges, see that fire-buckets are filled, scavenge the area about the hut for cigarette packets and waste paper, stack blackout screens. In twenty minutes the hut shines with an unbelievable, absolute, mass-produced cleanliness.

We, also, must have no loose end of hair or patch of skin which soap and water may have missed. It is made quite clear that we'll be extraordinarily lucky if we get away with anything of that sort, even once. Greatcoats and gas capes must be hung on their proper pegs, and folded into taut smoothness. Towels must be folded "into four," and always hung neatly with the number outwards.

A SOLDIER'S NUMBER

Every soldier has a number. It's more important than his name, for identification. There can be ten men of the same name in a company; but no two of the same number. Every item of kit must be stamped with this number, if only for the protection of the person who owns it. "Things have a habit of disappearing in the Army," says the corporal. That is to say, if a soldier is short of, say, a pair of socks, and happens to see a stray pair lying about, he is apt to pick them up. It

"COME TO THE COOKHOUSE DOOR, BOYS"

We take our knives, forks, spoons and mugs, and go to our restaurant

isn't stealing; it is "scrounging," which is somehow rather different, though utterly forbidden by regulations.

The hut is off our minds. In the course of the morning the company commander will come round to look at it, accompanied by the sergeant-major, or the orderly sergeant with his dreadful "book." Untidiness is bad discipline: a crime. Crime, in the army involves swift punishment. Punishment involves physical discomfort—fatigues, drills, loss of liberty. The argument is: it is much more comfortable in every way to be tidy and clean in one's personal habits.

"YOU'VE GOT TO LIVE TO THE BUGLE"

The bugle is the soldier's clock. It regulates his daily life

Cookhouse sounds *Come to the cookhouse door, boys,* the best-known call in the world. We take our knives, forks, spoons, and mugs, and go readily to our restaurant.

Food in the Army is variable, but on the whole it maintains a precarious average. In wartime, soldiers, like civilians, eat what they can get. But the diet of the soldier really depends on the purchasing power of his ration allowance.

He has to be fed on what can be bought for the modest allowance agreed upon by the Government. He gets three meals—breakfast, at about seven in the morning; dinner, at midday or twelve-thirty; and tea at five. In peace time, of course, food is more plentiful and varied, because prices and supplies are steadier. If cleanliness in the barrack-room is a religion, in the cookhouse it is a fanaticism. Vegetables are got ready by men on fatigue, under the cold eye of a cookhouse sergeant. Every potato is scoured like webbing before a parade: cabbages are "dug out" until they are as free of grit as cap badges, and almost as bright. The cookhouse must be ready for any surprise inspection. Utensils are burnished like buttons. Tables are scrubbed white. All men employed in cookhouses are subjected, at short intervals, to careful medical examinations.

ARMY FOOD

The quartermaster must balance the menus with his accounts. That means to say: if you get an exceptionally good dinner on Sunday, you are likely to get an exceptionally poor one on Tuesday.

THE BRITISH ARMY

In wartime, ceremonial gives place to reality. (Below) The Trooping of the Colour.

IN WAR AND PEACE
(*Top, left*) *A march-past in battle-dress.* (*Top, right*) *An armoured division on parade*

Breakfast might consist of a rasher and a half of bacon, one and a half slices of bread and margarine, porridge and tea. Or, instead of bacon, there might be "bags of mystery"—two small sausages, of a special army pattern: a kind of short Lee-Enfield sausage. A typical dinner would include meat, potatoes, greens or beans, and "duff," which might mean boiled rice or fruit tart, but most often consists of some kind of plain pudding. It all depends on what can be bought, and for how much. Meat might be stew, eked out with swedes and carrots; or, once in a while, roast beef. It is most likely to be stewed and then baked under a crust. Tea, also, is an incalculable meal. It has been known to include eggs and chips. More generally, there is some sort of pie or pasty, or meat roll, with two slices of bread and mar-garine, a little jam, and, naturally, a pint of strong tea in a mug. While nobody complains of overfeeding, nobody has any reasonable grouse about starvation.

FOOD GRUMBLES

Food is brought to the long scrubbed tables in square containers. Plates are distributed from a pile previously stacked up by the messmen. The men who happen to be sitting at the top of the table distribute the contents of each container in twelve equal portions. We eat under the eye of the quartermaster, who walks round to see that everything is running to order, and that the distribution of food is even. All must feed alike.

In the Army a man gets the habit of eating, without argument, whatever is placed in front of him, and of grumbling

AN ARMY FIELD KITCHEN

Great care is taken over Army food in the field as well as at home, though conditions are harder. Here is a joint being cooked in the field ovens, while logs are cut in the background

PHYSICAL TRAINING

Instead of dull exercises, physical training now contains many of the elements of games

about it, no matter what it is. Since time immemorial, there has never been any grouser so persistent in his grousing as the serving soldier. Any serious complaint about food is considered and dealt with. The officer comes into the restaurant, and asks: "Any complaints?" Everybody roars "No sir!" But everybody grumbles on in the same breath. Grumbling is the soldier's hobby. After breakfast we get ready for the first parade.

In the Army, any duty is a "parade." The small but serious responsibilities of the man under military discipline are rapidly woven into the life and thoughts of the recruit. The Army becomes his life.

The day frequently begins with physical training, in the open air if the rain holds off. In the old days, the P.T. instructors concentrated entirely on the dreariest kinds of Swedish drill; wearisome bendings and stretchings, which bored most men to tears. Now, while employing highly scientific methods of muscle building, they have introduced an element of play into P.T. Many of the exercises assume the air of games. One thing entirely new to the Army, is unarmed combat, a strenuous pastime.

UNARMED COMBAT

This is a kind of all-in wrestling. It is calculated to make men thoroughly efficient in self-defence against any imaginable opponent, of any weight. Furthermore, it develops individual confidence and courage. We pick partners, and, under the supervision of the instructor, rehearse subtle tricks of roughhouse fighting — arm-locks, hammerlocks, and throws evolved by the masters of ju-jitsu and catch-as-catch-can.

Nobody gets hurt. Naturally enough, muscles get bruised a little, and once in a while a ligament is strained. You can't build a soldier without a few aches and pains. If a man does happen to damage himself—and recruits, raw from civil life, are certain to feel some effects of this new, highly physical existence—his in-

civilian life: he hasn't much of a bedside manner; but he has something better—a desire to get his patient completely cured and back to duty in the shortest possible time. The M.O., with the dental experts and the hospital specialists behind him, helps to maintain a really remarkably high standard of fitness among soldiers.

No sickness, and no possibility of sickness, is ever ignored. X-ray specialists are

LEARNING THE PARTS OF A RIFLE

Weapon training is a most important part of the work of any soldier. This squad is being instructed in the details of the breech and bolt mechanism of their Lee-Enfield rifle

juries, whatever they may be, are dealt with very quickly and efficiently by the medical officer. The first pains of the soldier in the making are nearly always in his feet. The new, heavy boots, or the un-accustomed stamping which drill in-volves, raise blisters. Bruised, skinned, or blistered feet are the commonest casual-ties with which the army medical officer has to deal. He isn't like a practitioner in

always available to settle any dubious point of diagnosis. The idea of fitness has assumed an overwhelming importance in the minds of those who command. They have learned that an army marches not only on its stomach, but on its feet, teeth, throat, liver, heart, lungs and state of mind. The complete soldier must be fit.

Between the physical training instruc-tors and the medical officer, the recruit in

UNARMED COMBAT
Training in the art of self-defence and practice in disarming men makes this important

RECRUITS AT BAYONET DRILL

The fixing of the bayonet is a drill movement. Having replaced it in the scabbard, these
men are pausing to gain uniformity before completing the drill of "unfix bayonets"

the modern army grows fit whether he
likes it or not. He has no alternative.

The parades of the morning go on until
twelve, and every minute is filled.

The modern soldier has to learn many
things. The recruit in wartime has to
learn many things quickly. So much
depends on the rapid and thorough training of reliable man-power. There is, at
first, a great deal of drill. There is more in
drill than at first meets the eye. Quite
apart from the better appearance of well-
drilled men, there is another aspect. Men
trained to instantaneous and accurate re-
action to a word of command make better
soldiers. Well-drilled men march better
and acquire a greater reliance on each

other. They fight better, therefore, being
more mobile and better disciplined.

The drill movements are hammered
into us until they become almost instinctive. Hour after hour, day after day, tire-
less and patient, the instructor goes over
and over the wheels, forms, turns and
halts, and the numerous movements in
arms drill whereby one becomes completely familiar with the feel of rifle and
bayonet. We learn to salute, also, since
correctly timed and placed saluting is part
of the essential machinery of good military
discipline and manners. Then, more
important still, comes weapon training.

Drill is designed to teach us how to
march, and carry our weapons with

firm precision. Weapon training teaches us how to use them to the best effect.

First, we are taught the names of the parts of the rifle, together with their function. The sergeant explains the Short Lee-Enfield, screw by screw. He tells us how to clean it, for rifle cleaning is a necessary part of every soldier's daily routine, and a dirty rifle is, like insubordination, unforgivable. It is our best friend, we are warned, and must be treated as such—with exquisite care.

No British soldier is allowed to forget the occasional value of cold steel in warfare. There comes a time, in every war, when one fights man-to-man; and then arrives the mad moment of the bayonet. The fixing of the bayonet is a drill move-ment. But the use of it is among the very few things in the Army that permit of individual handling. We are taught how to come "On Guard," and how to make that deadly little three-inch stab at throat, breast, stomach or groin; how to parry, right or left; bring round the savage butt-stroke to head or jaw, and make a kill. But beyond the skeleton of prescribed method, the modern soldier uses his bayonet as it suits him, and according to his size and reach. Unorthodoxy is very useful here.

We must also know that wicked little iron egg called the hand grenade. We are instructed, first, with dummies; we learn what makes them deadly, and how they work. Soon, gingerly putting in our first fuse, and screwing back the base plug, we

BAYONET PRACTICE

No British soldier is allowed to forget the occasional value of cold steel in warfare. Much practice is necessary on dummies to render determined bayonet thrusts instinctive

shall throw live bombs and see them fall, and hear the vicious bang of their explosion and the whine of jagged fragments overhead. An invigorating experience.

Soon, also, we shall feel the strong, curiously liquescent recoil-that-is-not-a-recoil of the Bren Gun firing in savage bursts. But now, we must know the Bren from foresight-blade to butt-strap—all the diabolically clever yet divinely simple processes of the mechanism that makes up the deadliest of light machine guns. We must get the feel of it; learn to run with it, place it, correct it if it stops, and change its hot barrel in the minimum possible number of seconds.

We shall feel, also, something of the ruthlessness of the gangster, when we handle the evil-looking blue Tommy Gun. We shall learn the joyous little explosion of the mortar, and see its cylindrical bomb sail away and burst in a cauli-flower heart of dust and smoke five hundred yards away. But in the meantime, day by day, between the foot-aching routine of drill and the good clean fatigue of physical training, we have to acquire knowledge of these weapons, by dummies and diagrams explained in detail by the indefatigable sergeant.

LESSONS IN FIELDCRAFT

He also, with an officer, will teach us how to move in open country. We shall learn something of tactics, night operations, trench digging and field engineering, map reading, and the incredible business of camouflage, by means of which we may, like men in a fairy tale, clothe ourselves in invisibility.

The routine of the recruit is, at first, taken up with learning the rudiments of the things he'll simply have to know. In the peace time Army, the soldier must

PRACTISING AN ASSAULT

We shall throw live bombs and see them fall and hear the vicious bang of their explosion

A CAMOUFLAGED SNIPER
Here is a fine example of a man effectively dressed to tone with the surrounding country

attend school and acquire a certain standard of education. In war, there is no time for that: the education of the soldier is purely and simply soldiering. There's a lot to teach him, and not much time for him to learn it in. Most of it can be taught directly. The rest he learns, so to speak, as he walks and breathes in the camp. He learns the habits and manner of speech of the soldier, as the baby learns the habits and manner of speech of the man. Imperceptibly, he becomes military. There's no clearly defined frontier between the state of the recruit and that of the full-blown soldier. It simply comes to him in the atmosphere of the hut and the square. He walks differently, talks differently and thinks differently. He can't see the change himself; but his sergeant can. It is the reward of his labours.

After seven or eight weeks, it is usually said of the recruit that he is beginning to look something like a soldier.

OFF-DUTY RELAXATION

Having eaten and drunk things military with his daily bread, lived to the bugle, heard and spoken of nothing but things that concern the army, his air and attitude have altered. He has forgotten the feel of shoes and ties. He is one with his regiment. He has become part of the whole.

Only the evenings ever belong to the individual, in the army.

The day officially ends about five in the afternoon. But there are still some

THE EFFECT OF CAMOUFLAGE

A soldier in battle-dress is here contrasted effectively with one in an "observer suit"

things left to do. Equipment must be got ready for the following day: gaiters must be cleaned, boots polished, webbing "dug out." But in due course, slow and ruminative on relaxed legs, the soldier tries to amuse himself.

The N.A.A.F.I.—"Naffy"—provides a kind of background for comradeship off parade. Tea and "wads," beer and pies, can be got quite cheaply, and consumed in an atmosphere of khaki, in which somebody very often gets a tune out of a piano, and somebody sings. The same excellent institution provides comfortable reading-rooms and good libraries. The stout-hearted artistes of E.N.S.A. move always from camp to camp, providing very good entertainment for nothing, or

next to nothing. And again, there is always the battalion concert. Out of the mass of recruits there always emerge some entertainers. Sergeants sing—sometimes resembling eagles trying to chirp. Ammunition boots are changed for thin shoes: soldiers dance. Sometimes, some ambitious master-mind gets a cast together and produces a play. It all has to be squeezed into odd moments. Duty and entertainment in the Army keep severely apart. A rehearsal is "no excuse for anything." The R.S.M. will take a severe view of any kind of neglect of the most trivial duty—but you may revenge yourself in a skit upon him at the next concert: though it is more than likely that he will laugh quite as loudly as anybody else. He remembers his own early days.

On parade, in the Army, nobody is quite human. Off parade, everybody is, somehow, quite remarkably human.

MILITARY LAW

The rules of the Army are dangerous things to break. In the course of his daily life, the modern soldier must constantly watch himself—watch himself, until correct observance of military law and procedure becomes second nature.

Early in his Army life the recruit is made familiar with matters pertaining to crime and punishment. Drunkenness, desertion, neglect of duty and stealing are among the gravest of crimes—apart from such monstrous things as treason, espionage and cowardice—of which, thank God, very few of us might ever be guilty. Army law is gentle, up to a point. It makes allowances. Absenteeism does not become the major crime of desertion before a certain number of weeks. The new recruit is always given the benefit of any doubt. A wide margin is allowed for possible ignorance of what is right and proper. But let it once become apparent that a man is a "chancer," and he finds himself caught in the cogs of a machine from which there is no escape. He may get away with things once or twice—make excuses that afterwards expose themselves as flagrant lies, and still get away unpunished. But his moment comes. Extra drills, extra fatigues, and C.B. constitute the most commonly inflicted punishments. It's possible to avoid them; but there is scarcely a soldier in the British Army who has not, at some time or other in the course of his service, "got in the book" for something in the way of a trivial offence. Time wipes many little delinquencies off a soldier's conduct sheet. There is many a stately sergeant-major who has been a hell-raiser in his time, and nobody thinks any the worse of him for that.

A soldier is born into trouble as the sparks fly upwards: it is part of his every-day life. A drill here, a fatigue there, a few days of C.B. are all in the day's work. He learns to take whatever comes to him with a perfect equanimity. Discipline is severe, but not too severe. If he wants to be lawless, he knows in advance that he has to pay for it; and so, when his punishment comes, takes it and pays it off.

It's the daily life—the atmosphere—that makes the finished soldier, far more than scheduled training.

In peace time, the recruit signs on for a period of years—so many to serve, and so many on the Reserve. Nearly all soldiers in wartime sign for the duration. Many men have taken to the Army as a career, a job. As the platoon sergeant wisely said to us:—

"You get regular pay. You get plenty of holidays with pay and cheap travel by

LOADING A THREE-INCH MORTAR

Practice in the use of mortars is part of infantry training. Good team work is vital

BRITISH SOLDIERS EMBARK FOR SERVICE ABROAD

"You see the world. You go abroad to India, or China, or Africa. . . ." In peace time or war the British soldier becomes an experienced traveller in all parts of the world

rail. You get your clothes, board, lodging and washing free. You see the world. You go abroad to India, or China, or Africa. If you want to work, you can take a corporal's class, and become a lance-corporal, and so start on the way up and up towards the highest kinds of promotion. After twenty-one years you get a pension. You have to be very bad indeed before they give you the sack. If you want to be an officer, and can pass the examinations, there's nothing in the world to stop you. It's a democratic army. If any man-jack of you sets his heart upon being a general, there's no earthly reason why you shouldn't become one. Use your heads, do your duty, and live reasonably like good soldiers should. Then you'll be all right."

The day ends. At nine o'clock—tattoo—the orderly sergeant comes in, yells: "Stand to your beds," and looks to see if we are all here. We are. He goes away. Talk breaks out again. The end of the day finds us in a thoughtful mood.

We talk of many things: of war, and peace, and homes, and people. But in the end we talk only of the Army. All talk leads back to that in the end. It has been a day. We have got through it. Every day that comes and goes will settle us a little more comfortably into the new, strange way of life. Civvy Street is far away.

We have "made down" our beds; trousers and battle blouses laid out to crease between the folds of the long-folded blanket; one blanket doubled between two more laid on singly, the whole tucked in tidily; the hard little sausage of pillow neatly tied up in the coarse whitish pillowslip—everything set for sleep. We lazily consider the future.

One of us announces his intention of signing on for seven years. He wants to be one of the men that Kipling wrote about: a swaggering sergeant under a tropical sun. The Army has got into his blood.

Another wants to be a cook. A third wonders what it is like to be a military policeman. Two more decide that they are going to try and "take tapes," be N.C.O.s. A quiet boy says he proposes to make inquiries about being sent to an O.C.T.U., where officers are trained.

We climb into bed. The scrubbed wooden boards give springily. They will have to be scrubbed again on Saturday, when we swab the entire hut.

"When you come to think of it," says a little Londoner, "it's a busy life, ain't it? You don't really get much time to be homesick in. Do you, mate?"

Even if one could think of nothing else, that is one of the advantages of our new, peculiar daily life. The day being over, we want to sleep.

Lights Out blows.

Eight hours of sleep between now and reveille—and then, another day. . . .

FINAL THOUGHTS

This then is the life of a British soldier. It is a strenuous life, perhaps an unnatural one—but it has great attractions. Men become fit and proud of their fitness. Their minds are quickened and their powers of leadership have plenty of scope. Gone are the days of bullying and blind obedience. Modern warfare demands intelligence and initiative—the army tries to develop both. A soldier's work today is something of which a man may be proud.

A TROOP CONCERT

These troops are listening to some of their own companions entertaining them in the field. A surprising amount of "local talent" always comes to light among the ranks of any unit

TROOPS MARCHING OUT FROM CAMP

Our highly organized Army often begins the day with a brisk march to the parade ground

CHAPTER 2

Organization and Control

Committee of Imperial Defence. The composition of the Army Council and the duties of its members. Army Commands at home and abroad. Infantry and motorized divisions. Armoured divisions. Corps and Armies. The National Army. Officers and N.C.O.s. Dominion troops

I N Britain, war policy is laid down by the Cabinet or by a smaller body selected from and representing the Cabinet. Where naval, military or air matters are in question it is usual to call into consultation the head of the Service concerned. In fact, it is rare in total war that any question of policy that concerns one Service is not of concern to all three Services. Co-operation is vital.

In peace time the larger defence questions of the day were studied in detail by the Committee of Imperial Defence. Usually presided over when in full formal session by the Prime Minister or by the Minister of Defence as his deputy, this body delegated most of its work to technical sub-committees, on which expert opinion was fully represented. One of the permanent sub-committees working under this system before the Second World War, was that comprising the three heads of the fighting services, known as the Chiefs of Staff Sub-Committee. This, in technical terms, acted as "a Combined Chief of Staff in commission." It was the body responsible to the Minister of Defence (who often presided at its meetings) and through him to the Government, for professional advice on all matters concerning war and preparations for war. As regards the Army, its representative on this sub-committee was the Chief of the Imperial General Staff, who is the military head of the British Army and the successor to the former office of Commander-in-Chief.

The control of the British Army is now vested in the Army Council. This is a combined body of military and civil members, presided over by the Secretary of State for War and *collectively* responsible for advising him in all measures of higher military policy. In addition to this collective responsibility, the members of the Army Council *individually* act as the heads of various departments of the War Office and of the Army. They are concerned each with one particular branch of military organization and activity. Thus, of the three military members, the Chief of the Imperial General Staff, besides being the senior professional adviser of the Secretary of State, is in charge of war plans and of the whole general conduct of war in its broadest sense. (Fig. 1.)

C.I.G.S.'s DUTIES

He is responsible for what forces must be raised and maintained if the military policy of the Government in peace or war is to be carried out. He laid down or supervised the training plans of the whole army, officers and men, Regulars, Territorials and Militia, as they existed before September 1939, and also of the new National Army that was later created. He apportions under the overriding authority of the Government the available forces between garrisons, home defence and the various theatres of war, and appoints the higher commanders and staff officers. He maintains relations with the armies of the self-governing Dominions—hence his title of Chief of the Imperial General Staff. His responsibilities, in short, are onerous, widespread, and vital, such as only the very best available British soldier could hope to shoulder with success.

The other military members of the Army Council are the Adjutant General to the Forces, who is responsible for recruiting the men the Army needs, for their organization, for their discipline, and for their moral and physical welfare; and the Quartermaster General to the Forces, whose duty it is to provide everything that the Army requires in order to live. to move and to fight. They furnish

Financial Secretary, who acts as intermediary between the War Office and the Treasury. The latter has to see that the Army gets what money it needs and that the money it gets is appropriately, economically and usefully expended. One of the Under-Secretaries is a permanent one; he is a Civil Servant of tried ability who has risen to his position by long service in the various grades. The other three non-military members are politicians. They change with every successive change of Government and sometimes more often as promotion to higher offices of State comes their way. Such are the composition and duties of the central governing body of the British Army today and such are its members' individual duties.

ARMY COUNCIL

MILITARY MEMBERS	CIVIL SERVICE MEMBER	NON-MILITARY MEMBERS
CHIEF OF THE IMPERIAL GENERAL STAFF	PERMANENT UNDER-SECRETARY OF STATE FOR WAR	SECRETARY OF STATE FOR WAR
ADJUTANT-GENERAL TO THE FORCES		UNDER-SECRETARY OF STATE FOR WAR
QUARTER-MASTER GENERAL TO THE FORCES		FINANCIAL SECRETARY

Fig. 1. *The main sub-divisions of the Army Council are shown above. The only permanent member is the Civil Service member, the others being subject to military and political change*

and care for, replace and repair, all the human and material stuff of which an army is composed. They are men providers, and food and weapon providers, on a scale greater than anything normally known in civil life. Their responsibilities are world-wide, enormous, and vital; those who are chosen for these two high offices must be, and always are, soldiers of outstanding grasp and ability (Fig. 2).

There are also non-military members of the Army Council—the Secretary of State, who is its head and is responsible to the Prime Minister, to Parliament and to the country for the Army and all to do with it; two Under-Secretaries who, in addition to deputizing for him if required, each have various important responsibilities in the War Office; and the

Below the Army Council in order of seniority come the various Commands of the Army at home and abroad. Abroad these commands range in size and importance from the vast area of the Middle East down to small, but often vitally important, local ones such as Malta or Bermuda. At home there are in peace time six large commands and two smaller commands, Northern Ireland and London, which are known as "districts." The six large commands are Aldershot, the first home and chief training area of the British Army; Scottish, covering all Scotland north of the Border; Northern, including the whole of the north-east part of the country as far south as the Wash; Western, covering the northern and western areas from the Border to the

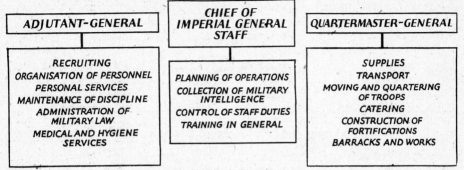

Fig. 2. *The main duties of the three military members of the Army Council are here shown.*
Their work is onerous and only men of exceptional military ability are fitted for it

Bristol Channel; Eastern, including East Anglia, the Home Counties, and the East Midlands; and the Southern, covering all the southern counties between the Straits of Dover and the western mouth of the Channel. These large commands are further sub-divided, mainly for recruiting purposes, into zones and areas. The bulk of the troops quartered in their borders, whether Regular, Territorial or Militia units, are organized in divisions and brigades as they would be if called on to take the field. In addition, all units not included in such formations, all depots and training establishments, and all garrison units, come under the general officer of the command (Fig. 3).

A command is, in fact, an administra-tive area created for purposes of con-venient organization. Areas have different requirements and unequal facilities for accommodation and transport.

Aldershot in peace time, despite its small area, is the most important com-mand of all and its general is usually a picked man—earmarked for command of any field force that may be sent overseas in time of war. Two divisions are usually quartered at Aldershot in peace; one division is stationed in each of the other three main commands, Southern, Eastern and Northern, while the Western and Scottish Commands include fewer units. These are regular troops only: each com-mand also included before the Second World War three or four Territorial

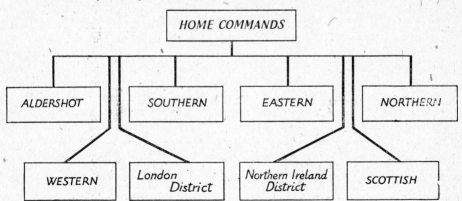

Fig. 3. *The army at home is divided into six main commands and two subsidiary "districts."*
The number of troops in any command varies according to facilities and tactical needs

divisions which just prior to its outbreak were doubled in number. A number of Militia divisions were also being organized, but these were amalgamated in September, 1939 to form the united wartime National Army of the Crown, in which there were neither Regular nor Territorial nor Militia formations.

OVERSEAS COMMANDS

In the overseas commands the same general organization holds good. In the Middle East Command in peace time there were two divisions and a number of non-divisional troops; in some of the smaller garrisons there were only a few coast defence troops and local forces. Generally speaking, the principle governing the size of these overseas commands was that they should be large enough to maintain themselves in case of need until help could be expected to reach them from home. Consideration was, of course, in each case given to the probability and likely scale of attack. Thus Gibraltar, the smallest area of all, had to be strongly held because of its great importance as the guardian of the western gateway of our Imperial sea route to the East via the Mediterranean. On the other hand, the British West Indies and Atlantic islands are so unlikely to form objectives for surprise attack that they are lightly held.

INFANTRY DIVISION

The higher organization of the Army in wartime is superimposed upon, rather than designed to supersede, that of peace. Field forces dispatched overseas are under specially appointed commanders responsible directly to the War Office. The basic formation of the field force is normally the Division. This includes units of all arms, so organized as to enable it, if need be, to carry out an independent operation of war on its own. The exact composition of the British division has varied considerably in detail from time to time, but its main constituents now always include three infantry brigades of three battalions each (making nine in all), a regiment of artillery (in all, seventy-two guns), an anti-tank gun battery, a motor cycle reconnaissance group, a company of engineers, a signal detachment, a field medical unit, and the necessary divisional transport for its supplies and ammunition. The total strength of the division is about 12,000 men at full establishment; its commander is a major-general and under him are three brigadiers for the infantry brigades and one for the artillery.

The motorized division has much the same general organization and composition as one of the normal type. Additional motor trucks and lorries also form part of it, so as to allow of the whole formation being transported for long distances at high speed by road, or for shorter distances at lower speeds across country.

ARMOURED DIVISION

The composition of the armoured division is very different. Its main element is one formed by the two tank brigades which include both heavy and light tanks of the cruiser type; these form the striking and assault portion of this very powerful body. The Divisional H.Q. is armoured and mobile; it has also its own protective screen of scout-cars, and cyclists. For reconnaissance there is a regiment of armoured cars, together with scout-cars, and solo and combination motor cyclists. For mopping up and consolidation there are motorized infantry battalions. To prepare and cover the attack are field, anti-tank and anti-aircraft artillery batteries, and engineer units, which carry mining and bridging equipment. Workshop, light repair and vehicle recovery units are furnished by the Royal Army Ordnance Corps, and a mobile medical unit by the Royal Army Medical Corps. There is, in addition, a full allotment of mechanical transport vehicles for

GALLANTRY MEDALS OF THE BRITISH ARMY

1, Victoria Cross; 2, George Cross; 3, Military Cross; 4, Distinguished Service Order;
5, Military Medal; 6, George Medal; 7, Distinguished Conduct Medal. The official
order of precedence of these medals is V.C., G.C., D.S.O., M.C., D.C.M., M.M., G.M.

the bringing up of supplies, ammunition stores, petrol and spare parts. The total strength of an armoured division is about 10,000 men, though it is variable.

Though these various types of divisions form the main combatant portion of the British Army, they by no means make up the whole of it. There are many other units which stand outside the divisional organization. Among these may be mentioned the army tank battalions, with their infantry tanks; the medium and heavy artillery batteries; the multifarious types of skilled technical engineer com-

Army forward from port or railhead to the points near the fighting zone where divisional transport can take over from them; the heavier ordnance units that have to maintain and repair the fleet of mechanical vehicles with which a modern army cannot dispense; the medical casualty clearing stations and base hospitals, and the huge network of units of all sorts on the line of communications and at the base. So numerous are they that normally their strength will form one-third of a fully modernized and equipped British Army, or half that of the units

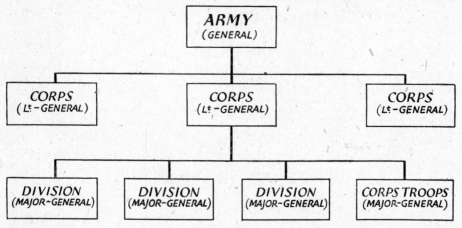

Fig. 4. *Above is shown the upper organization of British Army units. The number of Corps in an Army, or Divisions in a Corps, is variable. Local conditions make this inevitable*

panies; the larger signal units, providing intercommunication between divisions and higher formations; the intelligence detachments that deal with information about the enemy, and the denial to him of information about our own forces; and the larger reconnaissance units that play the role formerly belonging to the independent cavalry. There are many units, moreover, whose normal function is not so much fighting—though this they may also be called upon to do at need—as assisting the purely fighting troops. Among them are numbered the bulk of the supply and transport services, that carry all the varied requirements of the

embodied in the divisions of all types.

Some of these units come under the control of the next higher formations above the divisions, the Army Corps. The corps is a lieutenant-general's command, and usually includes two, three or even four or more divisions, though three is the most usual allotment. In addition, there are at the corps commander's disposal units of medium and heavy artillery, engineers, signals, reconnaissance troops, and a large apportionment of transport, ordnance, medical and other administration services. The total strength of a corps may number from 30,000 to 60,000, the average being about 45,000.

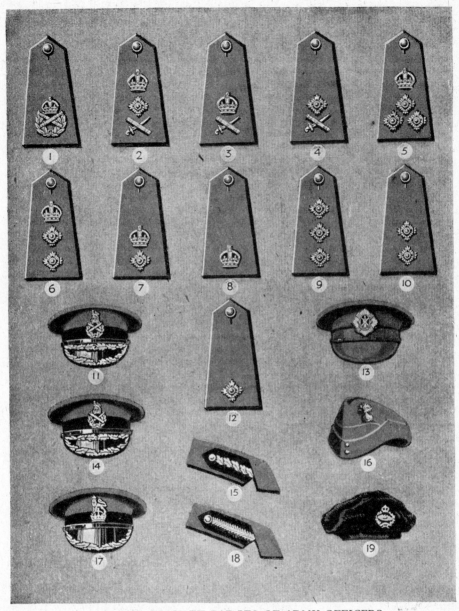

CAPS AND EPAULET BADGES OF ARMY OFFICERS

1, Field Marshal; 2, General ; 3, Lieutenant-General ; 4, Major-General ; 5, Brigadier ; 6, Colonel ; 7, Lieutenant-Colonel ; 8, Major ; 9, Captain ; 10, Lieutenant ; 11, Field Marshal ; 12, Second Lieutenant ; 13, Forage cap ; 14, General ; 15, General (gorget patch on lapel) ; 16, Field service side cap ; 17 and 18, Staff officer below rank of general (gorget patch on lapel) ; 19, Beret, Royal Tank Regiment. A Field Marshal, General, or Staff officer below the rank of general has red cap bands and red gorget patches on lapels

When, as in France at the end of 1914, a British Expeditionary Force numbers more than four corps, a new higher formation is frequently introduced, known as an Army. An army usually comprises anything from two to five corps and in an expeditionary force there may be anything up to five armies. The army is a full general's command, and it too will have an allotment of special troops, mostly heavy artillery, infantry, tank, and engineer and technical units, as well as special administration services of its own. An army may therefore number anything from a quarter of a million men upwards according to the number of corps it contains. It was not until the war of 1914-18 that Britain ever sent overseas enough troops to any one theatre of war to necessitate their formation in armies, and for the expeditionary force that went to France in 1939 a corps organization proved sufficient. The French, the Germans and the Russians in 1914-18 had recourse to a higher formation still, the Group of Armies, but this has never been found necessary in the British Army owing to its smallness of numbers.

PEACE TIME RECRUITING

The peace time method of recruitment of the British Army, both officers and men, was up till six months before the outbreak of the Second World War on a voluntary basis. The Regular Army numbered eight motorized and two armoured divisions. In addition there was the Territorial Army, part-time soldiers who did a number of drills or exercises and spent a fortnight in camp each year. In the spring of 1938 it comprised seven anti - aircraft and nine normal type divisions, with one mobile and three motorized divisions. In March, 1939, when Europe was fast drifting towards war, the decision to double the strength of the Territorial Army to a total strength of twenty-six divisions was taken. In July

of that year, moreover, compulsory service in the Army for young men between the ages of twenty and twenty-one was introduced for the first time in history. Before either of these two measures could take anything like their full effect, the Second World War broke out.

WARRANT OFFICERS

The new British Army in the making was once more refashioned into a great National Army including all Regular, Territorial and Militia units. This grew, with the calling-up for service of age-group after age-group, into a host of men numbering close on four millions. The majority of them are, of course, private soldiers but in between them and the officers come two classes known as non-commissioned and warrant officers. These are specially selected for their powers of leadership, efficiency and knowledge. They draw higher rates of pay and wear special badges. There are various ranks, those from lance-corporal up to company (or other such unit) quartermaster-sergeant, being classed as non-commissioned officers, those further upward to regimental or garrison sergeant-major as warrant officers, who hold a personal "warrant" conferring on them their recognized powers of command. No body of men has a finer tradition or has done better service than have our non-commissioned and warrant officers, "the backbone of the British Army," as they have frequently and rightly been called

COMMISSIONED OFFICERS

Most of the officers of the peace time army were educated at public or secondary schools, and entered one of the two cadet training colleges, the Royal Military College, Sandhurst, or the Royal Military Academy, Woolwich, after a competitive examination. Here they went through an eighteen months' training course, followed in the case of those selected for one

BADGES OF WARRANT OFFICERS AND N.C.O.s

1, Staff Sergeant-Major, 1st class; 2, Regimental Sergeant-Major and other Warrant Officers, 1st class; 3, Warrant Officer, 2nd class; 4, Company or Battery Sergeant-Major; 5, Company Quartermaster-Sergeant; 6, Sergeant; 7, Corporal or Bombardier; 8, Lance-Corporal or Lance-Bombardier; 9, Musketry instructor; 10, Physical Training instructor; 11, Signaller. There are other specialist badges, but they are too numerous for inclusion

BRITISH PARATROOP READY FOR ACTION

Britain is training some of the best of her troops in the specialist arts and duties of the parachutist. When dropping from a transport plane an overall is worn over his uniform. Once on the ground this is discarded and the paratroop, as above, is ready for action

of the mechanical or scientific branches of the Service, by a post-graduate technical course. The necessity for such course was gradually extended with the growth of military mechanization and the increasing application of science to the art of war. Eventually it was the general rule rather than the exception for young officers to undergo some form of such post-graduate training in modern war.

advance knowledge of soldiering from the point of view of the men whom it would afterwards be his duty to lead. The coming of war also brought before the selection boards a far wider choice of suitable candidates drawn into the Army by compulsory service. Regard was no longer paid to the former limitations of age and social standing which had automatically grown up or been officially laid down in

INDIAN TROOPS ON ACTIVE SERVICE

These men are members of the Indian Signals Corps, who have done notable work in the Middle East. Under the supervision of an N.C.O., they are busily collecting their stores

In 1939, the system of the war of 1914-18 was reverted to whereby every future officer had to get his commission through the ranks, a change which had already been approved in principle before the war. This enabled some previous practical judgment to be formed as to the real ability of seemingly suitable candidates. It also gave the young officer-to-be some

peace time. The period of training spent by the officer candidates at the officer cadet unit, of which a good many came into existence all over Britain and the Empire, was short. The large proportion of those who survived this highly intensive and thoroughly practical course might justly regard themselves as the flower of the army and its worthy leaders.

B.M.A.—B*

It is certain that never, save perhaps in the middle and later stages of the war of 1914-18, has any British Army of the past enjoyed so high a standard of leadership.

INDIAN TROOPS

Just as the Army drew on the best latent military talent of the land for its officers, so the influx of the physical and moral pick of the British people into its ranks raised the standard of its peace time recruitment up to a level fully equal to that prevailing in any continental conscript host. This improvement was, of course, essential if the full value was to be got out of the new weapons of war placed at the disposal of the present-day soldier by science and engineering and technical skill. Without trained men to wield them the best of weapons are of no avail.

Apart from the units of the British Army stationed overseas, all the great self-governing Dominions of the British Commonwealth of Nations maintain forces of their own. The Indian peace time army consisted of six divisions, two of which were stationed on the turbulent north-west frontier and four formed a field army available for dispatch overseas.

The Indian military contribution to the British war effort in the Second World War attained large proportions. The total number of Indians under arms soon approached the million mark. Units of the Indian Army played heroic parts in Libya, in Kenya, in Italian East Africa, in

SUDANESE DEFENCE FORCE

Members of this native force protected the southern frontier against the Italians in Abyssinia. They are a highly disciplined body, who fight brilliantly in tropical climate

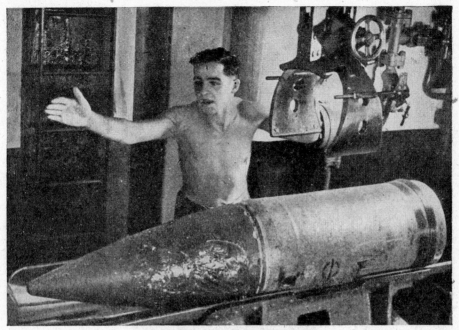

UNDERGROUND SHELL STORE

In some British naval bases the ammunition stores are deep underground. This gunner, stripped to the waist in the clammy heat, is preparing to hoist a shell up to the guns

British Somaliland, and in Syria. They bore the main burden of the operations in Iraq and Persia. They have been stationed in garrisons in Egypt, in Palestine and in Malaya. India's potentialities as an arsenal of man and manufacturing power are in fact capable of limitless development. Their growth is now notably rapid.

DOMINION TROOPS

The contributions of the Dominions of Canada, Australia, New Zealand and South Africa to the Empire military effort also need but little description here. A Canadian corps of three divisions has been quartered in Britain waiting for any German attempted invasion to materialize. Some units went to France, and others had a spell of duty in Iceland, or took part in the expedition to Spitsbergen.

The two Australian divisions and the New Zealand division, after a short period of service in Britain, were sent to North Africa in the autumn of 1939. Their deeds there, and in Greece and Crete, have made their name as world-famous as that of the Anzacs of the war of 1914-18. The South African army shouldered the main burden of the operations which conquered Italian East Africa in a few short spring weeks of 1940. They placed to the credit of British Imperial arms one of the swiftest and most complete victories of their history. A brilliant share in this epic was also taken by the native troops of the King's African Rifles, the West African Frontier Force, the Sudan Defence Force, and many others who proved themselves great fighters.

At the same time, in the Mediterranean, gunners of the Royal Malta Artillery dealt successfully with raiding Italian aircraft and speed boats. Against such Empire unity no foe can in the end prevail.

BRITISH TANK OUTSIDE TOBRUK

An enemy mine exploding in front of one of our tanks. The craters are useful as cover

CHAPTER 3

The Royal Armoured Corps

The cavalry of today. Reconnaissance, security, assault. Tanks used in co-operation with infantry. Tanks used independently. Armoured cars, cyclists, scout-cars. "I" tanks and cruiser tanks. Training of crews and their duties. Aerial co-operation. British tanks in France and Africa

THE Royal Armoured Corps of today is the heir of the cavalry of yesterday. But instead of riding on horses, it is mounted in mechanical vehicles— tanks of various types, armoured cars, scout-cars and motor cycles. Part of it it inherits direct from the old line cavalry regiments. Indeed, all these still form integral parts of the corps as such, and retain their old titles, badges and battle honours. Another part of it, the Royal Tank Regiment, is the descendant of the young Tank Corps of the war of 1914-18. Short as is its history, it yields to none in its pride in the deeds of its fathers and in its will to live up to them.

THREEFOLD DUTIES

The duties of the cavalry of old times, too, have been taken over by the new mechanized horsemen of today. These duties were threefold and may be summed up in the words: reconnaissance, security, assault. They remain the same now.

The advent of aircraft has, of course, relieved ground troops of much of the work that formerly fell to them under the head of reconnaissance. Aircraft have an infinitely wider range of vision and radius of action. Their reports are more quickly and surely rendered, and they can discern and send back information not only of the outer country of the enemy's forward lines (beyond which the cavalry of old times could rarely penetrate), but of what is going on in the very heart of his army and

even in his back areas. But there are conditions of weather and sometimes of ground too which limit the activities of reconnoitring aircraft and tend to make their reports inaccurate. It is often impossible, without an undue strain on available air resources, to maintain a constant hour to hour watch over the enemy. For close and detailed inspection of ground, moreover, the airman usually flies too high and too fast, particularly if his activities be opposed. During the night hours air reconnaissance is impossible, so the resulting gap in the work has still to be filled in by the mechanized cavalry. It is an arduous task.

It will thus often fall to their lot to push forward far in front of the main body strong reconnaissance patrols, consisting first of motor cycles or motor cycle machine gunners, followed by armoured cars, scout-cars, or light tanks in whatever combination may be most suitable to the particular conditions. Their main task may be to find out where the enemy is or, sometimes, where he is not; if a certain point has yet been reached or is held by him; if a threatening movement, perhaps already reported by the air force as having begun, has yet assumed dangerous proportions; or if a certain area is clear for the occupation and the advance of strong forces of their own side. Any of these duties and many others may be assigned to the mechanized cavalry, and, in the majority of cases, if the information

A MODERN RECONNAISSANCE GROUP

These motor cyclist units are trained to act as forward patrols ahead of the main body

required is to be worth having, it will have to be fought for. Therefore the reconnoitring body must be equipped not only with fast-moving vehicles, such as motor cycles or scout-cars, but with other slower ones with considerable fire power, such as motor cycle machine gunners, armoured cars, or light tanks. They must brush aside any weak hostile resistance and see what is behind it, or, if need be, force stronger enemy bodies to show their position and strength by deploying to fight. With a modern air arm and a modern mechanized cavalry force at his command, a general of today should have a reasonably clear picture in his mind at any given moment as to where his adversary's forces are and be able to form a moderately good guess as to what they are about. Both in range and power the mechanized cavalry are a great advance on the former horsed variety in the carrying out of the vital duty of reconnaissance.

Another role, closely connected with reconnaissance, is that of security. In all war, however much is known about the enemy's positions, his intentions are always more or less a matter of guess-work. Particularly is this the case today, when the high rate of mobility and manœuvrability of mechanized armies makes it possible for surprise attacks to be launched practically without warning. Troops from widely separated concentration areas in rear of the front can converge rapidly by swift night marches on some chosen weak point in the hostile line.

MECHANIZED PATROLS

Moreover, if a general's own air force be too weak to carry out its task of reconnaissance, his information of his adversary may be anything but accurate and complete. Therefore, if his army is to rest securely and safe from surprise, and is to avoid being caught unawares and unready by sudden hostile attacks in force, it must be covered in front by a screen of troops. These must be capable not only of giving early warning of such attacks, but of cushioning them and slackening down their pace of progress, so as to give their comrades in the rear, time to take up their positions for battle. This is again the duty of the mechanized cavalry which furnishes not only the small rapid-moving forward observation posts and patrols in close contact with the enemy, but also the stronger piquets and supports in the rear which can fight for the time and space required by their army to man at leisure its positions of defence. In this role each type of vehicle has its part to play. Motor cyclists, motor-cyclist machine gunners and scout-cars are useful as forward patrols, with armoured cars and light tanks acting as mobile fighting reserves.

Valuable however as are mechanized forces in these essential duties, their principal role is that of assault troops. Just as the modern mechanized cavalry regiments of the Royal Armoured Corps now carry out the reconnaissance and pro-tective duties of the light horse of former days, so its tank battalions have undertaken in attack and counter-attack on the battlefield itself the role formerly played by the dragoons and cuirassiers of the heavy cavalry reserve. There are two forms, however, in which this role can be played, and two contending schools of thought have long disputed as to which is the true one for armoured groups under modern conditions. We shall deal more in detail later with these conflicting views; here it is enough to say that both are recognized and accepted in the Royal Armoured Corps, which contains units organized, equipped and specially trained to carry out efficiently both duties.

ARMY TANK BATTALIONS

In the first view, tanks may be used in close co-operation with infantry, closely supported by artillery, in deliberate systematic attacks on strongly fortified positions firmly held with secure or well-guarded flanks. Under these conditions only frontal attacks will be possible, and

RECONNAISSANCE CARS

British lightly armoured cars with Bren guns climbing a road on the look-out for the enemy

such attacks infantry alone, as was shown time and again in the war of 1914-18, could only carry out slowly with heavy artillery support and at fearful loss. Tanks must, therefore, be employed to lead the way, to break through obstacles and to cross trenches, to deal with enemy machine guns and mortars, and to hold the ground thus overrun until the infantry can come up and take it over from them. Special units, known as "Army Tank battalions" several of which are normally grouped to form brigades, are therefore maintained for this purpose as part of the Royal Armoured Corps.

ARMOURED DIVISIONS

More spectacular, however, is the work of the independent Armoured Divisions. The main body of such a formation comprises armoured car units, for its own reconnaissance and security purposes, and units of fast tanks with wide ranges of action forming the main body. Motorized

infantry, close-support artillery of various types, engineers, signal units, and other arms and services also form part of the armoured divisions. By constant training and practice together, they are forged into powerful far-reaching weapons capable of carrying out important tasks on their own. A wide sweep round an enemy's flank to strike his rear communications, and cut off his retreat; a rapid pursuit through a breach made in the lines so as to turn defeat into disaster; a delaying action to hold off at arms' length a superior hostile force and prevent it interfering with important operations elsewhere; these, and other similar operations, may well fall to the lot of an independent armoured division in the course of a campaign, and it is for roles such as these that it is organized and fitted out.

Details of the present organization of the Royal Armoured Corps cannot, of course, be given here, even were they of great interest to the general public. This

A TANK IN HILLY COUNTRY
This "Matilda" tank weighs twenty-six tons. It has a two-pounder gun and a crew of four

RECONNAISSANCE REGIMENT ON THE MOVE

Ahead of the armoured divisions move armoured cars, Bren carriers and motor cyclists.
These form reconnaissance brigades and it is their duty to prevent surprise by the enemy

organization is, moreover, always subject to change at short notice especially in wartime, according to the lessons of recent experience in the field. Before the Second World War the organization of all Royal Armoured Corps battalions, with whatever types of tanks they were armed, was on the lines of the former horsed cavalry regiments and consisted of a head-quarters squadron, and three fighting squadrons with the necessary administration, organization and transport. The army tank battalions are army troops; that is, they are not normally allotted to the divisions comprising the army but remain under the direct control of the army commander himself and are allotted by him to divisions or corps for special tasks as required. The battalions forming part of the independent armoured formations on the other hand, were, before the war, allotted in the proportion of two or three medium tank battalions to one battalion of light tanks. A number of light and close-support tanks were also included in each medium tank battalion—which, for that reason, often came to be better known as "mixed" battalions.

RECONNAISSANCE BRIGADES

The armoured division consisted of three of these armoured brigades with the units attached as described above. Mechanized cavalry regiments, equipped with armoured cars and light tanks, each with its allotment of scout-cars, motor cycles,

(I) DIVISIONAL H.Q.	ARMOURED COMMAND VEHICLE. SCOUT CARS WITH BRENS. MOTOR CYCLISTS	
(II) ARMY CO-OPERATION SQUADRON COMPONENT	LYSANDER PLANE. MOBILE WIRELESS VAN.	
(III) GROUND RECONNAISSANCE UNIT	(a) ARMOURED CARS : SOME WITH BREN GUNS : '' '' 2.PDR. A/T GUNS. MOTOR CYCLISTS. M/CYCLE COMBINATIONS.	
	(b.) LIGHT TRUCKS WITH TROOPS IN THEM.	
(IV) ARMOURED BRIGADES	(a) ARMOURED REGIMENTS. VALENTINES. MATILDAS.	
	(b.) MOTORISED INFANTRY. (I.) BREN CARRIERS. (2.) TRUCKS : 3 OR 4 TIMES MORE THAN IN III (b.)	
(V) 'HORSE' ARTILLERY ANTI-TANK UNITS LIGHT A·A·UNITS MOTORISED INFANTRY	25. PDR. GUN-HOWITZER. 2. PDR. A/T GUN. BOFORS GUNS. SOME IN BREN CARRIERS '' '' TRUCKS	TWICE AS MANY AS IN IV (2)
R.E. UNITS	LORRIES CARRYING GIRDER BRIDGE SECTIONS	
(VI) R.A.S.C. DIVISIONAL TRANSPORT	"A" ECHELON LORRIES	PETROL : AMMUNITION : WIRELESS REPLACEMENTS.
	"B" ECHELON LORRIES	FOOD OF ALL SORTS : CANTEEN STORES, ETC: LORRY SPARE PARTS, ETC:
	3 TIMES AS MANY VEHICLES IN "B" AS IN "A".	
R.A.O.C.	(I) STORES OF WIRE, TYRES, SPARE CATERPILLARS, ETC. (II) TANK RECOVERY VEHICLE. (III) LIGHT WORKSHOP, (MOBILE).	
R.A.M.C.	FIELD AMBULANCES.	

COMPOSITION OF AN ARMOURED DIVISION,

An armoured division is complete in itself. The divisional and brigade headquarters are housed in Armoured Command vehicles (see page 90); close co-operation is maintained by wireless with the aeroplanes of the Army Co-operation squadrons. Preceded by their reconnaissance units, the armoured brigades comprise the main strength of the formation. Motorized

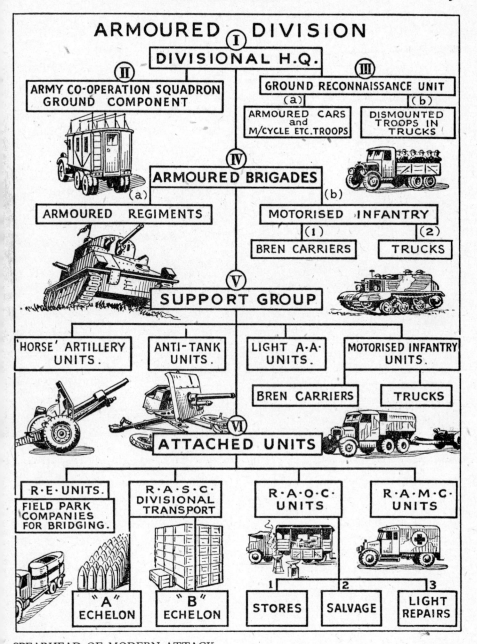

ARMOURED DIVISION

(I) DIVISIONAL H.Q.

(II) ARMY CO-OPERATION SQUADRON GROUND COMPONENT

(III) GROUND RECONNAISSANCE UNIT
(a) ARMOURED CARS and M/CYCLE ETC. TROOPS
(b) DISMOUNTED TROOPS IN TRUCKS

(IV) ARMOURED BRIGADES
(a) ARMOURED REGIMENTS
(b) MOTORISED INFANTRY
(1) BREN CARRIERS
(2) TRUCKS

(V) SUPPORT GROUP
'HORSE' ARTILLERY UNITS.
ANTI-TANK UNITS.
LIGHT A·A· UNITS.
MOTORISED INFANTRY UNITS.
BREN CARRIERS
TRUCKS

(VI) ATTACHED UNITS
R·E·UNITS. FIELD PARK COMPANIES FOR BRIDGING.
R·A·S·C· DIVISIONAL TRANSPORT
R·A·O·C· UNITS
R·A·M·C· UNITS
"A" ECHELON
"B" ECHELON
1 STORES
2 SALVAGE
3 LIGHT REPAIRS

SPEARHEAD OF MODERN ATTACK

infantry, "horse" artillery, anti-tank units and light A.A. guns are in close attendance. There are also attached engineering, supply, repair and medical units. Such a formation is able to penetrate enemy defences rapidly. It carries enough infantry to consolidate any **ground won, and is strong enough to resist counter-attacks before the main body arrives**

"VALENTINE" CRUISER TANKS MOVING

These tanks are the basis of Britain's light cruiser and " I " tank strength. They are very

motor cyclist machine gunners and transport, were also organized in reconnaissance brigades of three regiments each during the early stages of the war in France. They soon proved their worth.

More interesting to the general public are the types of vehicle with which the Royal Armoured Corps is now equipped. But here, too, full details cannot, of necessity, be given. These vehicles may be divided into two categories, the one designed primarily for use on roads such as motor cyclist machine gunners, scout-cars and armoured cars, the other category for cross-country work, including all types of tanks. The motor cyclist machine

gunners ride on motor cycle combinations which are fitted with armoured shields and they are armed with automatic weapons and rifles. They can move at high speed on roads and can also go both fast and far across country. The scout-car, formerly merely unarmoured light cars with high clearance and a crew of two, are now lightly armoured and carry light automatics of various types. They may in time supersede the cycle combination. The armoured car carries a crew of three or four, has a good road speed, and a wide radius of action. Being well armoured and armed with an anti-tank machine gun and a machine gun coaxially

FORWARD OVER THE BROW OF A HILL
manœuvrable, weigh about sixteen tons, and have a two-pounder gun as main armament

mounted in the turret, it is a fast, useful fighting machine. All these can leave the road and go across country at need, but, being wheeled vehicles, this is their exceptional, not their normal, role.

The various tanks with which the Royal Armoured Corps is armed fall into three classes: the light tank, the "I" tank and the cruiser tank. The light tank type is now gradually being superseded for all purposes by the light cruiser type. Designed for reconnaissance and security duties, the last model to be used by the Royal Armoured Corps carried three men, weighed some six tons and had a road speed of thirty miles an hour and an average cross-country speed of fifteen to twenty miles an hour. The new light cruiser type is heavier, weighing some ten tons and its road and cross-country speeds are not so high. It is more thickly armoured and formidably armed, and its crew is three men. Its radius of action and petrol consumption are remarkably good. The "I" tank is designed for working with infantry so that speed and range of action are less important than protection and good armament. The type known as "Valentine" (its predecessors had been nick-named "Matilda," no one quite knows why) is a sixteen-ton machine, with a crew of three; it can do fifteen miles an hour on the road and eight to ten miles an hour across country, and is very manœuvrable. Its armour is invulnerable to any known enemy anti-tank projectile, and its anti-tank gun mounted with a heavy machine gun in the turret can knock out any German tank it may meet.

TWO TYPES OF TANK

The medium tank, of which the models called the "Crusader" and the "Covenanter" are the latest, is similarly armed, but more lightly armoured; it is considerably faster both on and off roads and has a greater range of action and cross-country capacity. For all the work it has been called on to undertake it has proved itself a most excellent vehicle.

The time is therefore within sight when the Royal Armoured Corps will have only two main types of tanks, the "I" tank for work in close co-operation with infantry, and the cruiser tank for independent work. These types will comprise both light to medium and heavy models for various roles and duties.

Yet, even the best of vehicles and the most formidable armaments, the thickest armour, the fastest speed and the widest range of movement, are of little use to an armoured unit if the personnel of the unit is unskilful and ill-trained. The Royal Armoured Corps is able by reason of its comparatively small numbers to pick and choose its recruits. It has therefore been able to demand, and get, from the many keen and ambitious youngsters offering themselves, those keenest and best qualified by intelligence and civilian experience. The men of the corps are a fine type.

A "CRUSADER" TANK IN ROUGH COUNTRY
This is a new British medium cruiser tank. It is more powerful than the "Valentine"

AN AMERICAN TWENTY-EIGHT-TON TANK

This American tank has been used by the British. It is comparable with the British " Crusader "

and the tasks on which they are often engaged call for a form of discipline very different from that popularly associated with the Guards Brigade. The relations between the higher and lower ranks in the Royal Armoured Corps is bound rather to resemble that in vogue in the Royal Navy or the Royal Air Force, where all are brought into closer and more frequent contact by being engaged together, often in small groups, on highly technical tasks. Technical knowledge and skill is a prime necessity for all ranks of the corps, just as horsemastership and horse management was for the former cavalry officer or man. This expert knowledge of their primary weapon, once horse but now vehicle, still remains a matter of pride and of tradition among tank personnel.

Particularly stressed is the importance of careful and systematic maintenance and overhaul of vehicles. As a tank or a car off the road is, for the moment, non-existent—save as an incubus—every effort is made to keep them in service as long as

possible and to get them back to it as soon as possible, if they should be temporarily put out of action. No category of vehicle in civil life ever gets such motherly and ceaseless attention as those of the Royal Armoured Corps, and this seemingly almost excessive care and labour has repaid itself over and over again when the corps has gone into action. Next to the admirable design and workmanship which produced its fine machines, the time spent in the humdrum, dirty and back-breaking work of maintenance has been the main factor in ensuring that its units can go into action almost, if not quite, at full strength. The labour is amply repaid by results in the stress of action.

TANK TRAINING

But, training in vehicle maintenance is not even half the battle in mechanized warfare. A heavy responsibility rests on the small crews that have to drive, work and fight the tanks, for if they are ill-trained or unskilful the best machines

CUPOLA
PERISCOPE
TURRET TOP
LOADER
SIGHTING VANE
BESA MACHINE GUN
GUNNER
2 POUNDER QUICK-FIRING GUN
COMMANDE
MIRROR
SIDE LAMP
PERISCOPE
AIR INLET
TURRET TRAVERSING GEAR
HEAD LAMP
DRIVER
2-POUNDER SHELLS
PLY GLASS
RIGHT TRACK CONTROL LEVER
GEAR SELECTOR→
SEAT RAISING & LOWERING GEAR
LEFT TRACK CONTROL LEVER
INNER PLATING
TRACK
IDLER WHEEL
TRACK

A BRITISH HEAVY INFANTRY TANK—
This is one of our large infantry tanks. It is very heavily armoured against machine guns and anti-tank weapons. Driven by Diesel motors and with an automatic gearbox, it weighs about twenty-five tons. It has a crew of four men—the commander, a gunner, a loader and

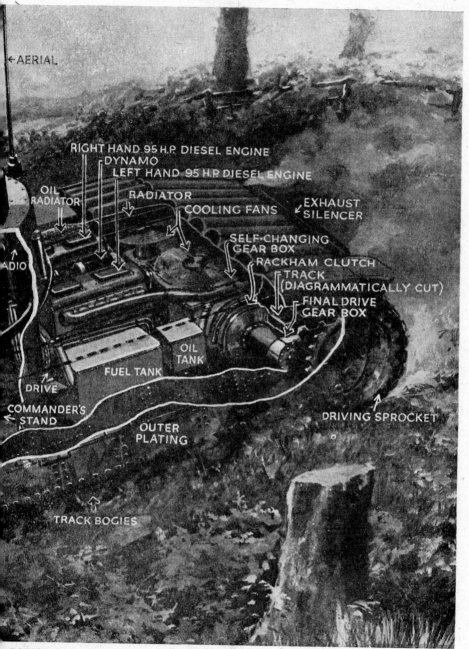

AERIAL

RIGHT HAND 95 H.P. DIESEL ENGINE
DYNAMO
LEFT HAND 95 H.P. DIESEL ENGINE

OIL
RADIATOR   RADIATOR
                              COOLING FANS   EXHAUST
                                                    SILENCER
RADIO
                              SELF-CHANGING
                              GEAR BOX
                              RACKHAM CLUTCH
                              TRACK
                              (DIAGRAMMATICALLY CUT)
                              FINAL DRIVE
                              GEAR BOX

                    OIL
                    TANK
         FUEL TANK
DRIVE

COMMANDER'S
STAND   DRIVING SPROCKET
                    OUTER
                    PLATING

TRACK BOGIES

POPULARLY KNOWN AS A "MATILDA"

a driver. Communication inside the tank is by telephone and outside by wireless. It is armed with a two-pounder gun and it has also a Besa machine gun. Some models have, in addition, smoke vents for making a smoke screen. The driver steers by two track-controlling levers

will be wasted on them. The driver, the gunner and the wireless operator all have to be masters of their various jobs, and not only of their own jobs but of each others' too, in case someone should become a casualty. Thus every member of a tank crew, before going on to specialize at his own task passes through an elementary training in driving both tracked and wheeled vehicles, in gun and machine gun firing, in wireless, in vehicle maintenance and in running repairs. Specialization is thus firmly based on a good groundwork of general knowledge, which, quite apart from its value in case of emergency, greatly facilitates the working of each tank crew as a team instead of a collection of individuals. They work as one man.

The tank driver is usually regarded as the key man of the crew and it is on him that the responsibility rests for his vehicle's mechanical efficiency. It is his job to get it to the place where it is wanted, to manœuvre it in action, and to extricate it from any of the very many difficult or perilous situations in which he may find himself in the course of battle. If it becomes unserviceable by reason of any but a major defect, it is for him to get it going again if this is in any way possible. His is an exhausting, responsible and nerve-racking job, yet rare and of little

BRITISH TANKS ENGAGED IN

All tank crews must be trained to manœuvre with certainty and precision. Here we see

value is the driver who would ever yield it up willingly to any one else. Tanks, like other inanimate objects, have their own individual peculiarities. No one knows these better or can get more out of his particular charge than the driver who has long been familiar with it in all its moods and motions. Even tanks have moods.

Yet, though he stands lower in corps ranking and in corps prestige, the gunner has a no less important, perhaps a more important, role to play. On whether he can pick and hold his target, and hit it, depends the whole efficiency of the tank as a weapon, and often the survival of both tank and crew in the stress of battle.

Therefore, the utmost trouble is taken, and rightly taken, to ensure that the tank gunner knows and can do his job. Theoretical instruction is followed by all sorts of practice. There are miniature ranges, where tiny tanks controlled by the instructor, career across country made of sand, diversified with replica woods and houses, roads and hedges; and here, behind an air rifle, the embryo gunner learns the practical rudiments of his art. Later, before a similar sort of target, he comes to handle the real guns but fitted with an attachment which allows them to fire small calibre ammunition. Here, poised on a device which hurls and

ELEMENTARY DRILL MANŒUVRES
tanks performing ordinary parade ground evolutions. Later they will learn battle movements

swings and jerks him about in realistic imitation of the motion of a tank, he becomes familiar with another branch of his work. Finally comes the open range, where, beginning with standing shots at stationary targets at short distances, he progresses to the battle practice where nothing is spared to face him with as close a copy as possible of his real job in war, with only the enemy's bullets and shells left to the imagination. After that he is a gunner, full-fledged and ready for action.

THE TANK COMMANDER

The most responsible job of all, however, is that of the commander, who is not usually an officer, but a junior non-commissioned officer or even a senior trooper. Besides controlling the tank, and issuing orders to the driver for speed and direction of advance, and controlling the fire of the machine gunners, he is himself the gunner for the main armament, the coaxial gun and machine gun in the turret. He has to handle the tank in such a way as to bring all its fire to bear most effectively on the enemy from the most suitable position and direction. He has also to receive and acknowledge orders from his troop commander through the wireless telephone as well as pass on to his superior any useful information as to what he may himself see and hear of the situation around him, the movements of the enemy and our own forces, and the course of the action. A well-handled tank is a most powerful weapon, and there can be few finer commands than this for a young and enthusiastic soldier today.

All the while that the training of the

LEARNING TO FIRE FROM A TANK
This tank gunner, seated in an imitation tank, is learning gunnery on a miniature range

LEARNING TO DRIVE A TANK

Much training is needed to accustom a tank driver to the uneven movements of his vehicle

personnel of the tank crews themselves is going on, the higher leaders, from troop commanders to brigade and divisional commanders, are thinking, experimenting, learning themselves and teaching their subordinates, how to work in small and large formations to the best advantage. Tactical exercises, theoretical and practical, staff tours on the map and on the ground, conferences and discussions, drills and manœuvres, are the means by which the doctrine is threshed out, approved and taught. Not only has each armoured unit and formation itself to be fashioned and hardened into a reliable and efficient instrument of war but these in turn have to learn to work in with other armoured units and formations, as well as with those of other arms. The army tank

battalions are constantly discussing and practising their methods of co-operation with infantry and artillery and though the co-operation of the independent tank bodies with other troops is less constant and direct, much time and thought must be devoted to it. Armoured troops, too, nowadays lose much of their value without aircraft to assist and support them. Now that the vital importance of such co-operation has been emphasized by events in the Low Countries and France, as well as by the Middle Eastern campaigns, this subject is engaging great attention.

CORPS TRADITION

Thus the Royal Armoured Corps stands today, and thus it prepares itself for war. Young as it is, and short as is its

DIAGRAMMATIC VIEW OF A BRITISH

This typical British cruiser tank, though not of the very latest design, has a speed of some twenty miles per hour across country, a crew of four, and weighs about sixteen tons. Its main armament is a two-pounder gun and a Besa machine gun. The crew need careful

LOADER

CUPOLA

← AERIAL

RADIO

COMMANDER

RADIATORS EITHER SIDE

AIR LOUVRES

340 H.P. "V" TYPE PETROL MOTOR

COOLING FAN

AIR CLEANERS TO CARBURETTORS

FUEL TANK

GEAR BOX

EXHAUSTS

FINAL DRIVE

DRIVING SPROCKET

MARK IVA MEDIUM CRUISER TANK

training as space is cramped. The commander with his head in the cupola controls the crew (and keeps in touch with other tanks) by wireless telephone. The gunner directs the turret by means of hydraulic traversing gear. The gun recoils within a few inches of his right ear

ARMY TANK AT A TRAINING DEPOT

It is on such older types of tank that personnel are trained in driving and gunnery

history in its present form, its units have long and glorious traditions. It is firmly resolved to live up to these and feels itself fully capable of maintaining and enhancing them. Let us make a brief survey of these traditions before we go on to glance at the achievements of the corps in war.

CAVALRY TRADITION

The Royal Armoured Corps is in one sense one of the oldest, in another sense one of the youngest, in the British Army of today. It includes in its ranks all the former regiments of horsed cavalry, and the earliest born of these cavalry regiments was first raised as long ago as 1661. It also includes the Royal Tank Regiment, which under the title Heavy Branch Machine Gun Corps, and, later, Tank Corps, was formed only in the middle of the war of 1914-18. Thus on one side the corps is nearly three centuries old, on the other a mere quarter of a century old.

Yet this combination of age and youth may rightly be considered symbolical, for though armed with the most up-to-date and formidable fighting weapons of the day, its role on the battlefield is almost as old as armies themselves.

There is neither space nor need here even to outline the long career of honourable achievement of the former cavalry arm of the British Army. The pageantry of splendid horses and gay uniforms conjured up by the very names of Dragoons, Dragoon Guards, Light Dragoons, Lancers, Hussars, is now a thing of the past, but some of their deeds—the great attack which decided the day at Blenheim, the furious charges of the Union and Household Brigades at Waterloo, the death ride of Balaclava—are part not only of the British Army, but of Britain's story. Every one of these famous regiments had its peculiar day of remembrance, when it celebrated some doughty action of the past or some signal honour bestowed upon it by a British sovereign. But the war of 1914-18 showed clearly the limited usefulness of men mounted on horses on battlefields seamed with trenches and barbed wire, and dominated by the machine gun and the tank.

Accordingly, it was decided to mechanize part at any rate of the cavalry of the British Army and to reduce in number those units remaining on a horsed basis. These changes took place immediately after the close of the war of 1914-18, and the first two cavalry regiments to be mechanized, the 11th Hussars and the 12th Lancers, were given armoured cars in place of their horses. Then in 1936 eight more cavalry regiments were converted from a horsed basis, to be equipped with armoured cars, light scout-cars, or light tanks. Within three years the revolution already so widely begun was com-

pleted. Early in 1939 the whole of the cavalry lines except for the two senior dragoon regiments, the Royals and the Scots Greys, were incorporated in the newly formed Royal Armoured Corps and were mechanized on the same basis as those units already so converted. At the same time the Royal Tank Corps, its title amended to the Royal Tank Regiment, was embodied in the new corps.

TRADITIONAL COMPROMISE

To preserve regimental traditions as dear to the unit as they are valuable to the Army, the old cavalry regiments retained their titles, badges of rank, and battle honours, and the promotion of their officers was to be carried out on a unit basis up to field rank, after which it was to be by selection on a corps basis. This typically British compromise, however anomalous in appearance, worked

TANK CAMOUFLAGE IN THE DESERT

In the desert camouflage is very necessary to hide vehicles from enemy aerial observation

B.M.A.—C

TESTING THE SMOKE-CHUTES OF A TANK
Many modern British tanks, as above, carry their own smoke-screen mechanism

smoothly and to general satisfaction in the short period of trial up to the outbreak of the Second World War. What was more important, by that time the equipment of the cavalry regiments allotted to form part of the British Expeditionary Force going to France had been completed. The former horsed cavalry wing of the Royal Armoured Corps was thus ready for its new mechanized role, and right well was it played in that disastrous campaign in Flanders in the early summer of 1940, which found its heroic conclusion in the evacuation from the beaches of Dunkirk.

THE ORIGIN OF THE TANK

The story of the Royal Tank Regiment is too well known, and has been too often told, to need more than summarizing

here. It was born of the deadlock that spread over the western war front at the end of 1914, when barbed wire and trenches penned the armies in and their bristling rifles, machine guns and cannon made the narrow no-man's-land between them impassable by living men.

Yet as early as that December of 1914 the ingenious brain of a field officer of British engineers had found the means and the method of using it. Armed and armoured vehicles on cross-country tracks, to be used by surprise and in mass to drive a great hole through the hostile fortified lines and open the road to victory—that was the idea of Colonel Swinton, whom the Royal Tank Regiment has always regarded as primarily its true father and prophet. Yet a year and a half elapsed before Colonel Swinton's first practical project materialized with the appearance of the earliest tanks on the Somme battlefield in September 1916. And more than a year more was to pass before the new weapon was used as from the first he had foreseen that it must be used, if its role was to be decisive of victory. That year from September 1916 to November 1917 was one of constant effort and as constant disappointment on the part of the personnel of the Tank Corps and of those who had faith in it. More than once during this time of trial, the very existence of the Tank Corps hung in the balance, and it needed the triumph at Cambrai to establish it firmly as an indispensable part of the British Army.

At this battle, fought on November 20, 1917—a day ever since celebrated as a festival by the Royal Tank Regiment— tanks were for the first time since their inception used in great numbers by surprise, and in the forefront of the attack. They gained a swift and signal victory.

TANK CORPS BECOMES FAMOUS

The four months of victorious advance which led to the collapse and surrender of the German armies a year after the battle of Cambrai finally set the seal on the great fame of the Tank Corps. At the

INSTRUCTION IN THE PARTS OF A TANK

On the blackboard are drawings of a chassis and tractors of a British tank. By understanding their working the driver will be better able to effect any necessary running repairs in action

OVERHAULING A BRITISH TANK

The maintenance of modern mechanical vehicles is a vital and difficult job. In battle, wear and tear is severe, especially on the tractors. The latter are heavy and cumbersome, as may be seen from the huge roll of tractor above. They are most vulnerable yet very strong

battle of Amiens on August 8, 1918, which marked the opening of this decisive campaign, they played the leading part and in almost every one of the succeeding battles they took a prominent share, the importance of which a few figures will emphasize better than many paragraphs of words.

During this period the Tank Corps fought on thirty-nine days and many of its personnel were in action fifteen or sixteen times. There were two thousand individual tank engagements, and as a result of these over eight hundred machines were sent into the repair department for attention; of these two hundred were so successfully dealt with that they were able to return to fight again. Of the combatant personnel of the corps, 10,000 in all, no less than one in four became casualties in these three months—a high percentage.

"PLAN 1919"

Yet great as was the role played in 1918 by the new arm, a still more extensive and original one had been designed for it had the campaign in the west gone on for another year. This "Plan 1919" was based on the idea of an annihilating blow at the enemy's brain, represented by his headquarters, and at his stomach, represented by his supply services. Five thousand tanks of all types were to take part in this gigantic operation. Though never to be executed, the idea was to bear worldwide intellectual fruit—and not unfortunately intellectual fruit only—in quarters other than those for and in which it was first so brilliantly designed.

With the coming of peace the Tank Corps, like the rest of the British Army, shrank to very small proportions indeed. In the depression of the post-war troubles, it may be noted its units bore their full share and saw service in Ireland, in Russia, on the Rhine, in Palestine, in Iraq and in India. Later the Royal Tank Corps saw active service in the Shanghai expedition in 1927, and in India, this latter service both in the form of "duties in aid of the civil power" to prevent or repress disorder among turbulent elements in the great cities, and also among the ever-turbulent and warlike tribes of the North-West Frontier. All over British India and native states from Waziristan to Bangalore, absolute confidence came to exist in the power of armoured car and light tank units to put right any form of trouble or disturbance.

TANK CORPS REORGANIZATION

When it became clear that Britain could not safely count on the peace of Europe being unbroken much longer, and the reorganization and strengthening of the Army began, the Royal Tank Corps was increased by several extra battalions.

In a mechanized corps, however, size is no accurate criterion of efficiency. The quality of its armoured fighting vehicles—their speed, radius of action, endurance, armour and armament—is a much more reliable one. As important, if not more so, are the training of the personnel in their fighting and mechanical duties, the quality of the leadership, and the doctrine of tactical employment.

OUT-OF-DATE VEHICLES

When the war of 1914-18 ended, all our machines were of a type designed as infantry-accompanying tanks, and had throughout been used as such. New types were obviously needed and all the earlier tanks were replaced by a new medium vehicle with a good turn of speed, well armed, but too lightly armoured for use against a first-class adversary. This remained the standard equipment of the British tank battalions for nearly fifteen years. But by the time the rearmament drive began it also was overdue for replacement. Unfortunately and unnecessarily, there were different technical and tactical ideas as to what should replace it, and design and production were unduly held up. The Munich crisis thus found no unit of the R.T.C. fit to take the field in a European theatre of war, though the new models had by then been agreed on and were in course of manufacture.

AUXILIARY WEAPONS

Prior to this a new light tank had also come into existence. The first type was a two-man machine, but a short period of practical manœuvre ground experience with them, proved conclusively that for fully efficient fighting vehicles they were under-manned and all units were therefore rearmed with a new three-man model. It was with this that both the cavalry and tank units of the Corps went to war in 1939.

The development of tank design, as well as methods of training, depend largely on the prevailing doctrine of the tactical use of tanks, and from the international discussion as to what this role should be there emerged two schools of tactical thought. The one, which was especially favoured in France, saw in the tank only a weapon of accompaniment. It was admitted generally that tanks by

AT THE DRIVING SEAT OF A TANK

The range of vision of a tank driver is very limited. This driver has the armoured visor open, and his area of vision is better than it would be when the visor is closed for action

TANK CREWS RESTING ON MANŒUVRES

Whenever tanks are motionless precautions are always taken against surprise. This tank is under tree cover from aerial observation and the men have their Bren guns at hand

themselves could overrun but could not permanently clear or hold ground, and that even in the first task they would have to expect far more serious and better organized resistance than they had ever met with during the war of 1914-18. Therefore if they were not to suffer heavily and perhaps fail, they must be closely supported by artillery and work in close conjunction with infantry throughout the battle. Speed was of less importance than good armament and heavy protection, and though progress might be slow it would be sure. In the ideas of this school, the tank was thus just another—admittedly the most powerful—of the many auxiliary weapons the role of which was to facilitate the infantry advance, the only proved and assured means of winning victory. This school based itself on the solid ground of 1914-18 experience, when the tank had always been a weapon of accompaniment and according to it always should be so employed.

INDEPENDENT WEAPONS

The other school poured scorn on the whole idea of the infantry-accompanying-tank, and saw in this procedure the waste of a most valuable weapon. It must not, in their view, be hampered by being fettered to a less powerful and slower moving arm. It must use its great speed and high capacity for manœuvre and fighting to strike swift, far-ranging, deadly blows at far-distant objectives. It must be used in great masses to ensure instant and complete success and to allow of relentless

A LIGHT AMERICAN TANK

The use of light tanks has been severely curtailed. They did not stand up well to the heavier enemy vehicles. In Africa, however, these American tanks have done well for Britain. They are speedy, easily manœuvrable, and particularly well suited to desert conditions

and continuous pursuit, so as to exploit that success to the full. Aircraft must serve as its long-range and close support artillery; motorized infantry, light artillery, engineers and other arms as required must accompany or follow it closely, assist it to keep moving and deal with any resistance it was not strong enough or had not time to subdue quickly. The ideas of this school are those that had inspired the Allied plans of campaign for 1919; the tank must not be a secondary but the primary weapon; on it would devolve the role of queen of the battlefields, and that of the other arms would be to facilitate and consolidate its victories.

Both these schools had their British adherents, and in the end the doctrines of both were officially accepted. The ideas of the second, the independent tank school, were, in fact, first worked out experimentally by the Royal Tank Corps, despite paucity of numbers, shortage of vehicles and equipment, and lack of adequate training ground. So it came about that at the beginning of the Second World War the Royal Armoured Corps was organized, as described above, so as to be able to play both roles as and when called upon to do so.

Not many reliable and detailed accounts have been received of the work of the Corps during the early hostilities of the Second World War, but enough is known to make it clear that it has more than lived up to its famous traditions. Owing to the time lag in rearmament the British Expeditionary Force that went to France in the autumn of 1939 included no independent armoured division; the only purely tank units to go overseas were an Army tank brigade of two battalions with their "I" tanks. It was not till the summer of next year when the great German offensive broke on the Western Front that the Royal Armoured Corps first came into action. Its armoured car and reconnaissance regiments were the earliest of all the B.E.F. to become engaged. After covering the advance of the army into Belgium they reached the line of the Dyle and pushed out beyond it to form a forward screen, behind which the defence of

that river line could be organized. Within a few hours of their arrival they were subjected to heavy pressure, which increased rapidly and menacingly. Although the light tanks with which they were principally armed were unsuited for close fighting in stationary positions, they put up a fine performance at the cost of heavy losses in men and vehicles. Many of these latter might have been rendered serviceable again had not the order for retirement come before the damage to them could be repaired. From the line of the Dyle, which the B.E.F. had been compelled to abandon because of the yielding of the

A VALENTINE "I" TANK

These modern British armoured vehicles have proved excellent in support of attacking infantry. They are strongly armoured, speedy, and have great power of manœuvre

B.M.A.—C*

COVENANTER CRUISER TANKS

Among recent types of British cruiser tanks are the Covenanters. They are fast, well armoured,

DRAWN UP FOR INSPECTION
low in construction, and are armed with a two-pounder gun and A.A. machine guns

front on either flank of it, the cavalry rearguard took a prominent part in all the stubborn step by step fighting in which our troops were engaged right the way back to the North Sea coast at Dunkirk. By the time this port was reached there were few armoured fighting vehicles left in any cavalry unit, and those that still remained had to be abandoned and destroyed on the dunes. Most of the personnel, however, got away in safety after their severe experiences, and some lived to fight another day in the Middle East, in more fortunate circumstances.

TANKS IN FRANCE

In the course of the long retreat the two Army tank battalions had opportunities of showing their mettle. Hopelessly outnumbered, often without clear orders in the general confusion, constantly anxious for their supplies, fuel and replacements, they acquitted themselves admirably under every test. Usually these tests took the form of small attacks, carried out at the request of local commanders to relieve a compromised position or extricate comrades from awkward or perilous situations. Almost always they had to go in at short notice, sure of encountering great odds but knowing little else of what lay around and before them. In the later stages of the campaign small parties of tanks or isolated machines sometimes came face to face with the enemy to their mutual surprise and had to shoot their way out. Rarely did any unit have a chance to take part in any well-organized, set-piece attack, where it could really give of its best.

One of the few such occasions occurred on May 21, 1940, at Arras. The Tank Brigade concerned, consisting of two battalions, had only just arrived after a 300-mile march from Brussels; it had seventy infantry tanks available for action, but the crews had had no time to overhaul or repair them after the long trip.

Nevertheless, the attack duly took place—ordered that same afternoon, though the units had only arrived in the early dawn hours. The whole force, despite strong enemy resistance, swept right round Arras from north to west, crashing through anti-tank defences and causing demoralization among the German infantry. Crowds of the latter came running towards our machines with their hands up, handing their weapons in through the open flaps to our crews inside, and climbing up on the roofs, still with their hands high, for a ride into captivity. By the time they had advanced five miles, however, the tanks were far ahead of the infantry with whom they were co-operating, and were much scattered over a wide area of the battlefield. There were very few battle casualties for the armour of the machines kept out all the German anti-tank fire, but many tanks had mechanical breakdowns and had to be abandoned on the field. When, after what (so far as the tanks were concerned) had been a highly successful day, the battalion rallied, it was found that only a small residue were in running order. Yet these were able to beat off a surprise night attack by the enemy.

STRONG TANK ARMOUR

When the personnel of these two battalions, which had also had to leave behind those of their excellent machines that had survived to reach the Dunkirk beaches, arrived back home they were able to report that their tanks had stood up splendidly to all the tests of the campaigns. The hostile anti-tank guns, whether mounted in enemy machines or on the ground, had never succeeded in penetrating their armour; nor had what hits they made had any ill effects on the crews inside the machines. One case was narrated where a tank had received twenty-six hits without one going through. The German tanks, on the other hand, had proved much inferior to ours and in enemy duels with anything like equal numbers had been worsted. With a fair field and no favour, the Royal Armoured Corps was confident of its superiority over the German Tank Corps: but in Flanders it had been too small to be able to pull its full weight.

TANKS IN LIBYA

The independent armoured division only reached France for the last stage of the campaign after the evacuation from Dunkirk (June 1940) of the bulk of the British Expeditionary Force. Its first and only big battle took place in the Somme valley. Here it was ordered to co-operate with French tanks and infantry in an attack on one of the bridgeheads south of the river which the Germans had seized and were holding. This operation was a failure, but the Armoured Division did all that was asked of it and more, driving its way deep into the hostile defences and holding on there grimly while the French infantry behind it slowly and with difficulty made their way forward to relieve it. By the time they arrived, however, the impetus of the attack had been lost and the ground our tanks had won was soon lost too when the Germans counter-attacked in force. Our losses in men were light but many tanks which had temporarily been put out of action could not be refitted in time to be got away. All the rest were left behind at the evacuation ports when the remains of our forces were withdrawn after the French capitulation.

The disappointing, though creditable, experiences of the Royal Armoured Corps in France were more than compensated for by their brilliant record in the Middle East. After Italy's entry into the war our army in the Western Desert of Egypt, very much smaller and less well equipped than that opposed to it, went through anxious and dangerous months. But the hostile advance was so slow and timid that time was gained for our forces to receive reinforcements and material enough to put them more on an equality with the Italians. The credit for this was largely due to the bold and successful harassing and delaying tactics carried out by the units of the Royal Armoured Corps, operating forward of our prepared defensive positions. In nearly every little skirmish and raid they proved their superiority over their adversaries. Before the winter set in the enemy had come to a definite halt well out of attacking range of our main forces. Only highly efficient troops, under bold and enterprising leaders, could have achieved these invaluable results with such small resources.

When after several postponements, the time came for General Wavell's Army of the Nile to pass from defence to attack, it was the Royal Armoured Corps that formed the spearhead of its advance. The first staggering blow at Sidi Barrani, which annihilated the Italian advance guard and set the tide of our victory in full flow was largely the work of our army tank units and of General Creagh's armoured division. It was an operation that had to be carried out strictly to a limited timetable if it were not to be altogether abortive, for owing to the long approach march to be accomplished before the battle could begin, only a very short time could be allowed for fighting and winning it. The secrecy and speed of this march was in itself astonishing.

CYRENAICA CONQUERED

The enterprise, tactical skill and combat efficiency shown by our armoured units in the battle alone enabled a complete success to be won well within the allotted time limit. So annihilating had been our victory here that it was possible to continue the offensive without a pause to allow the enemy to recover. What had originally been intended as only a large-scale raid, developed into a grandly designed and perfectly executed offensive,

BRITISH MATILDA TANKS

The Matilda is the original modern British cruiser tank. It has proved highly efficient, particularly in the desert. These tanks are advancing in open formation to counter aerial

which in a few weeks culminated in the conquest of the whole of Italian Cyrenaica.

In the battles of Bardia, Derna and Tobruk the British tanks, now acting in close co-operation with British and Dominion infantry and artillery, once more did yeoman service and added greatly to their laurels. But their greatest triumph was in the final victory of the campaign at Benghazi.

Here our armoured troops, after carrying out a long desert march, in conditions and over country which to the enemy appeared impossible, got round in rear of the main body of the Italian Army in Benghazi and cut its line of retreat southward along the coast road. Our leading tank units were heavily outnumbered and there was a long and fierce battle in which the Italians, using their tanks recklessly and desperately in great masses, were more than once on the point of breaking through the barrier across their path and making good their escape. But they were always checked at the critical

moment. At length the arrival of other forces to the help of our men and the threat of our main body closing in on the enemy's rear, caused them to give in and surrender. It was the fine marching of our armoured force that had made this complete and decisive success possible at all, and their great fighting qualities which had the principal share in achieving it. Benghazi was the proudest day in the history of the Royal Armoured Corps since the famous battle of Amiens on August 8, 1918.

These Libyan victories of our tanks were all the more noteworthy for having been gained by comparatively small forces over an enemy greatly superior in numbers and by no means of poor fighting quality, as might be too hastily assumed from the extent and completeness of our success. The Italians fought with their machines expertly and gallantly, but their machines were not so good as ours. Once they realized this, it had an understandably depressing effect on their

ADVANCE ACROSS THE DESERT
and artillery attack. The battle manœuvres of modern armoured vehicles much resemble those of a fleet, and these Matildas bear a distinct resemblance to naval units at sea

morale. Nevertheless right up to the end we had to fight hard for our victories. Next to the fine quality of our machines and the expertness of their handling, the high standard of maintenance and mechanical efficiency achieved throughout the operations was a primary factor in the success of the campaign.

The unfortunate sequel, by which all the fruits were lost, was due to the fact that the Germans managed to surprise us by the concentration of large armoured forces. Our garrison in Cyrenaica had been much weakened by the demands of the campaign in Greece. The Germans, it seems, were as much surprised by their success as we had been at Sidi Barrani, and their forward movement came to a halt when it reached the Egyptian frontier.

The lessons of these campaigns have merely confirmed the soundness of the pre-war doctrine and methods of the Royal Armoured Corps. The first is that quality, particularly in mechanized warfare, will always defeat quantity if the odds are not too unequal. The side that can produce the better machines, in the better order, manned by the more skilled crews on the battlefield, can hold its own against greatly superior numbers. It may even, if well led and lucky, gain startling and perhaps decisive victories. But good men and good machines are not good enough: only the best will do, for in war the margin of superiority for victory can never be too large, and the enemy too will be striving for that same superiority with all his ingenuity and resources. Secondly, though quality may often get the better of numbers, only numbers, as Nelson once said of naval warfare, can annihilate. What is wanted for decisive victory is not only better tanks and better tank crews, but more tanks than the enemy. The Royal Armoured Corps has brilliantly shown what it can do against odds. When it is so happily placed as to have all the factors of victory, quantitative as well as qualitative, on its side, it will be able to surpass even its already noteworthy deeds

BRITISH TRANSPORT ON THE TOBRUK-BARDIA ROAD

One of the features of modern warfare is the need for speed. These British troops are motorized and able to follow the armoured vehicles into action without becoming exhausted

CHAPTER 4

Tactics in Modern Warfare

The aim of belligerents. The changing balance between offensive and defensive action. The tank and the aeroplane as offensive weapons. The armoured division and its tactics. "Fifth Column." Defence in depth. Air-borne attack. New demands on leadership and equipment

THE aim of war remains today what it has always been for each and every belligerent—to break the enemy's antagonistic will and impose his own. This holds true whatever the purpose for which that will is to be exercised, whether it be imperialistic, economic or idealistic. Once the clash between these purposes has led to an outbreak of war, the two belligerents tend to follow either an offensive or a defensive policy or strategy. The one pursuing the offensive purpose normally considers itself the stronger, not necessarily or exclusively in numbers, but in the balance of the factors that make for victory in war. The side that has the negative purpose, usually if not always the side which has nothing to gain, adopts a defensive policy. This, though powerless to give positive results, is the only one possible with inferior resources. If successful, it will at least baffle the aggressor's purpose. The attacking nation will strive for as complete and quick a victory as it can achieve, so that it may most cheaply and surely accomplish its purpose in the war. The defending nation will try to spin out the contest by avoiding decisive battle or accepting it only on conditions which reduce its opponent's superiority. It will hope to reduce its own comparative weakness and in time wear away the strength of its foe.

The general outline of war is as true to-day, and will be as true tomorrow, as it was in the days when men first fought. Methods, weapons, conditions have all, of course, changed, and will again change rather in detail than in general outline. The broad principles, however, on which the wise leader wages his campaigns and on which good troops base their conduct are eternal. Mobility and the power of surprise are still the master weapons in the assailant's hands. A watchful security, and a wise use of his inferior force are the best resources of the defender. Close co-operation between the various parts of armies and between armies themselves, a wise choice of military purpose and the unswerving pursuit of it until achieved—these are the keys to success in war equally indispensable to both sides.

THE HUMAN ELEMENT

Victory will fall to the side that enjoys superiority in the balance of military factors, and always to that which makes the best use of them. And whatever the methods, weapons or conditions are, one factor remains constant—man. It is men, whether they be generals or soldiers, that make wars, and, basically, their military human nature remains in character the same through the ages.

At various times in history there has occurred a shift in the normal balance of factors forming the offensive and the defensive, so as to tip it decidedly in the one direction or the other. The war of 1914-18

THE GERMAN JU 87B (OR STUKA) DIVE BOMBER

The use of dive bombers in close support of attacking infantry and tanks was one of the key novelties in modern tactics at the outset of the Second World War. The psychological effect was at first very considerable. The Ju 87b has since been proved rather less effective to morale and vulnerable to defending fighters. It remains, however, a weapon of great power

showed an inclination in favour of the defensive factors, which became overheavy in the scale compared to those for the offensive. Among these factors were the growth in the size of armies and the increased complexity of their maintenance; the wider extent of the area covered by operations; the enhanced fire power of new weapons, such as machine guns and heavy artillery, and the greater dependence of armies on the total war effort of their nations. All these made for ponderousness, slowness and congestion and militated against movement, speed and flexibility of operation. The up-to-date means in opposing armies for finding out what each other was about, such as aeroplanes and wireless detection, made it difficult for either to surprise the other. The huge scale of necessary preparations

for any major operation reduced the possibility of achieving a rapid or decisive victory. Lack of mobility and weight of attack on the side of the assailant, and the mustered strength and fire power available to the defence, rendered it difficult for the victor to make much of any partial success. The war ended rather because the conquerors had worn down the vanquished by a combination of means, many of them other than military, than in consequence of any spectacular defeat on the classic lines of Waterloo or Sedan. The Germans in the west, when the Armistice was signed, were nevertheless as completely at an end of their powers of resistance as any beaten army in history. A repetition of the war of 1914-18 might reasonably have been expected to display this same character of a long drawn-out, slow-moving drama, braked in its tempo and clogged in its development by an over-balance in favour of the defence.

The Second World War of 1940 was different. Instead we saw a swift series of dramatic episodes, culminating in the catastrophic finale which overwhelmed in a brief spell of fighting measured in weeks only, the most renowned army of Europe. France went the way of Norway, Denmark, Holland and Belgium, and the Germans, after a career of victory which had cast all Western Europe beneath their heel, had suffered fewer casualties than in the four months of fighting on the Somme in 1916. Yet the Somme fighting had brought the attackers only the paltry gain of a few square miles of battle-torn ground. The scales between offence and defence had been violently and amazingly tipped in favour of the attacker. The same phenomenon, moreover, repeated itself on a smaller scale, but with no less swift and dazzling results in Libya, in Abyssinia, in Yugoslavia, in Greece and in Crete. Once more war had been invested with its old character of a dreadful and impassioned drama, once more campaigns had become brilliant and fruitful works of art, instead of toilsome and costly mechanical operations. In what lay the secret of this violent and amazing change?

Two weapons had brought this about and restored to the offensive form of war as much power as it had ever had in any previous age of history. Yet neither of them were new weapons. One, the aeroplane, though invented early in this century, had before 1914 been regarded by soldiers only as an interesting toy. By 1918 it had become an indispensable adjunct to armies and navies, yet little more than an adjunct. An air force was

VALENTINE TANKS FIRING AS THEY ADVANCE
The power of modern tanks is here well illustrated. No country deters them, their guns are powerful and their defensive armour is strong. At speed they are difficult to hit

used mainly as an eye, rarely as an arm. Its recognized roles were to see what the enemy was doing rather than to stop him doing it, and to direct the fire of artillery rather than use fire or bomb power itself. Only in the last few months of the war did the British attempt to extend this limited field of activity by the use of an independent force to strike at long-range targets of industrial rather than strictly military importance. The Germans, also, had tried with but little success to accomplish this by the use of Zeppelins and, later, of aeroplanes.

The second of these revolutionary weapons was the armoured fighting vehicle known as the tank. The war of 1914-18 had brought it to slow and painful birth. Only the Allies used it at first and they used it timidly and badly. The Germans so under-estimated its possibilities that they not only refused to adopt it themselves, but neglected to provide themselves with special weapons against it. Yet at Cambrai, and later during the final Allied advance of 1918 in the west, the tank led the way at every stage and proved itself to be the tool of victory. Not even by the end of the war, however, had the tank emerged from its chrysalis stage as a weapon of great power but of short range, crippling limitations and hazardous unreliability. Only in an Allied plan of campaign drawn up for use in 1919 was the use of a powerful independent force of tanks, charging through the enemy's battlefront to attain long-range objectives far within his back areas, even imagined. The idea was to bear much fruit later—but the reapers were to be the Germans and not the Allies.

GERMAN REARMAMENT

France and Britain, who in 1919 had the largest air force and tank fleet in the world, in the next two decades allowed them to decay amid dreams of world peace. Germany meanwhile was dreaming of an armed revival and a war of revenge, and as far as possible she was preparing for both. By 1936, under the new Nazi régime, she was once again powerful in arms. In Spain she was able under the eyes of an apathetic world to try out the new engines and methods on which she relied for victory in the forthcoming sequel to the war of 1914-18. These new tactics were further tested in Poland against a brave but weak and unprepared enemy. After further improvements, they then triumphantly proved themselves in the new Armageddon in the west in the summer of 1940. They thus became the pattern of present-day war, to be copied by both sides, and unfortunately for Britain with far more skill and success by the enemy than by the Allies.

ANTI-TANK DEFENCE

The chief difficulty of the attacker in 1914-18 had been not so much to break *into* the strong network of the defenders' fortifications, but to break *through* it. A heavy concentration of fire power and assault weapons could always make a certain amount of progress, though with ever decreasing speed and increasing difficulty as it went. But before it could get right through, its momentum was exhausted by the depth of the obstacles before it, or the increasing tenacity of the resistance of the hostile reserves. There was no power of driving home a strong and speedy attack. The slow-moving tanks had too limited a radius of action and the artillery could not support the infantry beyond a certain line without having to shift position at a great expenditure of time and labour. The new tank of the post-war period was designed to move faster and farther, and much was hoped from it. But anti-tank defence too had increased in power and variety since 1918, so that the issue of the duel between the two remained a matter for speculation. French military thought generally

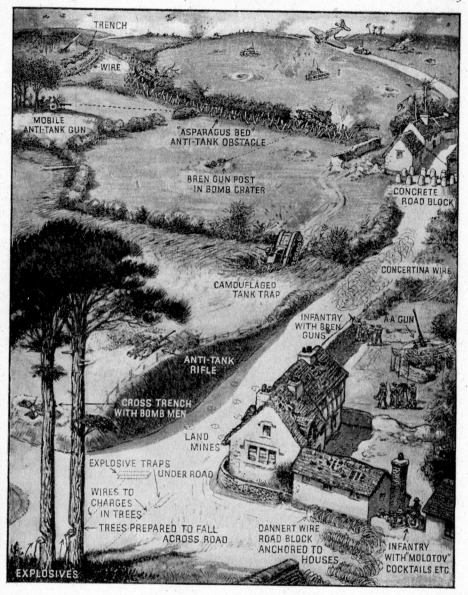

TRENCH

WIRE

MOBILE ANTI-TANK GUN

"ASPARAGUS BED" ANTI-TANK OBSTACLE

BREN GUN POST IN BOMB CRATER

CONCRETE ROAD BLOCK

CONCERTINA WIRE

CAMOUFLAGED TANK TRAP

INFANTRY WITH BREN GUNS

A-A GUN

ANTI-TANK RIFLE

CROSS TRENCH WITH BOMB MEN

LAND MINES

EXPLOSIVE TRAPS UNDER ROAD

WIRES TO CHARGES IN TREES

TREES PREPARED TO FALL ACROSS ROAD

DANNERT WIRE ROAD BLOCK ANCHORED TO HOUSES

INFANTRY WITH "MOLOTOV" COCKTAILS ETC.

EXPLOSIVES

TYPES OF TANK OBSTACLES

The revolutionary use of armoured fighting vehicles in modern warfare has made it essential to develop defences against them. Modern defence in depth consists of many devices. There are "asparagus beds" to slow them up while anti-tank weapons fire at them; concrete road blocks, wire, mines and tree traps block roads; there are also anti-tank ditches. Besides all these, anti-tank guns and rifles, "Molotov cocktails," and other weapons are used by the defending infantry. Aerial support in defence is also vital, while A.A. guns keep off enemy dive bombers. Tanks without air support are much less dangerous

The object of the Bren Carrier is
to transport Bren guns rapidly to
any required spot. The carriers
are here retiring, after leaving
their guns in the foreground

A MODERN BRITISH ARMOURED CAR

Armoured cars are much used in desert warfare. Provided they do not encounter heavily armoured tanks, their mobility and light armour is effective. The crew consists of a commander, a wireless operator and a driver. The armament consists of Besa machine-guns

considered that the tank, as in the war of 1914-18 could best be used in close co-operation with the other arms. This involved in effect accepting the latter's crippling limitations in matters of speed and range. The Germans, imitators always, but ingenious, painstaking and open-minded in military matters, found the answer to the problem of attack in quite a different technique.

ARMOURED DIVISIONS

This technique involved the use of armoured fighting vehicles, not merely as the spearhead, but as the main weapons of the attack, with the air arm as their accompanying artillery. These vehicles, mostly light and medium tanks, with a small assortment of heavier vehicles, formed the hard core of a Panzer or armoured division. To prepare the way ahead of them they had armoured cars and motor-cyclist machine gunners. For close support there were batteries of field artillery and batteries of anti-tank guns and machine guns. To occupy the ground that the tanks had overrun there was infantry carried in motor transport, able to keep up with them and allow them to go ahead from one bound to another with the minimum of delay. There were engineers to get the tanks across water obstacles, maintenance and workshop personnel to keep them in running order, and wireless and able signallers to maintain inter-communication. These were the components of the Panzer division which, in addition, had its own aircraft— the crews constantly living and working with it, so that the co-operation should be fully comradely and comprehensive. The new armoured corps was the elite of the German Army. Nothing was spared to equip it as efficiently and fully as possible; much was expected of it and its work fully came up to expectations.

The new armoured tactics consisted of an assembly of these divisions in great force and in secret before the chosen area of attack, and a vigorous mass advance after a crash bombardment of the hostile defences by guns and aircraft. Any obstacles were charged through, brushed aside, or overcome in some way by the leading waves of tanks. Often these hurled themselves into the anti-tank ditches to block the flanking fire of guns sited to command them, and thus formed a bridge over which their following comrades could cross. They even ventured recklessly into minefields through which, if they were destroyed, it would then help their comrades to clear a way. Used thus, with reckless disregard of loss, at full speed and with maximum weight, the tank units would certainly, at one point or several, succeed in bursting a way into the heart of the hostile defence network.

In all this first stage of the attack, the "break in," the co-operating aircraft of the Panzer divisions would prepare and smooth the way.

Their first task was to cripple or destroy the hostile air force. If this were not possible, it was hotly engaged to prevent it giving warning of the coming assault. By the intensive concentration of aircraft, mostly bombers, but dive bombers in particular, this first purpose was achieved.

THE DIVE BOMBER

If perhaps all the hostile machines could not be destroyed in the air or on the ground, violent and sustained bombing attacks on their aerodromes would keep them grounded and out of action for the time being. The air on the battlefield could thus be kept clear for the shorter-ranged

ROAD OBSTRUCTIONS IN FRANCE

This is an example of bad road obstruction. Modern vehicles are well able to make a detour around such elementary road blocks

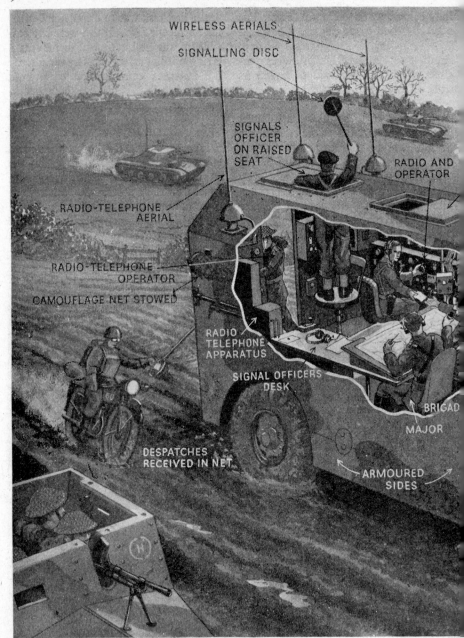

THE ARMOURED COMMAND

In a modern armoured division the tank brigades are controlled by their commanders from armoured command vehicles. These are armoured offices containing seven men. In front, next to the driver, is the intelligence officer. Inside, near a large wall map, sits the brigadier and his brigade major. There are also a signals officer and wireless operators

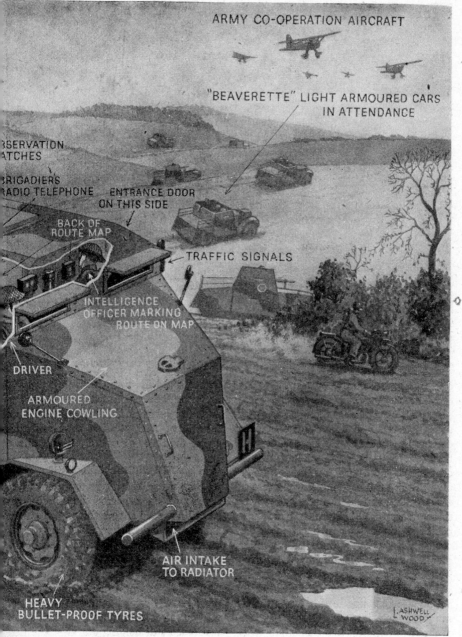

ARMY CO-OPERATION AIRCRAFT

"BEAVERETTE" LIGHT ARMOURED CARS IN ATTENDANCE

OBSERVATION HATCHES

BRIGADIERS RADIO TELEPHONE

ENTRANCE DOOR ON THIS SIDE

BACK OF ROUTE MAP

TRAFFIC SIGNALS

INTELLIGENCE OFFICER MARKING ROUTE ON MAP

DRIVER

ARMOURED ENGINE COWLING

AIR INTAKE TO RADIATOR

HEAVY BULLET-PROOF TYRES

L. ASHWELL WOOD

VEHICLE OR DORCHESTER

Communication is constantly maintained by wireless with all other vehicles and aircraft. Dispatch riders also deliver messages into a net. Being the nerve-centres of an armoured division these vehicles are carefully screened by light armoured cars, Bren carriers and armed motor cyclists. Although not tracked vehicles, they can negotiate quite rough country

HAULING AN ASSAULT BOAT INTO POSITION

Light boats are much used to ferry small groups of infantry across rivers. The men who have crossed them constitute a protective bridgehead, while more substantial crossing arrangements are made with pontoons or box girder bridges by the special engineering units

dive bombers to do their work. Easy prey to hostile fighters in aerial combat, these machines, as much by their moral as by their material effect, are formidable to defending troops on the ground. It was their task to put to flight or neutralize any centres of anti-tank resistance which might hold up the continued progress of the attacking Panzer formations. Many of these, discovered beforehand or suspected to be lurking in likely localities, could be dealt with at once; others which revealed themselves during the action would be engaged with great promptness, and accuracy, thanks to the close wireless liaison always maintained between the air squadrons and the ground troops. As soon as the dive bombers had done their work and before their victims could recover their shattered nerves and rally, armoured fighting vehicles and infantry were upon them. In this way any formidable de-

fences, sited in great depth and strongly held, could be penetrated from end to end with a speed incredible to those who from the war of 1914-18 drew false analogies about the likely course of any new one.

THE BREAK THROUGH

Once a break through, even if only a small one on a narrow and precarious front, had been successfully effected, the assailants would lever and wrench it yet wider open by swift and bold use of the tactics of infiltration. All forces within reach of the gap were collected to pour through it, leaving to their slow-moving, more heavily armed comrades the task of dealing at leisure with any islands of resistance still holding out after the first wave of battle had passed them by. Moving at full speed, the skies above and before them swept and kept clear by their co-operating aircraft, the countryside ahead and on the flanks submerged by hordes of speedy motor-cyclist machine gunners and hurtling armoured cars, the tanks and their supporting motorized arms would thrust boldly and unhesitatingly ahead in their appointed zones of action. Some, fanning out on either side of the gap through which they had passed, would turn in on the flanks and rear of the unbroken portions of the hostile defence line. This would widen in both directions the area of confusion and enable other comrades temporarily held up there to join in the victorious advance. But most of them would thrust forward deeper and even deeper into the back areas of the enemy. Here lie all the vital yet undefended administrative organizations, deprived of which an army can never fight or hold together for long. Headquarters, communications, dumps, depots, supply and transport columns, repair shops, railways, airfields—all were now the invader's prey, for it was impossible to provide them all with adequate local defence. Their effective destruction or even their temporary crippling meant

the most widespread confusion. Far beyond the range of even the boldest and farthest-flung of the mechanized ground troops, the aircraft began and carried on the same task. To disrupt the enemy's army as a fighting force by destroying the nerve centres, sinews and ganglia of its existence and resistance; to spread as wide and as deep as possible the mortal disease of panic, confusion and congestion—these were the new tactics in the field.

"FIFTH COLUMN"

So as to undermine morale much work was done even in areas yet further ahead where neither aircraft nor ground troops could penetrate. This was by the use of that systematic subterranean organization of spies, saboteurs, and traitors of all kinds, euphemistically comprised under the term "Fifth Column." By their nefarious aid even the helpless and harmless civilian population were turned into weapons against their own side. Stampeded on to the roads and kept on the run by a mixture of false or exaggerated rumour and of deliberate acts of brutal

CARRYING LIGHT PONTOONS TO THE WATER'S EDGE

Speedy bridging is most necessary in modern mobile warfare. Pontoon bridges, though vulnerable to aerial attack, can rapidly be thrown across water obstacles during an advance

terrorism and mass murder, they could be relied on to clog the roads of retreat and assistance for the forward troops of the beaten defence. Far and wide over whole provinces was spread an atmosphere of misery and fear, of defeat and disaster. Thus in Poland, in Norway, in the Low Countries and in France, strong and defensible places fell before a paltry pretence of attack or even before a miasma of menaces. Great historic lands, their physical and moral defences utterly demolished, collapsed as helpless prey before that breathless type of assault.

SPEED AND AIR POWER

By these methods Germany made herself master of Europe. Overwhelming air power not only on battlefields but over whole theatres of operations: overwhelming speed and might in the new mechanized tools of ground warfare; the organization of treachery and ruse to spread panic and terror and to destroy the enemy's morale and will to fight—these were the weapons by which these methods were put into effect—and by which alone they can be defeated.

That in these same methods lay the secret of victory in all modern war, and that their efficacy was not limited merely to the particular circumstances of a campaign in Western Europe, was shown by the equally remarkable series of British triumphs in the Western Desert of Egypt and Cyrenaica. Here a force, much smaller in numbers, but enjoying technical superiority both on the ground and in the air, attacked and defeated another equally highly mechanized and modernized army. In the space of a few weeks it was utterly destroyed at the absurdly low price of a few thousand casualties. Here, too, the combination of mechanized forces and aircraft handled with enterprise and skill triumphed over even greater technical, climatic and tactical difficulties than had confronted the German military

machine in France. The possibility of surprise hardly existed, the services of supply and maintenance were sorely strained, and the hot weather acted adversely on both men and vehicles. Even after all deductions for the indifferent quality of the opposition have been made, this was a military triumph as surprising as it was meritorious.

In Abyssinia, too, in Greece and in Yugoslavia, though the full application of the *blitzkrieg* methods of the 1940 summer campaign in the west could not be made owing to difficulties of ground and communications, the same phenomena were observed. The new form of attack had a swiftness, flexibility and weight which rose lightly over all these handicaps. The whole vast, rugged and trackless expanse of Italian East Africa was overrun between Christmas and the coming of the spring rains, the British columns performing amazing feats in the way of swift and synchronized advance. Yugoslavia and Greece were conquered by the Germans in a matter of weeks. The former, it is true, had been caught in unreadiness for war and the latter had already been engaged for some months in a successful but exhausting fight against odds. Yet the immense potency of the modern offensive was thus again and again demonstrated. Was there any reply to it? Or was it irresistible?

MODERN DEFENCE

From a theoretical point of view, it seems fairly obvious what the reply should be. In the war of 1914-18 the rigid strongly held trench defence zones were found to expose their garrisons merely to profitless annihilation under the devastating weight of steel that the attack could rain upon them. It was found necessary to thin out the garrisons of the foremost lines and deepen the zone of defence. In this way the attack was cushioned and encumbered as it

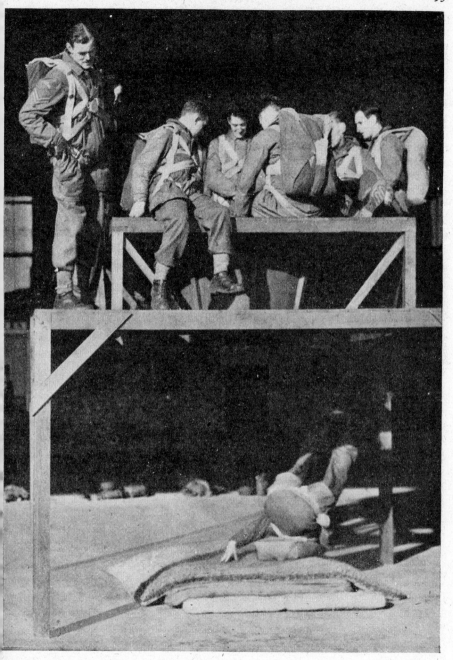

PARATROOPS LEARNING HOW TO FALL

When a parachutist comes to earth, there is a great risk of damaged limbs at the moment of contact with the ground. These men are learning to fall from a practice chute on a platform

progressed, until it finally lost so much momentum and strength that the ground it had won could be wrested from it again by the counterstroke of the defenders' reserves. Against an attack going "all out" this method proved effective enough. It failed, however, when the assailants adopted new methods and began to limit their efforts to a series of short bounds as far only as objectives up to which their artillery could give them strong support and cover. But now that the new mechanized onslaught of today has reverted to the "all out" form, with speed, violence and disregard of losses as its keynotes, it seems that the true line of defence against

it should be an adaptation of that which had earlier proved its worth. The defender must reduce to a minimum the proportion of his force devoted to holding his front lines. He must increase the depth of the battle zone by carrying it much further to the rear and must provide very strong and highly mobile reserves ready for a swift and powerful counter action at the shortest of short notice. These reserves must consist for the most part of armoured fighting vehicles and air squadrons. Even if inferior in numbers, these should be able to deal effectively with the intruders. The latter will already be nearing the end of their

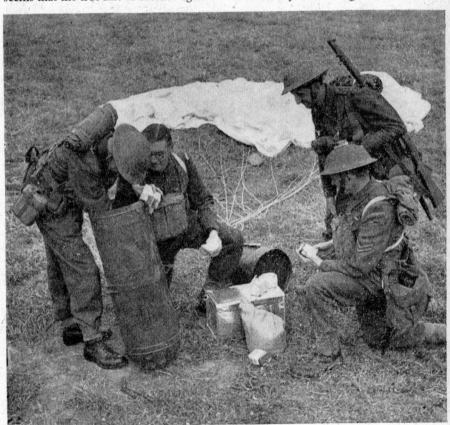

SOLDIERS UNLOADING A FOOD CONTAINER

Planes of the Army Co-operation Command practise the dropping of food containers to isolated groups of infantry. These men are unloading one of these containers when on manœuvres

A LYSANDER PLANE OF THE ARMY CO-OPERATION COMMAND

These planes are specially designed for reconnaissance work for the Army. The crews have a wide range of vision and are specially trained for their work. The pilot has to be proficient in map reading. The rear man is the air gunner. A reconnaissance conference is in progress

physical and moral energies if the forward defenders have done their duty. Anti-tank defences, artificial and natural, will be erected, selected in the heart of a defensive zone and towards its rear so as to check the hostile column in full tide of victory. The principle of a wall in front of the zone with the idea of preventing the enemy setting a foot inside it must be discarded. By judicious choice of country and by cleverly siting defences, the attempt will be made to canalize the lines of hostile advance so as to make easier the rapid and prepared action of the defending counter-attack troops. Constant all-round vigilance and instant readiness for action both on the ground and in the air, will be necessary to minimize the possibility of surprise. Stubborn resolution, courage and self-reliance will be called for on the part of the garrisons of the defended localities in the forward zone. They must be prepared to be passed by and surrounded in the rising tide of

hostile attack and may have to hold out for long periods before it ebbs again. In order that they may be able to do so, they must be made self-supporting in methods of supplies, ammunition and war material on the same scale as a besieged garrison, and lavishly provided with means of anti-tank and anti-aircraft defence. In the domain of energy, resourcefulness, self-reliance, initiative and enterprise the defence must match the attack. These qualities, the secrets of success in war, whatever the weapons used, must be displayed in the planning and preparation for the battle just as much as in the fighting of it. If there is to be any hope of success — even such success as defensive strategy and tactics can achieve—this is highly desirable and almost essential.

It is admitted that even this system of defence, though the only one that seems in any way promising, is far more difficult to apply in practice than to formulate in theory. The defender is always in some

BRITISH PARATROOPS PRACTISING THE DESCENT
*Paratroops are here seen descending from Whitley bombers. Containers full of ammunition
are dropping with them. The quicker men jump in succession, the closer together they land*

way inferior to the attacker, or he would
not be the defender. Under modern conditions that inferiority can be so rapidly
taken advantage of, and so ruthlessly and
thoroughly exploited, that effective re-
action is difficult. To be effective it must
be as swift and as forceful as the action it
is planned to counterbalance.

DEFENCE IN DEPTH

The purpose of the modern offensive
is to disrupt the hostile organization on a
wide front and to a great depth, to inter-
rupt communications and the issue of
orders, and to recognize and stifle any
attempted counter-attack before it can
begin to make itself felt. Defence in
depth is a formula less easy to apply than
to pronounce. Obviously there are limits

to the area of ground that even the
million-strong armies of today can occupy
and defend effectively. If they are to be
arranged in immense depth from front to
rear, they must either draw in their
flanks and so shorten their front, or else
must be strung out very thinly on a wide
front. Both these dispositions have their
perils; a short front risks being out-
flanked and enveloped; a thinly held one
cannot long put up effective resistance to
any serious attack. The larger the area
occupied, the more troops will have to be
locked up in defended localities and
devoted to purely passive defence. Few
will then be left available for the counter-
offensive, by which alone any ground lost
can be recovered, and the enemy be not
just held off but decisively repulsed.

Another application of attack methods, which has already shown its great and astonishing power in Crete, still further accentuates this necessity for the modern defence to spread itself over a wide field. The large scale use of air-borne and parachute troops is now added to a defender's other anxieties and preoccupations. Any day, if the attacker is possessed of command of the air, or any night, if such command is still in dispute, may see the descent of parachute troops in large numbers far behind the forward battle lines. Their mission may be purely destructive, the interruption or demolition of communications, the blocking of roads and railways, the temporary seizure of headquarters, command posts, signal centres, and telephone exchanges, the destruction of bridges and raids on supply and transport depots. Such work, even if not fully successful, will add considerably to the confusion and disorganization which it is one of the assailant's objects to bring about over a wide area. Before all the parachutists can be rounded up they will certainly have done much harm.

In Norway, the Low Countries and France their activities were mainly destructive, largely because their numbers were limited and the supplies and ammunition at their disposal were confined to what they could bring with them. Nevertheless, their direct influence on the course of these campaigns, though only local, was great. The panic and alarm caused by false or exaggerated reports of their arrival, often deliberately spread by traitor elements, were even more widespread and disastrous.

AIR ATTACK ON CRETE

In the Middle Eastern campaigns of 1941, and particularly in the invasion of Crete, this use of parachutists was developed into a well designed and completely novel form of air-borne attack, independent, in the first stages at any rate, of operations on the ground. In Crete, indeed, no such ground operations

BRITISH PARATROOPS SPEEDILY MOVING TO THE ATTACK

Intensive training is necessary for paratroops. When they land they are most vulnerable. It is essential that they land close together, remove their parachutes, collect their ammunition and stores from the containers, and make for any nearby cover at the greatest possible speed

were possible, for the only approaches to the island were by sea and of these the British Navy retained command till the end. But air command was throughout in the hands of the assailants, and this was the deciding factor. From this fully controlled air the Germans were able to rain down clouds of parachute troops.

AIR-BORNE TROOPS

With them came a formidable armament of light field guns, mortars, ammunition and supplies. Their arrival was preceded and covered by intensive dive bombing attacks. These put out of action the bulk of the ground anti-aircraft defence and sought to prevent the allied infantry and machine gunners from interfering with the actual arrival and assembly of the first of the invaders. There was, in fact, much interference, and the losses of the parachute troops were heavy. But they conquered and held enough ground to allow of their rapid reinforcement by other air-borne troops, carried in troop carriers or in towed gliders. These machines, cheap and mass produced, were got to land even at the cost of a crash which put them out of action for good, at any and every possible place in the captured areas. Recklessness of loss, if only the object aimed at were achieved, was as marked in this as in any German operation of war. Communication, quickly established by wireless with their base of operations on the mainland, brought the attackers any assistance and supplies asked for at short notice, as and where it was required. Close co-operation with the dive bomber aircraft which had covered their first arrival enabled them to consolidate and extend their foothold with rapidity. More and more troops were poured in as new space for their landing and more scope for their use offered itself. When once the attack had attained sufficient numerical superiority to offset its inferiority in armament, the issue of

the campaign was decided. With this victory the full power of an air-borne attack stood revealed for all the world to see. Yet another was added to the overwhelming and inextricable tangle of problems already besetting the unfortunate defender in modern warfare.

The statement that under the new technique, warfare has become an affair of areas, no longer of lines, is thus seen to be an understatement of the truth. In fact, the whole area of the defender's country must now be considered as a possible zone of battle. If the attacker has the requisite air superiority and resources in troop-carrying aircraft and gliders, he can now carry out widespread and far-flung air-borne attacks combined with intensive bombing. Experience appears so far to show that the most effective way of dealing with a flood of parachutists is to attack them at once before they can establish themselves—often a matter of minutes only. But how is this to be ensured over a huge area which may embrace the greater part or even the whole of a country, without risking a disastrous dispersion of forces and resources?

GROUND DEFENCE

Local levies, such as the Home Guard in Britain, are one possible answer to the problem. Much of the Home Guard's effectiveness, however, lies in the fact that at first it will have to deal with air-borne attacks alone, and that there are available to reinforce it at speed ample regular forces, better armed and provided than any hostile air-borne troops. The whole of these forces are unlikely to be simultaneously and urgently required to assist in repulsing a strong land attack. The defenders of a continental country cannot hope to be so happily situated. For them any proportion of their forces diverted to deal with—or even wait for—a powerful rear attack by air-borne troops is lost to the frontal battle, where its presence

BRITISH PARATROOPS DROPPING FROM A WHITLEY BOMBER

It is essential that paratroops follow one another rapidly when leaving their plane. These men are dropping in a group. Containers with arms and ammunition are also released at intervals

might have availed to stem the hostile tide or even to have turned it back.

Another point to be remembered in connection with the modern war of areas is that loss of territory, which was once a matter of comparatively minor military importance, is no longer equally so. In these days of "all in" war every resource of the belligerent countries and every adult member of their populations forms part of the national war effort. The destruction of important resources over a wide area is a legitimate purpose of operations. Success in this might be well worth achieving, even if the ground gained were not intended to be permanently held. Raids by land as well as by air forces, aimed solely against a vulnerable portion of the enemy's industrial war machine may be a feature of future war-

fare. The defender will have to guard against these as well as against attacks with purely military aims. The possible degree of elasticity, an essential characteristic of defence today, must therefore be limited by these and other such considerations.

INDUSTRY A FACTOR

It is clear that the problems of the defence under present conditions are most difficult and complex. It is, perhaps, not too much to say that against a competent opponent enjoying any marked superiority in the air arm or in the mechanized ground forces, they are all but insoluble. Only a highly industrialized country, well prepared and powerfully armed, can hope to engage in modern war without the certainty of being defeated and conquered. Such a conquest

PRACTISING LANDING FROM BARGES

With a view to the future, British troops are now being trained in landing from the sea by barges. These specially constructed boats are carried near to the enemy coast in warships and then driven ashore under their own power. They can also carry light mechanical vehicles

VALENTINES UNDERGOING BATTLE PRACTICE

An intelligent use of smoke screens, grenades and blank ammunition renders realistic much of the training of tank personnel. Crews learn to fight their tanks in all possible conditions

would be rapid and accompanied by devastating slaughter and destruction. The fate of the Low Countries and of Yugoslavia is symptomatic of the fate of weak or ill-prepared nations who dare to affront the modern god Mars in full panoply. The present military impotence of small and poor peoples, whose past histories contain so many a bright page of heroic battle against fearful odds, is one effect (and not the least important one) of the present heavy preponderance in warfare of the attack over the defence.

CHANGING WEAPONS

It is a common dictum that every weapon or change in tactics in time meets with its answer and that, sooner or later, the balance between attack and defence is restored. So the impenetrable but ponderous Greek phalanx went down before the supple flexibility of the Roman legion, so the armoured knight met his match in the

English archer and the Swiss pikeman; and the bow and the pike had, in time, to yield pride of place to musket and cannon. So now the firearms of today, the heavy guns, the rifles and the machine guns, have been outmatched by the combination of aeroplanes, tanks and mobile guns. This superiority too may be but temporary and uncertain and may pass when the right answer to it has been found. What is overlooked is that the discovery of these counterbalances to the preponderant weapon of the moment has never itself been a matter of moments but rather of long periods. During such a time wars have been won and lost, great empires set up and overthrown and the whole face of continents changed by these same preponderant weapons. Alexander the Great's phalanx spread Greek civilization and modes of thought over all the Middle East in its hey-day of military supremacy. The mailed horseman ruled the battlefields of Europe for some five hundred years before his supremacy came to an end. Even the brief period of less than a decade in which Prussian military weapons and methods enjoyed a temporary but definite supremacy between 1864 and 1871 enabled her to absorb Germany, extend her frontiers and establish herself as the first military power in Europe. For the weak and ill-armed, for the unwarlike and the unprepared, there is small comfort in this theory. Research may soon—for necessity is the mother of invention—bring to light some effective counter-weapon. But, meanwhile, the only effective answer to the aeroplane or the tank would seem to be another aeroplane and another tank. When a nation can match aeroplane with aeroplane, tank with tank, its defence is effective enough to deal with the new form of attack. If it can match two for one, and these two of better quality, it is able itself to wield the attack weapon, and so gain final victory.

OLDER ARMS STILL EFFECTIVE

We must not assume then that the older arms—the foot-slogging infantry, the machine guns which in the war of 1914-18 were lords of the battlefield, the guns of all calibres which paved the way for every attack—are all now outworn relics of a shadowy past, utterly without value for modern war. There are many circumstances in which these would be not merely the principal, but the only weapons that can be used. In mountains or forest country, in terrain where the mechanized forces cannot go or cannot be maintained, the older arms must still carry the main burden of the war. Here too, the defensive may well assert its superiority over the offensive, as happened in Albania where tanks had little room in which to work and could not operate in large numbers. In such country anti-tank defences cannot be rapidly overrun and will be able to take such a heavy toll as to

bring any small-scale mechanized attack to a halt. A crushing air superiority, however, will even have to be of permanent value. As the operations in Crete have shown, it will enable the older arms to achieve victory, though more slowly and with heavier loss than would have been the case had it been possible to use armoured fighting vehicles for the task.

THEIR CHANGED ROLES

Even in fully mechanized warfare, therefore, these older arms must play their parts. But these parts will be subordinate and auxiliary to those of the aeroplanes and the tanks, to which the leading role has, for the time being, definitely fallen. Where infantry once led the army, it must now follow to clear up the debris of resistance still holding out after the tanks have passed by. It must moreover be motor-borne in order that it may do so quickly and thoroughly over as wide an area as possible. The role of heavy artillery, requiring mountains of heavy shells to feed it, has now once again become limited to action before heavily fortified and densely manned positions. What is required of the artillery of today is that it should be no heavier than is consistent with high power of movement and manœuvre. It must be able to accompany or closely follow the troops it is supporting wherever they go, and be always in intimate and close touch with them, ready for constant service at short call. Engineers, too, have to be as highly mobile as those forward units, whether tanks or infantry, whom it is their principal duty to assist and maintain. Their bridging trains must be got up quickly and yet be capable of dealing with swifter moving and greater weights than ever before in history.

On the signal service, a particularly severe responsibility rests. The task of keeping in touch with each of the widely separated units of swiftly moving armies

BRITISH TANKS MANŒUVRING

Close-order driving in armoured vehicles is a difficult matter. Efficiency in manœuvre and gunnery are all-important in action. A driver learns to turn his tank anywhere at will

B.M.A.—D*

BRITISH PARATROOPS MARCH TO THEIR
Fully armed, with folded parachutes on their backs, these men are going aboard at an airfield.

operating over great areas of country is as difficult as it is vital to victory. The problems of collecting and dealing with casualties by the medical services have become not less important but far more difficult. The problem of the supply of food, ammunition, and especially petrol remains as vital as ever, yet more difficult than ever. Without petrol, tanks and lorries die on their tracks and become mere scrap iron—and though the daily distribution of food and ammunition can sometimes be dispensed with by mechanized columns, these cannot continue self-contained for long together. The supply services, moreover, like any other part of the modern army, can no longer think of themselves as non-combatant. They must be prepared at any time of the day or night to be attacked by aircraft or by enemy armoured fighting vehicles.

Europe's latest war has in fact not superseded these older arms—far from it.

It has made their roles less spectacular and less easy, but by no means less valuable or less vital than ever they were in the past.

On leadership, too, new demands are made. There is still the need for more forethought, for the wide grasp, for careful and detailed preparations, for prudence and a sense of realities and possibilities. But the call now will be even more insistently for alertness of mind, for swift decision, for boldness and for driving power. Only men of this calibre can handle to the best effect the powerful, fast moving, yet fragile weapons that modern war has placed at their disposal. The German Army has shown that it has known how to find, train and use such men. The British Army has proved, and will prove again, that it is no whit behind its foes in this respect.

Yet it remains true that no army, however brave, however venturous, however well led, can win without an ample and

PLANES FOR A PRACTICE FLIGHT
Armstrong-Whitworth Whitley bombers in the background are often used as transport planes

indeed superabundant supply of the best weapons that a rich and powerful country can devise and manufacture. Within certain limits, superiority in numbers can compensate for inferior quality, and this important factor of success in the past has been on the enemy's side. Until that numerical inferiority has been ironed out to something more like equality, no enduring military success is possible.

When all the soldiers of an army have been recruited and all the weapons needed have been made and issued, the men still have to learn to use their weapons before that army can take the field as an effective force fit to fight battles and win victories. That is not a matter of days or weeks, nor is time devoted to it other than well spent. No one would expect to become master of a highly technical civil trade after anything but a considerable apprenticeship. The army of today is an army of craftsmen. Nor is

there any settled standard of attainment for it other than something better than the best, for any army's job is not merely to attain a high technical degree of proficiency, but to beat the enemy. War is not a qualifying, but a competitive examination. Strength is not enough; only superior strength counts.

Yet with all war's new paraphernalia of complicated and variegated equipment, the basic factors of victory are today, and will be tomorrow, what they have ever been. Leadership, valour, skill, morale—these are not less but more essential than before. These can compensate for many, but not too many, deficiencies in the material factors of war, though it is neither wise nor just to rely on them to excess. But without these qualities, the best and most up-to-date equipment will merely in the end form so much booty for a better enemy. Moral and material factors must be combined for victory.

A BRITISH 3.7-INCH. A.A. GUN

These powerful guns have proved very successful. They are mobile and have an all-round traverse. The man in the right foreground is sighting the gun while the others load it

CHAPTER 5

The Royal Artillery

Anti-aircraft gunnery. Range-finders and predictors. Searchlights. Types of guns. A.A. organization. Coast artillery. Artillery of the field army. Anti-tank and mountain guns. Heavy guns, guns and howitzers. Divisional artillery organization. Parts of guns. Laying guns. Elementary ballistics. Observation posts and signalling. Types of gunfire

GUNS, and still more guns, of every kind are wanted today, as never before. The Battle of France showed the irresistible power of boldly handled modern tanks, against a force poorly equipped with aircraft, tanks, and anti-aircraft and anti-tank guns. In the Battle for Britain, on the other hand, the fighter pilots, making up by their quality for their smaller number, won by a narrow margin. Their heroic efforts were ably seconded by anti-aircraft guns. A shortage of anti-aircraft guns has, on several other occasions, proved a severe handicap to forces on the defensive.

When in 1914 the anti-aircraft gunner made his battlefield début it was the fashion to poke fun at him for his seeming inability to get his bursts into the same cubic mile of sky as his quarry. Soon he improved, and a year later was taking a steady, if small, toll. The average of all combatants for the whole of the war of 1914-18 was one aeroplane shot down by gunfire for every six to seven thousand shells fired. Striking evidence of a radical improvement since then in guns, ammunition, instruments, and methods is to be found in the mounting total of enemy losses. We know that the guns defending Britain have a bag of several hundred to their credit. This is a remarkable achievement when one takes into consideration the vastly increased speeds and all-round improvement in performance of modern aircraft. It is heartening to know that modern guns are proving to be a more formidable menace to contemporary aircraft than were those of the last war to the much slower ones of their day.

This question of speed and the great height at which he finds his target are the two things that mark off the anti-aircraft gunner's problem from that of the field and coast artilleryman.

The angle at which we have to raise our eyes above the earth to follow an aeroplane is known to him as the angle of sight. This angle is a relatively constant factor of secondary importance in a field or coast artillery shoot. To the anti-aircraft gunner it is a major factor and is one that may, and usually does, change continually in the course of a single engagement.

A.A. GUNNERS' PROBLEMS

The elements of his problem are, first, to burst his shell at a given point in the sky, and secondly, to ensure so far as lies within his power, that shell and aeroplane shall be at that point in space together at one and the same instant.

Let us suppose that the time of flight of the shell is twenty seconds. In this time an aeroplane moving at 270 miles an hour (in still air) will fly a mile and a half. This is the pilot's period of grace, and it is always open to him to make some unforeseen move while the shell is on its way up to him. Should he do so he will upset all calculations and the shell will in all probability miss him.

He may elect to change his course, his height, or his speed; any one of these, all three, or any two. It is necessary to make an assumption about what he will do. The simplest is that he will alter none of them; and fortunately there is some justification for this convenient supposition. He may fail to see the gun flash and fly on, unaware that he is being fired at; he may be "on course" for bombing and reluctant to make a change. We now proceed on this definite assumption.

Height is measured by a height-finding range-finder and, once found, is taken as constant for a shoot. Although course and speed are also taken as constant; the presentation of the target to the guns changes from moment to moment. The chief variables are angle of sight, as explained above, direction and range, on which time of flight, and therefore fuze length too, chiefly depend.

An instrument of complicated design and great precision—the predictor—is used for following the target. This robot mathematician keeps constant track of the momentary state of all the variables, measures the rates at which they are changing and, casting forward, "predicts" from these rates all the necessary data for the chosen future instant. Moreover, it keeps the gun crews continuously posted to the second by means of mechanical transmission with all the information they

A.A. SPOTTERS AT WORK

These men are adjusting a height-finding range-finder on to an enemy plane. When once they have found the height it is taken as being constant throughout the shoot. In view of the speed of modern aircraft, men have to be highly trained to register the height quickly

DEFENDERS OF BRITAIN'S CITIES

This anti-aircraft battery is firing a salvo at night against enemy raiders. The weight of metal hurled into the air makes anything except high flying extremely dangerous to the enemy. Modern methods of ranging and location have made A.A. fire very much more accurate than before

require for bursting their shells at the chosen point in the aeroplane's path at the precise moment when it is due to reach it.

This method assumes a target always in full view. No attempt is made to range, that is to observe the bursts and correct the fire on to the target by trial and error. The aim is to gain effect from the early rounds before the airman's attention has been drawn to the fact that he is being shot at. Here the element of chance comes in. Even if all the data have been accurately determined, shells will not fly nor fuzes burn—or "tick," for some are clockwork—to expectation with mathematical exactitude. Also a shell may burst very close to its target without the splinters doing any vital harm, though on the other hand, of course, a splinter from one bursting far off might kill the pilot.

In cloudy weather the target may be only intermittently visible, if indeed it is visible at all. By night, high flying aircraft are seldom effectively illuminated by searchlights and this brings us to the problem of the unseen target.

There is no burking the fact that, hard though it may be to get, exactly the same data by night as by day are needed by the guns. There are sound locators and methods for using them, but sound is at best a fickle medium susceptible to many disturbing influences. More modern methods for engaging the unseen target have been devised and are being used and developed; when guns now engage aircraft by night it is certainly no longer a case of a shot in the dark.

Anti-aircraft guns also have a subsidiary value. In addition to shooting to kill, they do so to deter and also to baulk. Further, their bursting shells serve as pointers for fighters to the whereabouts of enemy aircraft. Because searchlights and sound locators have only a small value as a rule as aids to shooting, it should not therefore be supposed that their total value is small.

The lights, even if they do not actually illuminate a target for a fighter pilot, at least give him some indication of the approximate position of the enemy. The power of modern searchlights has been increased; they can now be concentrated at a great height upon an enemy, unless the clouds are low and heavy.

The principal types of anti-aircraft guns are the 4·5-inch, the 3·7-inch and the 3-inch. They all use H.E. shell and gain their effects by their fragments or splinters (popularly miscalled "shrapnel," which is no longer used for the purpose). All the field army anti-aircraft guns and a proportion of those specifically allotted to home defence are mobile.

The remainder, including those allotted for the defence of the ports of the Empire, are static. The light anti-aircraft weapon, the Bofors gun, which fires chargers of four shells, each weighing approximately two pounds, is mobile. It is the particular and deadly enemy of the dive bomber. It has a rapid rate of fire, is designed to obtain direct hits on low flying aircraft and frequently scores them.

The anti-aircraft formation next above the regiment is the brigade. In the field, this is the highest anti-aircraft formation. At home, however, the Air Defence of Great Britain units have, above brigades, their own ladder of divisions, corps and finally Anti-Aircraft Command. The

A.A. ARTILLERY ORGANIZATION

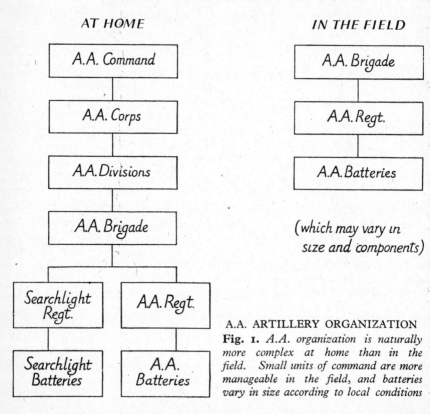

AT HOME

A.A. Command

A.A. Corps

A.A. Divisions

A.A. Brigade

Searchlight Regt.   A.A. Regt.

Searchlight Batteries   A.A. Batteries

IN THE FIELD

A.A. Brigade

A.A. Regt.

A.A. Batteries

(which may vary in size and components)

A.A. ARTILLERY ORGANIZATION
Fig. 1. *A.A. organization is naturally more complex at home than in the field. Small units of command are more manageable in the field, and batteries vary in size according to local conditions*

FIRING A BRITISH A.A. GUN

These guns are very powerful and mobile. As soon as the shell is loaded into the breech the lanyard is pulled. Another shell is ready in the background and will be loaded the moment the empty shell case has been ejected. The gun has an all-round traverse and the sighting and traversing adjustments are done by the two men seated in front near the wheels

general officer commanding-in-chief of this command works in the closest co-operation with, and to an extent, under the orders of the air officer commanding-in-chief, Fighter Command, R.A.F. (Fig. 1).

Coast artillery has two roles of first-class importance. The threat of invasion by sea was, in the Second World War, revived as a live issue and a working premise for many British defensive preparations. It is the function of coast artillery to deal wholesale with invading forces, sink them by the shipload, and reduce the survivors to a remnant to be handled in detail by the beach defences.

This potential and perhaps temporary role should not be allowed to obscure the age-old function of coast artillery, as

important today as ever it was. The ports at home and throughout the Empire required by the Royal Navy and the Mercantile Marine must at all times be protected against attacks by enemy surface craft of any kind from battleships to E-boats. Coast artillery guns, assisted close inshore at night by coast artillery searchlights perform this duty.,

Guns mounted on shore enjoy a four-fold advantage over guns mounted in a ship. Their target is large and conspicu-ous, whereas they are themselves often difficult to pick out from their background and surroundings. They have a steady platform, and the guns aboard a ship a moving one. Ammunition storage and supply are simpler to arrange on land than on the sea. Facilities for range finding are better from shore than from a ship.

The diversity of potential attacking ships is matched by the variety of coast artillery guns from 15-inch down to 12-pounders and even smaller pieces. Intermediate types are the 9·2-inch, 6-inch and 4·7-inch. It was a 6-inch battery which, though heavily out-gunned, gave the German cruiser *Blücher* a mauling off the Hartlepools in the war of 1914-18. Guns are used, not howitzers; and they use armour piercing, high explosive, or shrapnel shell according to the nature of their target and the calibre of the gun. The numbers and kinds of guns mounted at different places are governed by the importance of the place and the local probabilities and possibilities of attack. Compared with guns of the field army,

coast artillery guns, calibre for calibre, have a more rapid rate of fire. All the guns are kept at a high pitch of readiness. In fair weather or foul, by night as well as by day, gun look-outs, often clad in sou'-westers, do sentry-go in front of every gun and keep an unremitting vigil on the sea. Every hour or two they are relieved by other men from the gun detachments. These rest fully dressed in the gun floor shelters, close in rear, ready to spring into instant action at the first sign of the approach of a suspicious vessel.

There are two other types of artillery regiments that may be briefly noted here before going on to the artillery of the field army. First, there are the "Defence" regiments and batteries. Movable rather than mobile in the full sense, they are used for the local gun defence of coastal

LIGHT COASTAL DEFENCE GUN

Coastal watch is kept on the shores of Britain. This light gun is specially designed to deal with possible enemy sea-raiders in small craft. It is mobile and has a very high rate of fire

A HEAVY BRITISH GUN

This great gun is in sharp contrast to the coastal gun opposite. It is loaded by power apparatus and fires a very heavy shell. Naturally, it is slower to load and fire, and its destructive power is much greater. The emplacement is constructed of concrete and steel

and inland areas against the incursion of tanks and infantry. Secondly, "Maritime" regiments provide an organization for those artillerymen who go to sea to man the guns in our troopships. Like the younger members of a big family—and these two types are the youngest—they inherit the useful cast-offs of their elder brothers. They have indeed a miscellaneous, but useful, collection of guns.

The artillery of the field army comprises many types of regiments and batteries. The biggest class are those armed with 25-pounders, namely, horse and field artillery. The others are anti-tank, medium, heavy, mountain and survey regiments ; and there are some batteries of super heavy artillery.

Horse artillery regiments (they have no horses now, but the title will die hard) are included in the armoured divisions, where they continue to share the fortunes of the cavalry regiments (now in armoured fighting vehicles), their former comrades of the horsed days. The men are hand-picked. The officers are taken from amongst those who are alert in mind, quick physically, good quick "shots" with their guns, knowledgeable tactically, and with a good eye for country. Formerly they had also to be expert horsemen and horsemasters. All these qualities and more are required for the tempo of the rapid movements of spearhead troops in the hurly-burly of modern war.

Field artillery regiments, the preponderating type of artillery with the field army, are present in fixed proportions in the divisions. They stand in the same relation to infantry as do the horse artillery

THE BRITISH 25-POUNDER GUN-HOWITZER

This is the main armament of the field artillery. It is a compromise between a gun and a howitzer. While very mobile, it is well able to knock out enemy tanks and destroy other armoured vehicles. It can also effectively drop shells from a high angle behind enemy cover

regiments to the cavalry. Additional regiments, called army field regiments, are at the disposal of corps and higher formations for reinforcing purposes. The 25 - pounder which, having variable charges, is technically a gun-howitzer, is a general purpose weapon. It is used for harassing fire, counter battery and defensive fire, for barrage work and concentrations. For all these H.E. shells are fired. It has no shrapnel. It can also be used as an anti-tank weapon, for which role it has special ammunition.

2-POUNDER ANTI-TANK GUN

The menace of the modern tank with its power, speed and range, in a phrase its battle winning potential, lends great importance to the design and handling of the anti-tank gun. Anti-tank regiments have a proud post in the field army. They are fortunate in their weapon which has

already proved its worth. Designed expressly and exclusively for engaging tanks, the 2-pounders have no other function but to destroy as many of them as possible. The gun is accurate and has a high velocity armour piercing projectile which immobilizes any tank that is fairly struck within the prescribed ranges of engagement. The gun crews are trained to hold their fire until the chances of hitting with their very first round amount almost to certainty.

The rugged country of the North-West Frontier province of India is the peace time home of the mountain artilleryman. Wherever guns are required in places inaccessible to wheels or tracks the mountain batteries come into their own. Their weapon is the 3·7-inch howitzer which with its carriage and ammunition is readily divisible into separate pack mule loads. Like the old screw gun of Kipling's days the piece itself divides into two loads —chase and breech. The mules led by men on foot move at a fast walk on the level and can often be seen overtaking infantry in order to bring guns into action ahead of a marching column. "Where the infantryman can climb," they say, "there the mountain gun can go." The way they take their guns up and down the mountain sides to seemingly inaccessible spots has to be seen to be believed possible.

BIG GUNS

Big guns have a glamour of their own. They are to be found in the Medium regiments — 60-pounder guns, 6-inch howitzers; Heavy regiments — 6 - inch guns, 8-inch and 9·2-inch howitzers; Super-Heavy batteries—guns up to 15-inch and 12-inch howitzers. Most of these weapons were represented in the "siege" batteries of the war of 1914-18.

The difference between a gun and a howitzer may be noted here. Guns used invariably to have a single charge or weight of propellant, whereas howitzers had, and still have, a number of charges (Fig. 2). This matter of charges constituted by definition the technical distinction between the two weapons. The other difference is merely one of appearance. A howitzer is shorter and more stocky looking than a gun of the same calibre. The advantages that variable charges confer are: ease of crest clearance at short ranges, reduction in gun wear by choosing the smallest charge that will "make" the range, and the use of high projection to gain a steep angle of descent when attacking personnel or material behind or under cover. The introduction of variable charges for some of the guns

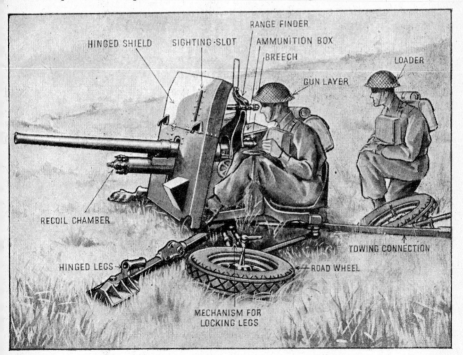

THE 2-POUNDER ANTI-TANK GUN
This is a light, highly mobile gun used against armoured fighting vehicles. The wheels are detachable and the legs are splayed. The armour-piercing shells fired can knock out tanks

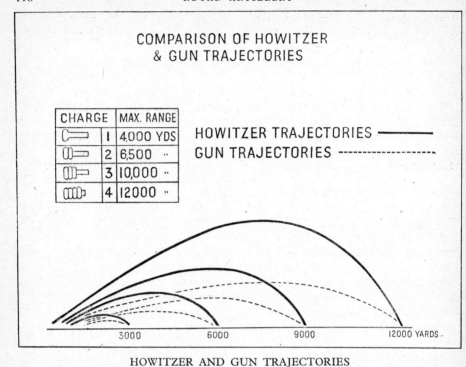

COMPARISON OF HOWITZER
& GUN TRAJECTORIES

CHARGE		MAX. RANGE
	1	4,000 YDS
	2	6,500 "
	3	10,000 "
	4	12000 "

HOWITZER TRAJECTORIES ————
GUN TRAJECTORIES --------------

3000   6000   9000   12000 YARDS

HOWITZER AND GUN TRAJECTORIES

Fig. 2. *The difference between guns and howitzers is that a gun has a single weight of propellant, whereas a howitzer has a variable number of charges. The steeper angle of descent of the howitzer shell makes it the more effective in attacking personnel behind cover*

has weakened the validity of the old definition, and has given currency to the well-known hybrid term "gun-howitzer."

For those interested in the shell weights of the different pieces, a good rough rule is that the weight of the shell in pounds is one-half the cube of the calibre measured in inches. For example, by this rule 6-inch and 15-inch shells would weigh respectively 108 lb. (half of 6×6×6 lb.) and 1,688 lb. (half of 15×15×15 lb.); actually a 6-inch shell weighs 100 lb. and the average weight of three types of 15-inch gun and howitzer shells is 1,797 lb.

MEDIUM AND HEAVY GUNS

Medium weapons have less mobility but considerably greater shell power than field guns. They are much used for counter battery work, and are intended for the destruction of material and field works rather than for attacking personnel. Heavy artillery and super-heavy artillery are used for longer range work and to secure greater disruptive effects.

Every gunner always wants to know exactly where his guns are, and in what direction and how far off his target lies. All the regiments ("less anti-tank"—to use a military phrase) consequently look to the survey units when in need of accurate data. These units have the triple function of surveying, flash-spotting and sound-ranging.

Surveying brings to mind the slow process of deliberate observation and measurement followed by leisurely calculation, and an atmosphere quite foreign to the stress and urgency of battle. Modern survey units, however, use quick field methods and seek results in hours rather than in days. The amount and accuracy of what they are able to do in a given period of time depends upon the state of their training, the amount of trigonometrical data available to them in the particular theatre of operations, and the nature of the terrain over which they have to work.

FLASH SPOTTING

Flash spotting and sound ranging have to do with the location of the enemy's guns. In the hours of darkness and half light the flash-spotters keep watch from a chain of stations from each of which an instrument is aligned on the flash when a gun fires, and on the core of the flash when it fires again. The rays from the different stations are plotted. At their intersection is the enemy's gun position. Working on similar lines, but in the medium of sound instead of light, the mechanical ears of the sound-rangers' microphones can detect the position of the enemy's guns and of our own shell bursts. Thus they go further than the flash spotters. The gunners adjust the position of the shell bursts until the sound rangers tell them that it is in the same spot as that from which the sound of the enemy gun came. Since flash-spotters and sound-rangers obviously cannot tell accurately where flash or sound came from until they know exactly where they are themselves, and in what direction they are looking or listening, it will be appreciated that they both seriously need what is known as internal survey.

In the Field Artillery, a very important man, entitled the Number One, and usually a sergeant, commands each sub-section. This consists of one gun with its

DIVISIONAL ARTILLERY.

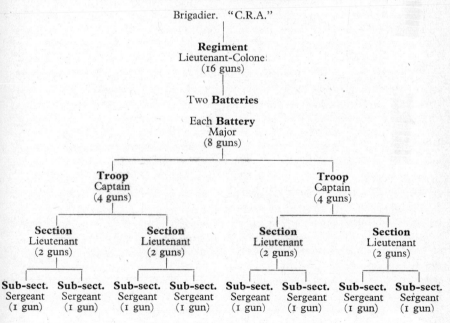

Brigadier. "C.R.A."

Regiment
Lieutenant-Colonel
(16 guns)

Two **Batteries**

Each **Battery**
Major
(8 guns)

Troop Captain (4 guns)		**Troop** Captain (4 guns)	
Section Lieutenant (2 guns)	**Section** Lieutenant (2 guns)	**Section** Lieutenant (2 guns)	**Section** Lieutenant (2 guns)

Sub-sect. Sergeant (1 gun) **Sub-sect.** Sergeant (1 gun) **Sub-sect.** Sergeant (1 gun) **Sub-sect.** Sergeant (1 gun) **Sub-sect.** Sergeant (1 gun) **Sub-sect.** Sergeant (1 gun) **Sub-sect.** Sergeant (1 gun) **Sub-sect.** Sergeant (1 gun)

THE COMPOSITION OF A REGIMENT OF ARTILLERY

Fig. 3. *Batteries vary in number of guns, but above is shown the usual make-up of a Field Artillery Regiment. The battery, or on occasion the troop, is the normal fire-unit in a regiment*

detachment and its complement of ammunition, equipment, and, if mobile, of transport. Thereafter like a multiplication table, the artillery regimental organization commonly runs: two sub-sections, one section; two sections, one troop; two (or more) troops, one battery; and two (or more) batteries, one regiment. Section, troop, battery and regiment have two, four, eight (or more) and sixteen (or more) guns each and are commanded respectively by a subaltern, a captain, a major, and a lieutenant-colonel. The last mentioned is the C.O., who shoulders the responsibility for the technical and tactical performance of his regiment (Fig. 3).

The variation of the number of guns in a battery is great. It may have one, two, three, four, eight, twelve and even sixteen guns, according to the type of artillery. The biggest coast and super-heavy weapons are to be found in single-gun batteries. A heavy battery has four guns; eight is the normal figure for field and medium batteries. Anti-tank and light anti-aircraft have the highest figures.

The battery, or on occasion, troop, is the fire unit—that is, the biggest unit the fire of which one man will personally observe or otherwise control on to one target. In coast artillery the fire command is the area of water over which one man will exercise fire control irrespective of the number of guns that can be brought

A BRITISH 9·2 HOWITZER FIRING

This powerful coastal howitzer, with its barrel at full recoil, is seen firing a shell weighing some 400 lb. The range of a howitzer is varied by the use of different charges behind the shell

THE EYES OF A COASTAL GUN

In the recording room of a coastal battery all the details of range, position and angle of sight of a target are worked out instantly on this telescope mechanism before the battery fires

to bear on it. Although guns are usually fought in troop or in battery, some may be dispersed in action singly: then the No. 1 steps into as fine an independent command as a non-commissioned officer could ever wish for.

A divisional artillery is commanded by a C.R.A. (Commander, Royal Artillery). Corps artillery units are commanded by a C.C.R.A. (Commander, Corps Royal Artillery). These two officers take their orders from the divisional and corps commander respectively. At each Army Headquarters, and at General Headquarters, artillery policy and technique are coordinated by still more senior artillery officers under the orders of army commanders and the commander-in-chief.

The gunner's true weapon is the shell and not the gun. But the gun serves two essential purposes: first, to confine the power gases behind the base of the shell so as to give it the desired initial, or muzzle, velocity; and secondly, to ensure that the shell, when fired from the gun, is projected in the correct initial direction.

To facilitate movement laterally and also up and down, the actual gun, piece or barrel, is mounted about its point of balance in a carriage (if it is mobile) or in a mounting (if it is static). Lateral movement is effected by means of a traversing gear, a common form of which is the worm allowing some degrees of movement on either side of a central line (Fig. 4). If more traverse is required the trail is lifted and the gun is pivoted bodily about its wheels. Anti-tank and light anti-aircraft guns have "all-round" traverse, the traversing gear operating on a circle.

For any up and down movement guns are provided with elevating gears, a feature of which is a toothed arc (Fig. 5). Common additions are an elevation indicator which shows the tilt of the gun in the firing position, and a quick-release arrangement to allow the gun to be moved directly to its firing position from a

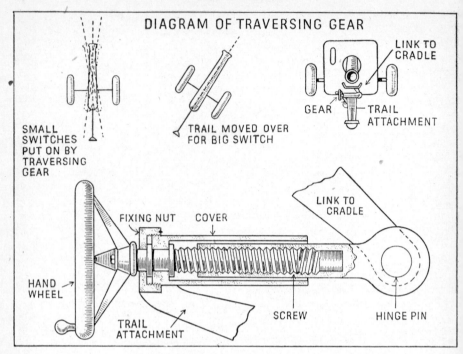

DIAGRAM OF TRAVERSING GEAR

LINK TO CRADLE

SMALL SWITCHES PUT ON BY TRAVERSING GEAR

TRAIL MOVED OVER FOR BIG SWITCH

GEAR   TRAIL ATTACHMENT

FIXING NUT   COVER

LINK TO CRADLE

HAND WHEEL

TRAIL ATTACHMENT

SCREW   HINGE PIN

THE TRAVERSING GEAR OF A GUN

Fig. 4. *By means of a hand wheel the barrel of a gun can be moved laterally through some degrees. To move the barrel farther laterally the whole trail of the gun is switched*

horizontal loading position by bearing down heavily upon the top of the breech.

The function of the breech mechanism is to facilitate rapid loading, to house the firing arrangements, and to prevent the escape of power gases. Some mechanisms close automatically as the shell is loaded. Examples of this are to be found in the 3-inch anti-aircraft gun and the 2-pounder anti-tank gun. Others are hand operated throughout; loading in the heavier classes is power operated. The firing mechanism usually embodies a striker which is cocked trigger fashion against the compression of a spring. The cocking and release is done in one motion by pulling the firing lever or firing lanyard (Fig. 6). When the spring is released a firing pin flies forward and striking a percussion cap on a primer or firing tube, ignites the cartridge or propelling charge. Some guns are fired electrically. The breech screw is locked in the firing position by the engagement of its threads with corresponding threads inside the gun just behind the chamber. These threads are of steel strong enough to withstand the enormous pressures (of the order of fifteen tons to the square inch) generated when the charge explodes. The pressure forces the sides of a brass cartridge case against the walls of the chamber, or by pressing against a mushroom head on the front of the breech screw squeezes out a circular sealing ring or obturator.

The elevation indicator, as said, marks the tilt or elevation of the piece relative to its carriage or mounting. The sights, broadly speaking, relate this angle, and also the horizontal direction in which the piece is pointing, to its target or to other known points on the ground. The fact that the guns of a high sited coast battery are at a constant level, within the limits of tide, above their targets is turned to account in the automatic sight, which is in effect a range-finder with a vertical base. The mere act of laying on the target through a telescope ensures that the correct range is on the gun. If the target as seen from the guns is moving, say from right to left, the required left lead is set on a deflection scale. This has the effect of moving the eyepiece of the telescope over to the left and so making the telescope itself point to the right of the target. The gun and sights are now swung bodily together over to the left until the telescope is pointing at the target once more. The gun now not only has the correct range on, but is pointing the right amount ahead of the ship to allow for its movement during the flight of the shell. Similarly, arrangements for deflection are included in the sights of anti-tank guns, certain anti-aircraft guns and field guns.

What might be called a standard set of sights as used with field guns, and with small modification with medium also and other types, incorporates other features. First, there is the sight clinometer (Fig. 7), for adding to, or subtracting from, the angle of elevation on the gun—informally referred to above as tilt—the amount due to the difference in level between gun and target. This amount is usually small except when shooting at aircraft. Next there is a dial sight for measuring horizontal angles. This consists of a circular plate graduated so that it can be set in degrees and minutes at any angle round the circle. By setting the sight to the appropriate angle and then turning gun and sight together until the latter is aligned on the aiming mark the gun will point in the required horizontal direction. The aiming mark might be any distant prominent point like a church spire to a flank, or aiming posts might be used. These are the little black and white painted metal rods, to be seen planted in pairs in front of or behind each gun in line with the dial sight. Then there is a telescope sight chiefly used for anti-tank

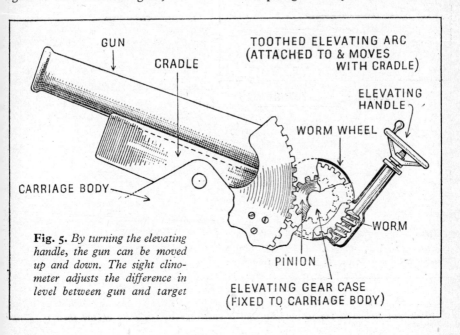

Fig. 5. *By turning the elevating handle, the gun can be moved up and down. The sight clinometer adjusts the difference in level between gun and target*

shooting, and finally an open sight for use when poor visibility prevents the layer from seeing his target clearly enough through the telescope.

The gunner is concerned with ensuring as best he can that his shell shall strike a given object or that it shall burst at a given point. Laying is simply the process of pointing the gun in the right direction to secure this result. Since a shell comes under the influence of gravity and has a tendency to fall from the instant that it leaves the gun, the muzzle must be aimed at a point higher than the target. The process of doing this is called "laying for elevation." The sights must also be pointed towards the target—this is called "laying for line." When these two operations have been accurately completed the gun is said to be "laid" (Fig. 7).

The two methods of laying are "direct" and "indirect." In the first the layer can see his target and aligns his telescope or open sight upon it, like a rifleman. Anti-tank, light anti-aircraft, always, coast artillery guns usually, are laid direct. Other guns can be laid direct at need. When the target is "on the other side of the hill," as it usually is in the field, recourse is had to indirect laying. The position of the target is found from a map, or by survey methods, or it may be necessary to get its direction, range and height from a point from which it is visible and then solve some triangles. The direction, or line, is set on the dial sight, range is set on the elevation indicator as at direct laying, difference of height is converted into an angle of sight and is set on the sight clinometer. The gun is then laid, and if a tunnel could be bored through the hill along the line of sight the layer would see his target at the end of it.

Over naval and aerial gunners, and

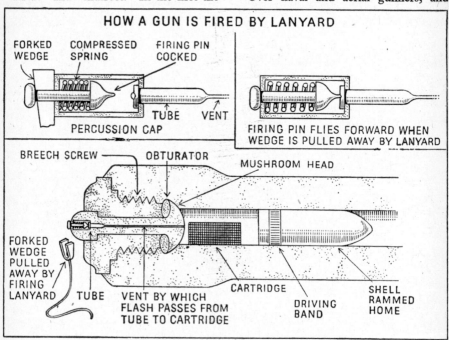

HOW A GUN IS FIRED BY LANYARD

FORKED WEDGE   COMPRESSED SPRING   FIRING PIN COCKED

TUBE   VENT

PERCUSSION CAP

FIRING PIN FLIES FORWARD WHEN WEDGE IS PULLED AWAY BY LANYARD

BREECH SCREW   OBTURATOR   MUSHROOM HEAD

FORKED WEDGE PULLED AWAY BY FIRING LANYARD   TUBE   VENT BY WHICH FLASH PASSES FROM TUBE TO CARTRIDGE   CARTRIDGE   DRIVING BAND   SHELL RAMMED HOME

THE FIRING MECHANISM OF A GUN

Fig. 6. *The firing mechanism has a striker which is released when the lanyard is pulled. A firing pin strikes a percussion cap and a cartridge at the base of the shell is ignited*

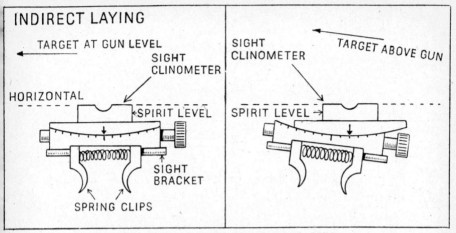

INDIRECT LAYING

TARGET AT GUN LEVEL

SIGHT
CLINOMETER

HORIZONTAL

SPIRIT LEVEL

SIGHT
BRACKET

SPRING CLIPS

SIGHT
CLINOMETER

TARGET ABOVE GUN

SPIRIT LEVEL

THE SIGHT CLINOMETER OF A GUN

Fig. 7. *By means of this instrument the difference in level between gun and target is either added to, or subtracted from, the angle of elevation on the gun. The difference, except when firing at aircraft, is usually small, but it is of essential importance to accurate shooting*

gunners in tanks, the artillery layer has the advantage of a gun at rest. But the practised dexterity of the skilled layer, and more than most, of the good anti-tank gunlayer, is acquired only by months of concentrated daily effort.

It has been explained how the primer or tube ignites the charge. As soon as this happens, power gas is given off by the exploding propellant. The explosion is not so violent as the detonation that shatters a shell into fragments. That does not mean that it is not forceful or quick. The propellant burns at an accelerating rate, giving off more and more gas, and the pressure in the chamber rises fast to the point at which it overcomes the inertia of the shell, and forces the latter to begin to move up the bore. The raised parts, or hard steel lands, of the spiralled rifling, biting into the soft copper belt or driving band near the base of the shell, impart spin to it and at the same time the driving band prevents any gas from escaping forward past the sides of the shell. The increasing pressure forces the projectile with accelerating velocity up the bore. The charge is not entirely consumed

until the shell has travelled between one and two-thirds of the total length of the bore. Thereafter the gas still expands under its own pressure and continues to accelerate the shell. About three hundredths of a second after the charge is ignited, the shell finally leaves the bore slightly further accelerated at the last instant by the escaping gas. It leaves spinning rapidly, right-handed as seen from behind, about its axis and propelled forward with tremendous muzzle velocity approaching 2,000 miles an hour.

If it were fired into a vacuum the combined effect of the propelling force, gravity and spin would be to make the shell travel in a symmetrical parabola, the gyroscopic effect of the spin keeping the axis always parallel to its position at the moment of projection (Fig. 8 A).

The resistance of the air, however, has several effects, some relatively simple, others highly complicated. In the first place the shell is moving so fast that the air cannot, so to speak, get out of the way. As a result it is compressed in front of the shell and exerts suction or drag behind it. The combined effect of these two forces is to retard the forward movement of the shell and alter the shape of the trajectory as seen from the side from a parabola to a curve along which the shell travels more abruptly downwards than it does upwards, the highest point being nearer to the target than to the original gun position.

The game of golf offers a useful analogy for the next two steps. Looking down upon a sliced golf ball it will be found to

This does not mean that the theory about the effect of friction is wrong; it is probably right. But another and more powerful factor comes into play to override the effect of friction and change the direction of the deviation. Air is viscous, or to use a homely word, sticky. It adheres to the surface of the spinning ball and is carried round by it to the front of the ball where it piles up and forms a shoulder on

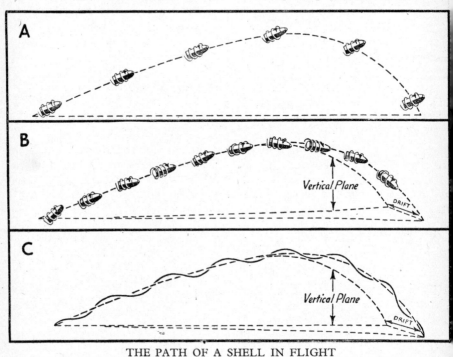

THE PATH OF A SHELL IN FLIGHT

Fig. 8. *If fired in a vacuum the axis of a shell would remain parallel to the position when fired (A). Air pressure changes its trajectory (B). In (C) the two flights are shown*

be spinning clockwise round an upright axis. It is also moving through the air in the general direction towards which it was struck. Like the shell it has a cushion of air in front though not nearly so compressed. We should expect that the combination of spin and friction would tend to make the ball roll across this cushion and deviate gradually to the left. It does nothing of the sort. It deviates, as every golfer knows, to the right.

the compressed cushion of air already there due to the forward motion of the ball. The cushion and shoulder together form a pad of greatest air density, and therefore of greatest air pressure on the left front of the ball, and this pressure, persistently applied, causes it to edge away gradually to the right and describe in its flight the curve known as a slice. So much for the golf ball, now for the shell.

Here again at first sight the unexpected

happens. A shell projected with a clockwise spin as seen from behind has an anticlockwise spin when viewed from in front and above. If the considerations of the previous paragraph hold good it ought to be deflected to the left, but in fact its deviation, or to use the technical term—drift, is to the right. Here again, however, a still more powerful over-ruling factor comes into play. The spin of the shell tends to keep its axis parallel to its original position. A glance at Fig. 8 (A) will show that if the trajectory there represented were in air instead of in a vacuum the resistance or pressure of the air would soon cease to act directly against the nose of the shell, and begin to impinge at an

nearly so. At a range of a couple of miles 100 shells fired from a gun of average performance may be expected to fall in an area of about 120 yards long and 30 yards wide. In shape an elongated "O," this area is called the 100 per cent zone (Fig. 9). The spread of shot is caused by the accidental errors that come from a host of unavoidable little variations from round to round—variations in the play of the gears, in the weight of charge, in the weight of shell, in the precise angle of the gun at the instant of projection, and the rest. When these act cumulatively we get the abnormally short, long, or wide round. The chances are, however, that they will tend to counteract one another to some

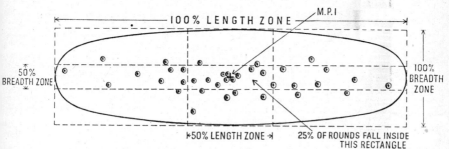

Fig. 9. THE "100 PER CENT ZONE" AND MEAN POINT OF IMPACT

angle to its axis. The effects of this pressure on the side of the spinning shell are peculiar. In the first place it causes the nose of the shell to rotate or "precess" about the trajectory which results in an approximation to the desired nose-on flight. Secondly, it keeps on moving the shell slightly but bodily over to the right, thus causing drift. As a result of these rather complex forces the general path of the shell through the air—or trajectory—takes the shape shown in Fig. 8 (B), round which its nose precesses, Fig. 8 (C). The resulting drift is compensated for either in the elevating gear or in the sighting gear.

If a succession of shells is fired from a gun laid each time in exactly the same way they will not fall on the same spot or even

extent, and the rounds will fall thickest near the centre of the "O." Its very centre is termed the mean point of impact (M.P.I.). It is of cardinal importance in gunnery that the M.P.I. shall be superimposed upon the middle of the target, when as a result, the maximum effect of the shelling will be realized.

Whenever possible the fire of guns is corrected on to the target from an observation point (O.P. or "O. Pip") by the process of ranging. If the O.P. is in or nearly in the line joining the guns to the target, the observer's task is simplified. The round that looks "left" to him is "left" from the gun, the round that he sees beyond the target is "plus" from the gun and so on (Fig. 10).

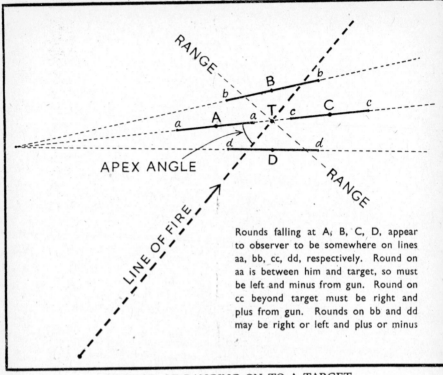

RANGE

B   b

A   T   C   c

a   a

APEX ANGLE

d   d

D

RANGE

LINE OF FIRE

Rounds falling at A, B, C, D, appear to observer to be somewhere on lines aa, bb, cc, dd, respectively. Round on aa is between him and target, so must be left and minus from gun. Round on cc beyond target must be right and plus from gun. Rounds on bb and dd may be right or left and plus or minus

METHOD OF RANGING ON TO A TARGET

Fig. 10.—*In the drawing the battery of guns is in the foreground firing along the "line of fire," while the observer is on the left of the target and is ranging from an oblique angle*

More often than not, however, his O.P. will be displaced to one side or other of his line of fire, and in consequence of his oblique view the observation of the fall of the shot will not be so straightforward. If he is to the left of the line of fire, then rounds falling between him and the target are left and short from the guns, rounds beyond the target are right and plus from the guns (Fig. 10). He gradually closes in on his target by altering both line and range until he has "bracketed" it between narrow limits. Then, selecting intermediate data, he shoots for effect.

The observation party consists usually of a trio: the observing officer, his assistant and a signaller. They are the eyes of the guns. Before opening fire the officer,

his companions close to him—one on either side—can be seen studying the ground round his target with his glasses. His assistant is busy doing calculations. Soon the signaller cries out "Shot one!" The assistant looks up to watch the target with his naked eye. If the officer is an old hand he will not put his glasses on to the target at once: that strains the eyes. He knows the time of flight and waits to lift them just before the shell is due to fall. He sees it. "More, four degrees, 3700!" he snaps out crisply. The signaller repeats this correction to the guns, and later says: "Through, sir!" to his officer.

The communication link between the O.P. and the guns is as vital as a life-line. The means employed is two-way radio-telephony (with remote control so that the aerial shall not give away the position of the O.P.), line telephony, or, more rarely, visual signalling. The N.C.O. in charge of the team of signallers in each battery has the important duty of establishing and maintaining these and all the other internal communications in the battery. Communication between the batteries and regimental H.Q. is the responsibility of a signal section from the Royal Corps of Signals.

The work of the static O.P.s is supplemented, particularly during mobile operations, by carriers equipped with radiotelephones and known as armoured O.P.s. Aircraft are also used for observing artillery fire, communication being by W/T (wireless telegraphy) or R/T (radiotelephony), one-way or two-way according to equipment and the circumstances.

When for any reason artillery fire cannot be observed it comes under the heading of predicted shooting. All the necessary data are obtained by calculation, and the accuracy and detail with which it is worked out depends upon the task in hand. If the safety of the infantry he is supporting is involved, as in barrage work, or his target is small, all the factors affecting the shooting of his guns have to be considered by the gun position officer (G.P.O.) in detail. Using survey methods and large-scale maps, line, range and angle of sight can be determined with great accuracy. But the line and range so found cannot obviously be put on the gun uncorrected.

In the first place, meteorological conditions of the moment affect shooting. A head wind reduces range, a following

A COASTAL DEFENCE POST

This great howitzer is being reloaded after a practice shoot somewhere on the defended coast of Britain. The next shell is about to be rammed home, followed by its charge

M.A.—E

OBSERVATION
POST ON TOP OF
HILL CAMOUFLAGED
WITH NETTING

OBSERVATION OFFICER

O.P. ASSISTANT
NOTING RANGES

O.P. SIGNALLER
ON FIELD TELEPHONE

COMMUNICATION BETWEEN AN OBSERVATION

The party at the observation post observe and correct the shots of the troop (or battery)
until the desired result is obtained. By means of line telephony, or wireless, communication

wind increases it. A cross wind deflects
the shell. The density of the air—which
depends upon its temperature, the baro-
metric pressure, and its humidity—
affects the carrying power of a shell. The
necessary data for the gunners' calculations are obtained by the help of the R.A.F.
and are supplied to them at frequent intervals in the form of meteor "telegrams".

The text is in code. "BAR 2990"
means that at sea level the barometer
reading is 29.9 inches.

Thereafter, each four-figure group is
read with the five-figure group immediately following it. The first two figures

Meteor "Telegram"

From	Meteor			
Originator's Number 26			*Date* 19	
BAR 2990	0749	05090		1052
10075	2050	18060	3048	28060
4045	36053	5041	43045	6036
45030				
Time of Origin 1200				

GUNS FIRING OVER
HILL ONTO TARGET
OBSCURED BY
RISING GROUND

TROOP GUN
POSITION

TELEPHONE
CABLE ROUTE

GUN POST AERIAL

LINEMAN

AERIAL

O.P. WAGON
LINE BEHIND
HAYSTACK

.OTE
.TROL WIRE
"WEEN
.EPHONE SET
D O.P.
NALLER

O.P. SIGNALLER
ON FIELD PHONE

RADIO TELEPHONE SET

SIGNALLER'S
MOTOR CYCLE

POST AND A TROOP GUN POSITION
*is maintained with the guns. The O.P. signaller's wireless aerial is kept at some distance
from the observation post in order not to give away the position of the latter to the enemy*

of each four-figure group refer to the shell's time of flight in seconds. The last two figures give the average air temperature it will meet in its flight.

The five-figure groups give (for the same flight) the average strength of the wind in feet per second (first two figures), and the bearing (last three figures) from which it is blowing. As examples:—

(*a*) If the time of flight to the target is 7 seconds, the groups 0749 and 05090 are selected. These give an air temperature of 49 degrees Fahrenheit and a 5 foot-second wind from a bearing of 90 degrees, or from the east.

(*b*) If the time of flight to the target is 50 seconds, the groups 5041, 43045 are selected. These give an air temperature of 41 degrees Fahrenheit and a 43 foot-second wind from a bearing of 45 degrees, or from the north-east.

In the second place the temperature of the charge and the weight of the shell have to be taken into consideration. Both these factors affect muzzle velocity. A rise in charge temperature increases it, a heavier shell reduces it; but at the same time a heavier shell has more staying power at long ranges. These are the main factors that must always be considered.

A POWERFUL ANTI-AIRCRAFT SEARCHLIGHT

Searchlights are still very useful as aids to A.A. guns and to night fighters. The great reflector is here being cleaned ready for action. Modern searchlights have much increased power

A great point about predicted shooting is the surprise effect gained by opening fire with guns which have previously kept silent. When surprise is of secondary consequence, and the "targets" can be seen, a modified procedure is used by registering them beforehand and obtaining the data by a preliminary shoot.

TACTICAL FIRE

Shooting by map alone is blind and liable to be very inaccurate: it is justified only when the target is large and speed in opening fire all-important.

Three standard methods are employed when firing for effect. At "gun fire" the specified number of rounds are fired independently from each gun at the interval ordered. At "salvo fire" the guns are fired simultaneously by order or at a given signal. At "troop" or "battery fire" the guns are fired in succession from the right at the prescribed interval. This method is used in preference to gun fire when it is desired to observe rounds from, and apply corrections to, individual guns. If, as is usual, the guns are firing along parallel lines, and the wind is blowing from the right, the order is given for the guns to be fired from the left in order to prevent the drifting smoke of the earlier bursts from obscuring the later ones.

The terms used for the tactical forms of fire suggest their own significance.

Counter-battery work brings to mind the artillery duel between rival batteries. Harassing fire, which is often directed against such targets as cross-roads to interfere with night movement, and defensive fire are both instruments of the defence. Defensive fire is put down only when the enemy are actually seen to be advancing to the attack.

Artillery fire in support of the attack may take the form of observed fire, barrages, smoke screens, and concentrations. When the enemy's defences are strong and in some depth, or his dispositions on the ground to be attacked are not known with any certainty, a barrage is desirable. It provides a moving curtain of fire just ahead of the leading tanks and infantry, systematically quartering all the ground over which the advance is to take place. Naturally enough, many guns and a great deal of ammunition are required for barrage fire. Concentrations of fire and smoke screens are more selective and economical. The first are directed against known nests of resistance, while smoke screens are used to blind the eyes of the defence. Observed fire is used if enemy movements are detected from O.P.s.

ADVENT OF MECHANIZATION

With the advent of mechanization, artillery mobility has been revolutionized. A remarkable diversity of creatures have been used in their day for moving guns about. "The expression 'horse,'" in the words of the Army Act, "includes a mule, and . . . this Act . . . shall apply to any

A CAMOUFLAGED GUN POSITION

Defence from aerial attack is vitally important today. This 6-inch gun has been carefully hidden. Though it is important to hide a gun, it is also vital to hide tracks leading to it

beast of whatever description . . . used for burden or draught . . . as if such beast were included in the expression 'horse'." In addition to the mountain artillery mule, which is still used, elephants, camels, and bullocks have been gun carriers and drawers in the past. Man, too, is not excluded, for artillery porters still carry the mountain howitzers through the bush on their heads today. The lighter loads are carried by individual men, the heavier ones, such as the breech and the chase, are carried on the heads of four men.

GUN TRACTORS

Advantages obviously accrue on mobilization if the army follows in peace the commercial practice of the country in the matter of its transport. And so almost all the Army Act "horses" have been ousted by their inanimate counterparts—caterpillars of different kinds, dragons, hathis,

quads, and some with less picturesque names. Not long ago guns were just towed, with the gun wheels unaltered, but it was found that speeds in excess of ten miles an hour even on good English roads, and less than half of that on rough French pavé, were liable to be detrimental to the equipment. Then rubber-padded tyres were tried and a slightly increased speed became admissible. The modern gun has pneumatic tyres of the type best suited to it and can now keep its place in a fast-moving motorized column. It is not confined to roads, and should it get into difficulties in cross-country movement the powerful winching gear and cable incorporated in the gun-towing vehicle can usually extricate it. Some guns are still carried in transporters and a very few are actually mounted on them, but the common practice is for the gun on a mobile carriage to be towed by a separate

FUZE SETTING IN AN UNDERGROUND STORE

Many coastal batteries have underground ammunition stores as a precaution against aerial attack. The fuzes are set and the shells then carried up to the guns, ready for immediate use

A QUAD HAULING A GUN

Quads are used to tow guns across country. This one, with its winch attachment, is hauling
a gun out of the mud. This saves the time wasted in waiting for a repair lorry

vehicle. Much-used types are Morris and Guy Quads for the 25-pounder and lighter guns, Scammell and A.E.C. vehicles for medium, heavy and certain super-heavy guns. The heavier types of these are divisible into a number of separate towing loads for which extra wheeled axles are provided when necessary. In addition to pulling the gun the towing vehicles carry its detachment of men and some ammunition for immediate requirements. Each regiment has a Light Aid Detachment (L.A.D.) of the Royal Army Ordnance Corps attached to it to help to keep the vehicles on the road by dealing with repair work beyond the competence of the gunner drivers and fitters. The super-heavy railway mountings are provided with special types of rolling stock. The trucks on which some of the guns are mounted are so designed that the platforms off which the guns fire can be lowered to rest on the sleepers. In this way they can shoot over a comparatively wide arc of fire. Others are fired off their (railway) wheels and they are only fired more or less in prolongation of the track because, if fired obliquely across it, the recoil might splay the rails. Curved spurs are constructed therefore, the chords of which lie parallel to the general direction in which it is intended to shoot. When the target lies more than a very few degrees off the alignment of the track at the particular point where the gun is, an engine is brought up to shunt the gun truck forward or back along the curve until the muzzle is pointing approximately in the required direction, small line corrections being taken up on a traversing gear.

BATTERY TRANSPORT

The transport of a battery is divided into a number of groups on the principle that each shall pave the way for the work of the next. The reconnaissance party comes first to choose the O.P.s and gun positions. Next, the "firing battery"— that is to say the guns with their immediate requirements in staff, instruments

O.P.

TROOP GUN POSITION

BATTERY COMMAND POST

TROOP GUN POSITION

TROOP GUN POSITION

FIRST LINE (COMMUNICATION GROUP) RENDEZVOUS

— J. MATHEW —

A BATTERY OF FIELD GUNS

When a field battery goes into action the O.P. is placed where it has a commanding view of the country. It is then linked up with the gun positions. Behind them is to be found

and ammunition. Then the "first-line" vehicles, loaded chiefly with more ammunition. And lastly, "B" echelon vehicles which come up to the neighbourhood of the gun positions at some convenient time, often after dark, with cooking pots, food and blankets. Having deposited their loads the drivers take them back to the wagon lines some distance in rear.

The good soldier of old always contrived somehow to keep his powder dry. The good gunner of today is ever solicitous about his ammunition too, making sure so far as he can that it is kept in good condition and that he does not run short of it.

He watches expenditure carefully, and sees to it that demands for more are lodged in ample time. Delivery to the guns takes place as a rule by night to avoid detection from the air, though at need, of course, it is brought up in daylight. At forward gun positions it often has to be humped some distance by hand. When a heavy expenditure is foreseen the necessary number of rounds per gun are dumped at the gun positions and the ammunition vehicles are refilled.

A fundamental principle of ammunition supply is that it is passed systematically and automatically from rear to front to

PRELIMINARY WAGON LINES

GUN GROUP
RENDEZVOUS

DEPLOYING INTO ACTION
*the battery command post. Guns wait at a gun rendezvous until their final action position
has been selected. The preliminary wagon line and first line groups get under cover nearby*

replace expenditure. Another is that in emergency all ammunition is, to some extent, common property. Replenishment in front of railhead is carried out by two links of mechanical transport. Each link has a fixed number of ammunition-carrying vehicles; fixed, that is, subject to some give and take to suit the varying number of units being served from time to time. The first link picks up at railhead and delivers to the second which carries it forward and hands it over to units at delivery point. This is done as far forward as possible consistent with reasonable safety—sometimes at the regimental or

battery wagon lines, and even at the actual gun positions—to reduce to a minimum the number of times ammunition is handled. The gunner's weapon is the shell. His job boils down to putting the right number of the right kind into the right place at the right time. For this, they must be ready to his hand at the guns.

Nevertheless, when all is said and done they remain as always an ancillary arm to support the operations of the Royal Navy and R.A.F. and the other arms of their own Service. It is pretty fair to conclude that although gunners win no battles, very few indeed are ever won without them.

A FINE PIECE OF DEMOLITION WORK

This great bridge over the river Vistula was thoroughly demolished by engineers of the Polish Army when Germany attacked Poland. Bridge demolition is an important part of the work of army engineers. They must also be expert in the construction of bridges

CHAPTER 6

The Royal Engineers

R.E. organization in the field. Construction of army accommodation overseas. R.E. in France and Belgium. Bridge demolition. Road cratering. Clearing minefields and "booby" traps. Bridge building and types of bridge. R.E. in Africa. R.E. at an overseas base. Railways and lines of communication. Road and aerodrome construction. Stores and materials. Defended ports abroad: Singapore. Transportation

THE work of the Royal Engineers is, in the main, either constructive or destructive. The remainder of their work in a theatre of war overseas can be divided into two spheres. These overlap to some extent, namely, the work of the field units, and of those on the line of communications and at the base. There are some types of units which may be employed on either.

In the field, the chief engineer (or, when the size of the force warrants it, the engineer-in-chief) is the head and co-ordinator of all engineer services. He is attached to the staff of the commander-in-chief, to whom he acts as adviser in all engineer matters. On his own staff he has branches responsible for R.E. intelligence, roads, water supply, etc. Chief engineers are also appointed to armies and corps, and a commander R.E. to divisions as well as for army and corps troops.

DEFENCE CONSTRUCTION

All demands and forecasts of requirements of stores are sorted and arranged by an officer on the staff of the director of works specially appointed for this purpose, subject to the general guidance of the engineer-in-chief. The distribution of available stores is made by this officer.

The work of the field units varies greatly with the theatre of war and the conditions prevailing. It is the responsibility of a commander or his staff to settle what defences are required, how they should be sited, fields of fire, etc. It is then for the R.E. officer to design them and supervise their construction, so that they fulfil the commander's requirements. Similarly in the case of accommodation either for men or stores, it is for the staff to say what is wanted and for the R.E. to produce it. As an example, consider the problem of accommodation overseas. Britain was found, on the outbreak of war, with a short stock of timber and after the invasion of Norway one of her best sources of supply was cut off. The R.E. had for a long time been in close touch with the makers of the Nissen hut, famous in 1918, and a modern much improved type was produced. The wooden lining was replaced by a corrugated iron one, thus not only practically eliminating the use of wood but removing the temptation to use the lining as a heaven-sent fuel supply. The occupation of Iceland, too, presented the R.E. with a difficult problem in housing. This was met by the use of special insulation between the walls and the lining, and also by an insulated floor.

During the lull before the German offensive in France in 1939-40, the field units were employed largely on the construction of concrete pill boxes, anti-tank ditches, obstacles, etc. These necessitated the employment of a large quantity of mechanical plant, such as heavy and light excavators, concrete mixers, stone crushers, etc., and all these had to be provided from Britain or the U.S.A. Among the biggest problems was the provision of the "aggregate" (or stone), required in enormous quantities for the concrete. The large quarries at Marquis in northern France were found to be inadequate to cope with the demand, and it was necessary to find suitable sites to open up new quarries and to provide the necessary machinery. So great was the amount of mechanical plant in use that special units were formed to use it and maintain it.

When the British Army moved forward into Belgium, the work of the field engineers changed at once. While on the move, however, there was little time to deal with more than rapid water supply or similar types of work. The move had been organized in complete detail and no unforeseen work was necessary. When the retreat began and during it, the main task of the R.E. was that of demolition. The retreat in 1940 was, from the demolition point of view, most successful. Though time did not allow for much work in the way of preparation, there is no known case of a bridge which was not blown up. Many such demolitions, moreover, were completed with great gallantry within

QUARRYING FOR "AGGREGATE" (OR STONE)

An immense quantity of stone is required for road making and general construction work. These men are hard at work in a quarry cutting out the "aggregate" for use in concrete

sight of the enemy. No less than 600 bridges were successfully demolished in this retreat with the total expenditure of 900 tons of explosives.

When time permits, the normal method for the demolition of a bridge is to attack it by blowing up the piers or abutments. When time is limited, the crown or haunches of the arches are destroyed. Though wet guncotton slabs or ammonal are the normal service explosives, gelignite, dynamite or any commercial explosives are used if necessary. If properly employed they are very effective.

The normal method of firing is by means of electric detonators, operated by an exploder; this exploder is a very efficient hand-operated dynamo. Usually an alternative method of firing is also provided with any charge, this being by safety fuze, joined through instantaneous fuze or fuzes to detonators.

To give some idea of the variety of the work of the R.E. in this retreat in Belgium and France, the following is the reply of the C.R.E. of one of the divisions which took part in the operations, to the question: "What did the R.E. do?"

"On arrival on the line of the River Dyle, divisional R.E. units were employed at once on the preparation of bridges for demolition and, later, on the preparation of defended buildings, special defence posts, dugouts for H.Q.s, etc. In fact, standard work was expected from them. Very little work had been done by the Belgians.

"In the initial stages of the retreat the sappers were generally disengaged very early and sent back to get on with the preparations for demolition of successive river lines in rear. A certain amount of additional delay was inflicted by road cratering. The supply of explosive was adequate, and there was no difficulty in completing the tasks given. As a matter of interest the 3rd Division R.E. blew up in all eighty bridges and 142 craters.

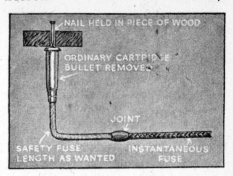

AN EMERGENCY EXPLODER

A nail driven into a cartridge ignites a slow-burning fuze. This gives time for getting a safe distance away. An instantaneous fuze connects direct with the explosive charge. The slow fuze is of any length needed

"When the B.E.F. evacuated the Lille sector of the French frontier defences and began to make its way northward to the coast, the employment of sappers became much more varied in its scope. There were still bridges to be demolished but there were also relief bridges to be built, and there began to be a demand for fighting soldiers. For example, at Commines, the 4th Division R.E. put in a highly successful counter-attack. North of Furnes the 3rd Division R.E. spent two days and three nights holding on to a vital sector of the last line of defence, the Furnes-Nieuport canal; they used hand grenades, a three-inch mortar and other strange weapons quite imperturbably.

"During the evacuation there was much to be done. Unfortunately the pontoon equipment had been destroyed, but improvised piers of lorries, decked with timber from beach huts and houses in the town, were built and used to capacity. Boat crews were in great demand, and many parties rowed themselves backwards and forwards until beaten by sheer exhaustion. One sapper in a small dinghy took off twenty-seven men, each trip being a good half-mile, and went on after being capsized twice by 'near misses' of

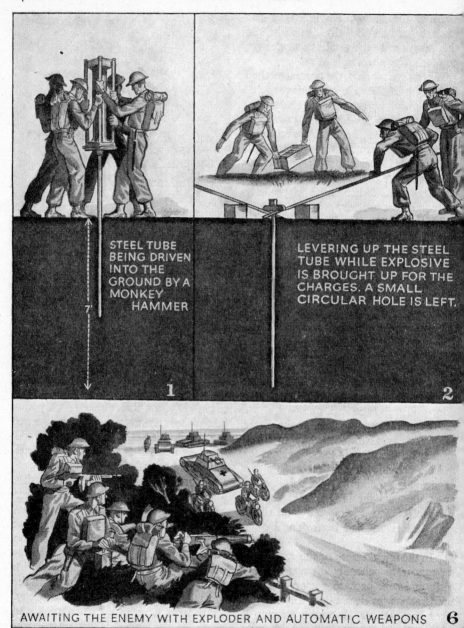

STEEL TUBE BEING DRIVEN INTO THE GROUND BY A MONKEY HAMMER

7'

1

LEVERING UP THE STEEL TUBE WHILE EXPLOSIVE IS BROUGHT UP FOR THE CHARGES. A SMALL CIRCULAR HOLE IS LEFT.

2

AWAITING THE ENEMY WITH EXPLODER AND AUTOMATIC WEAPONS   **6**

STEPS IN THE MAKING

The Germans introduced road cratering on a large scale into warfare. It has since become one of the main methods of blocking roads. First a hole is drilled down through the road surface with the aid of a "monkey" hammer. Into this a small charge is inserted in order to form a chamber at the foot of the shaft. This chamber is then packed with a considerable

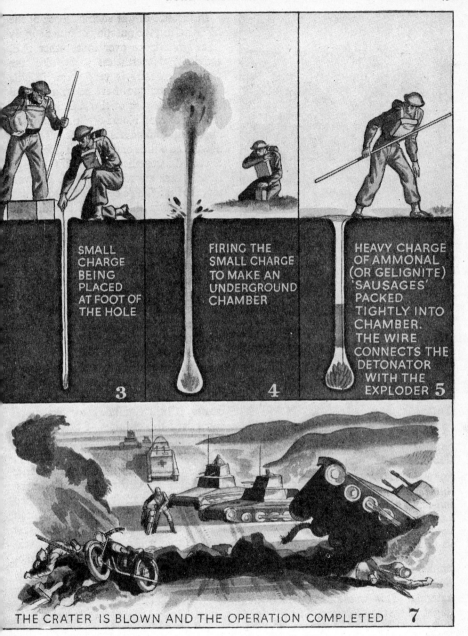

SMALL CHARGE BEING PLACED AT FOOT OF THE HOLE **3**

FIRING THE SMALL CHARGE TO MAKE AN UNDERGROUND CHAMBER **4**

HEAVY CHARGE OF AMMONAL (OR GELIGNITE) 'SAUSAGES' PACKED TIGHTLY INTO CHAMBER. THE WIRE CONNECTS THE DETONATOR WITH THE EXPLODER **5**

THE CRATER IS BLOWN AND THE OPERATION COMPLETED **7**

OF A ROAD CRATER

charge of high explosive, which is connected up to an exploder. It is then blown up either when the enemy is on the spot, or earlier in order to disorganize his transport at a suitably chosen place on the road. A narrow bottle-neck is a good place to choose as a detour is usually impossible. Clever cratering can be most effective in delaying the enemy

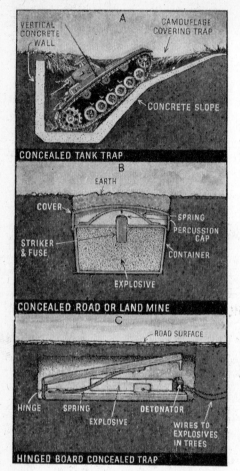

VERTICAL CONCRETE WALL — A — CAMOUFLAGE COVERING TRAP

CONCRETE SLOPE

CONCEALED TANK TRAP

B

EARTH

COVER — SPRING PERCUSSION CAP

STRIKER & FUSE — CONTAINER

EXPLOSIVE

CONCEALED ROAD OR LAND MINE

C

ROAD SURFACE

HINGE — SPRING — DETONATOR — WIRES TO EXPLOSIVES IN TREES

EXPLOSIVE

HINGED BOARD CONCEALED TRAP

ANTI-TANK OBSTACLES

Anti-tank obstacles are varied. Sometimes anti-tank ditches are constructed (A). Land mines (B) are also laid, and also hinged traps (C) which bring trees down across the vehicles as they pass under them

bombs. Losses were heavy at this stage."

Mention is made in the above of road cratering. This was an art which was taught us by the Germans. The secret of road cratering is to find a place or places where diversion of traffic is difficult. R.E. units carry special equipment for drilling into roads, etc., and then by means of a charge of explosives blowing a large crater in the road or elsewhere.

In theatres of war such as those of the Middle East, the question of water supply takes precedence over most other R.E. activities. Nevertheless here also the variation of tasks is very great. Middle East communiques have referred several times to the work of the R.E. in the removing of road blocks and the neutralizing of anti-tank mines. For the latter type of work an officer of the Indian Engineers, Second-Lieutenant Premindra Singh Bhagat, was awarded the V.C. He was, too, the first King's commissioned Indian officer to win this coveted award. The citation reads as follows:—

"For most conspicuous gallantry on active service in the Middle East. During the pursuit of the enemy following the capture of Metemma on the night of January 31-February 1, 1941, Second-Lieutenant Bhagat was in command of a section of a field company, sappers and miners, detailed to accompany the leading mobile troops (in Bren carriers) to clear the road and adjacent area of mines. For a period of four days, and over a distance of fifty-five miles this officer, in the leading carrier, led the column. He detected and supervised the clearing of fifteen minefields. Speed being essential, he worked at high pressure from dawn to dusk each day. On two occasions when his carrier was blown up with casualties to others, and on a third occasion, when ambushed and under close enemy fire, he himself carried straight on with his task. He refused relief when worn out with strain and fatigue and with one eardrum punctured by an explosion, on the grounds that he was now better qualified to continue his task to the end.

"His coolness, persistence over a period of ninety-six hours, and gallantry, not only in battle, but throughout the long period when the safety of the column and the speed at which it could advance were dependent on his personal efforts, were of the highest order."

Some "booby" traps also are often left behind by armies in retreat, largely to cause delay. These are sometimes of a primitive kind, such as a trip wire or some similar arrangement. Sometimes they are of extreme ingenuity. One of the duties of the R.E. is to find and neutralize these difficult and dangerous traps.

Reference has been made earlier to the R.E. work on demolition, especially of bridges. *When carried out by the enemy,* this entails heavy work in the erection of numerous bridges to take the place of those so thoroughly demolished.

The light foot bridges and the assault boats are manned and erected by the infantry, but bridges to take heavier loads are the responsibility of the R.E.

Various forms of bridging are carried as part of the equipment of the Army.

The standard pontoon equipment is carried by a R.A.S.C. unit, but its erection is the duty of the R.E. A very good and simple steel trestle is carried with the pontoon equipment. The use of pontoons is, however, limited. They are bulky to move about, require certain conditions of rivers and approaches and are very costly to erect when under observation.

Two types of standard steel bridges are also carried, the small and large box girders, which though carried in parts are rapidly connected up to make a continuous girder.

These bridges of standard equipment are, however, seldom at once available in sufficient quantities. The R.E. stores organization therefore holds a large amount of rolled steel joists of all sizes, which are available to supplement the

A KAPOK OR LIGHT BRIDGE

These bridges, constructed on kapok floats, are carried to the water already made up and pushed across it. A hinged ramp on the front of the bridge is used to scale the bank

HOW A GIRDER BRIDGE IS DEMOLISHED

The thoroughness of any demolition work must necessarily depend upon the time available in which to carry it out. In the case of a girder bridge a charge is placed at the foot of abutments on one bank to dislodge the supports. In order to smash up the girders themselves, charges are bound on to their top and bottom central parts. When the charges are fired from a distance the result is usually as shown here. If no exploder is available an emergency one (see page 141) is employed. Good demolition work not only renders a bridge unusable, it makes repair work impossible. The explosives are tightly packed to increase their effect

ROYAL ENGINEERS CONSTRUCTING ROADS

The construction of new roads is an important part of engineering work. Modern mechanized warfare makes big demands upon supplies along the lines of communication. For the cutting of new roads (top) the engineers use the most modern mechanical plant. Huge excavators cut away the top surface, other machines level it, and the top soil is carried away in lorries. A layer of small stones (below) is then put down upon the road and a concrete surface completes the job. Speedy road making is a vital factor in the supply of an advancing army. It is impossible to maintain a fast-moving modern army unless the supply roads are good

UNLOADING PONTOONS FROM THEIR SPECIAL LORRY

Some fourteen men carry the lower pontoon off the vehicle first. The top pontoon is then lowered by pulleys in the upright girders of the lorry and later is itself carried away

standard bridging equipment. Some heavy steel bridges are also held which, though slower to erect, are used for more permanent work. It is anticipated that in time a new form of bridge will supersede all other types of bridges, including to some extent the use of pontoons.

SOUTH AFRICAN ENGINEERS

Mention should be made here of the South African Engineers who, under the Chief Engineer East Africa, accomplished very fine work against the Italians in Africa. Both the men and the plant from South Africa must have been of the best. Their water supply companies were most successful and the road construction companies from Natal, the Cape and Transvaal were highly efficient. They built a first-class road at the rate of twelve miles a month. Other engineers from South Africa were also equally successful. Unprovided with the British

Army pontoon equipment, they used materials constructed at Nairobi and completed four bridges of 300 feet and one of 600 feet over the Rivers Juba and Tana. They bridged the wide River Juba in only seventeen hours.

These are only a few examples of the tasks which the R.E. may be called upon to do. Even the best of troops, however, cannot achieve real success in this type of work without materials. These materials could be available when and where they are needed solely by the use of great foresight on the part of the chief engineer (or C.R.E.) concerned.

For all these tasks which the R.E. with divisions may be set, there are three field companies in each division. During the war of 1914-18 nearly every C.R.E. of a division found it necessary to withdraw men from the field companies to form a small workshop and store. This probable need was met by forming in the pre-1939 years, divisional field park companies. They consisted of good tradesmen, sufficient in number for a small workshop and also for store-holding.

The calls on the R.E. are far from constant. It would, therefore, be most uneconomical to fix the strength of the Divisional R.E. at a figure which enabled them without help to cope with a peak demand. Each corps is therefore given a number of army field companies which can be attached as required to help the divisional field companies with a sudden rush. Except in name these army field companies are identical with the divisional field companies. When not employed with any division, they carry out numerous engineers' jobs, such as providing accommodation, etc., in the corps area.

When an overseas base is to be formed, and there is a line of communication from such base to the divisional or corps area, the R.E. units to be sent are estimated on the basis of the amount of work envisaged. It is seldom that the number required is over-estimated.

R.E. WORKSHOPS

When only a small force is sent, it may suffice to have only a workshop and park company to look after the collecting, receiving and distribution of R.E. stores. This unit consists of a small workshop section as well as a store section, together with two advanced park sections for forming forward dumps of stores and all necessary materials.

As the force grows and the amount of material to be handled increases, it is necessary to replace the workshop and park company by larger units. These consist of a base workshop, and a base stores

CARRYING A PONTOON TO THE WATER

When a pontoon is being taken to the water the men wear life jackets as there is always the possibility that they may go into the water themselves when joining up the sections

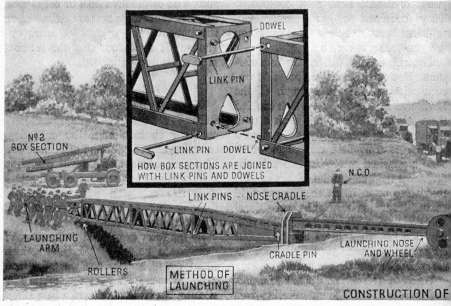

DOWEL

LINK PIN

LINK PIN   DOWEL

HOW BOX SECTIONS ARE JOINED
WITH LINK PINS AND DOWELS

Nº 2
BOX SECTION

LINK PINS   NOSE CRADLE

N.C.O.

LAUNCHING
ARM

CRADLE PIN

LAUNCHING NOSE
AND WHEEL

ROLLERS

METHOD OF
LAUNCHING

CONSTRUCTION OF

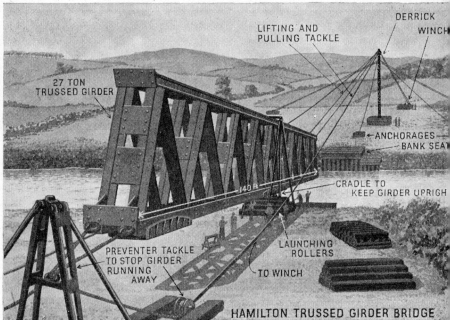

LIFTING AND
PULLING TACKLE

DERRICK
WINCH

27 TON
TRUSSED GIRDER

ANCHORAGES
BANK SEA

140 Fr

CRADLE TO
KEEP GIRDER UPRIGH

PREVENTER TACKLE
TO STOP GIRDER
RUNNING
AWAY

LAUNCHING
ROLLERS

TO WINCH

HAMILTON TRUSSED GIRDER BRIDGE

TYPES OF BRIDGING EQUIPMENT

*The sections of the small box girder (top) are connected up as in the inset. The span is 64 feet
and it is pushed on rollers across the river with a launching nose attached. The Hamilton
trussed girder (left) is a heavy bridge of two 27-ton girders, 140 feet in length. A double
derrick and winch pulls the girders across the river. Cables at the other end prevent them*

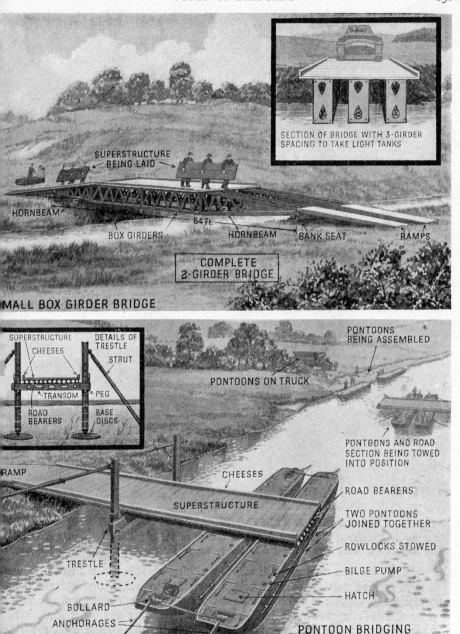

SECTION OF BRIDGE WITH 3-GIRDER SPACING TO TAKE LIGHT TANKS

SUPERSTRUCTURE BEING LAID

HORNBEAM

BOX GIRDERS 64 Ft. HORNBEAM BANK SEAT RAMPS

COMPLETE 2-GIRDER BRIDGE

MALL BOX GIRDER BRIDGE

SUPERSTRUCTURE DETAILS OF TRESTLE
CHEESES STRUT
TRANSOM PEG
ROAD BEARERS BASE DISCS

PONTOONS BEING ASSEMBLED

PONTOONS ON TRUCK

PONTOONS AND ROAD SECTION BEING TOWED INTO POSITION

RAMP

CHEESES

SUPERSTRUCTURE

ROAD BEARERS

TWO PONTOONS JOINED TOGETHER

ROWLOCKS STOWED

TRESTLE

BILGE PUMP

HATCH

BOLLARD
ANCHORAGES

PONTOON BRIDGING

USED BY THE ROYAL ENGINEERS

running away when past the point of balance. A regular pontoon bridge (right) consists of four essential elements and is suitable for carrying loads up to 30 tons. Pontoons, 21 feet in length, are joined together end on. These are anchored at intervals across the river. Road bearers are placed across the pontoons and on these the roadway is laid with a raised kerb

ERECTING A TRESTLE FOR A PONTOON BRIDGE

In order to provide a firm ramp from the bridge to the shore a steel trestle is erected.
This necessitates some men wading into the water to fix the girders firmly to the trestle

depot. The workshop is a large unit with the most modern wood and metal working machinery, capable of a considerable output either of repairs or new work. The base stores depot is a large fully equipped store-holding unit, capable of dealing with the large amount of R.E. stores required by a modern army.

The work of the R.E. at the base, as in the field, varies with the theatre of war

and the conditions. In France, it was necessary to build large camps, store-houses, hospitals, etc., as well as arrange for large electric and water distribution schemes. In the Middle East, available accommodation is even more limited. Enormous storehouses have had to be erected, as well as large cold storage plants. Electric light, water, drainage, roads, etc., have had to be provided. Not the least of the problems is that of the ammunition depots. The amount of ammunition of all kinds required by a modern army runs into very big quantities. In the war of 1914-18 cover from weather was all that was required, apart from the distribution of stacks to distances sufficient to prevent the spread of an explosion. Today the air menace necessitates splinter, or bomb-proof, covering and the provision of some concealment.

The tonnage of supplies to be handled for a force of any size is enormous. Though, in the first instance, road-fed depots may suffice, it is essential to change over to a rail-fed system as soon as possible. The existing railway system will generally decide on the layout to be adopted. Superimposed on the railway system, however, are the roads, store sheds, shelters, offices, etc., all necessitating a large amount of further labour and

MANŒUVRING PONTOON SECTIONS INTO POSITION

It is particularly in this strenuous work that life jackets are a necessary precaution. The heavy sections are moved into position by poles and are then locked together with bolts

materials. The methods employed depend on the local resources in skilled labour, but the design and responsibility is that of the R.E. The supply of local skilled labour is seldom sufficient nor, in many cases, of a high enough standard. R.E. units have then to be utilized. After initial experience in France, a new type of unit was decided upon—the Artisan Works Company R.E. This unit consists of skilled

no relation to the standards in this country. They, consequently, necessitated the construction of special transformers for use there. To cope with such difficulties an Electrical Mechanical Section was evolved, and one or more of these can be sent when such work reaches large enough proportions.

Reference has already been made to the fact that there is no clear demarcation

LOCKING TOGETHER THE SECTIONS OF A PONTOON BRIDGE

While some men in waders fix the boats together, others lay steel bars across them. On these a road surface of wooden planks is put down with a kerb to prevent side slips

men of the building trades, and their value was proved in France and elsewhere. Many are the problems which the R.E. have to solve on the layout of a large base, as the demands from the Ordnance and Supply Services for accommodation and power are on a big scale. In France the frequencies and voltages of electric power in different parts varied and bore

between the units required at the base or on the lines of communication, and those required in the forward area. Some units may, in fact, be used in either area as and when needed.

Of these are the Road Construction Companies, consisting of men highly experienced in road repairs and construction of all kinds and equipped with the most modern machinery. Similar units are the Well-Boring Sections, capable of deep boring for water or the distribution of that water above ground.

Another important and most useful unit is the Army Troops Company, which was used in great numbers in the war of 1914-18 and is a real link between the forward and back areas. It is a fully mobile unit with a high percentage of tradesmen and some machine tools; it is also a "Jack of all Trades" unit and is available for the more permanent work in the forward area, or to supplement the specialist units on the lines of communication and at the base. These units are all provided on the basis of estimated requirements.

It is not perhaps well known that among the more important of the R.E. duties in the field is the construction, maintenance and repair of aerodromes for the R.A.F. In France, so great was the demand for new aerodromes that it was found essential to create a new type of unit to deal with it, and General Construction Companies were formed.

AERODROME CONSTRUCTION

In the first instance, they were employed principally on new aerodrome construction. For this the methods used varied widely, depending on the type of plane for which they were required and the nature of the soil, etc. After construction came maintenance, which in the face of heavy enemy bombing was no sinecure. For several months after their withdrawal from France, many of these companies were employed on the maintenance of aerodromes in Great Britain.

At home, in peace time, it is possible to work out accurately and order in plenty of time, all the materials required for a job. This will ensure that the work is not kept waiting for lack of any particular item. It is clear that this is not possible in the case of the R.E., especially in the field, as their tasks cannot always be foreseen.

Though some stores such as sandbags, wire, etc., are supplied to the R.E. stores through Ordnance channels, the large majority are obtained by the R.E. Stores Organization, either through the appropriate branch of the Ministry of Supply or by direct purchase.

R.E. STORES DEPARTMENT

Before a campaign in France or in the Middle East, this branch, working on an appreciation by the General Staff, makes out a list of plant and materials which it is considered will be required initially. There is no golden rule, as these must vary with the theatre of war and also with the handling facilities at the port of entry.

The R.E. Stores Department has to compete with other branches for their share of the shipping tonnage available. As this tonnage and the handling facilities are limited, it becomes essential to settle an order of priority. This, at the beginning of a campaign, can only be done by intelligent anticipation. The shipments on this estimated basis go on until such time as the local R.E. commander has been able to make his own appreciation. Thereafter, shipments are to his order. On arrival overseas the plant and stores are taken into the R.E. base store depot and from there distributed as required.

Owing to competing demands for shipping there is seldom a surplus of stores or plant, and its distribution according to an order of priority is an essential. This is settled by the local R.E. commander on the instructions of the staff.

DEFENDED PORTS ABROAD

The motto of the R.E. is "Ubique" and it is true to say that wherever you find units of the Army, there you will find R.E. The work of the R.E. at defended ports abroad is of the same category as that in this country, with modifications to suit the local conditions and weather. Singapore, which represented a type of

SECURING HAULING TACKLE TO A HEAVY GIRDER

These heavy girders are hauled across a river by a derrick and winch tackle. The men are here attaching the nose of the girder to ropes from the tackle on the other bank. The tackle prevents the girder falling into the river when past the point of balance

strongly defended port, gives a good example of the variety of the work the R.E. may be called upon to do. .

It started with the clearing of the bush, then anti-malarial drainage, followed by the design and construction of emplacements, magazines, etc., for all types of guns, the design and construction of barracks, electric light (including generating station), water supply, storm and other drainage, recreation grounds, etc.

The emplacements for many of the heavier types of guns involved considerably more than the large lump of concrete, which is all that the onlooker from outside could see. They necessitated vast excavations and the building of underground engine rooms, magazines, shell hoists, telephone exchanges; in fact, a large house, shell- and bomb-proof, with the top surface at ground level and as far as possible invisible.

Apart from these directly military duties, the R.E. carry out several important though less conspicuous labours. The demand for timber in both army and civilian building is enormous. Skilled men from Australia, Canada and Newfoundland have been formed into the Forestry Corps of the Royal Engineers.

They have done excellent service both in Britain and in the Middle East. In addition, there are Tunnelling Corps, R.E., for the building of deep dug-outs for operation headquarters and similar work. Much highly skilled work has been done by them at Gibraltar. Such matters as the disposal of dangerous time-bombs are also an R.E. duty. The Bomb Disposal units are both skilled and courageous; their record is a notable one. The whole question of the distribution of mails to the Army is also the responsibility of the R.E. Formed mostly from G.P.O. staff, these units are highly trained and they get but little publicity.

The Transportation Service, though a part of the R.E., is under a separate directorate at the War Office and in the field. At the W.O. there is a Director of Transportation, who is responsible for all this work; in the field there is a corresponding appointment, in each case attached to the quartermaster-general. The work of the Transportation Service can be described shortly as the design, construction, maintenance and operation of docks, railways and inland waterways.

The Dock units consist of expert stevedores and dock operating units, and experts are also available for any dock construction. Some idea of the task accomplished may be gathered from the following weights of stores landed in France by the R.E. Docks units. They consisted of no less than 100,972 tons of

SWINGING A HEAVY GIRDER INTO POSITION

When the girder has been hauled past its point of balance it is liable to dip into the river. To prevent this the tackle in the foreground brakes the girder while the far derrick raises the nose and hauls it across. This is now termed the "derrick and preventor" method of bridging

ENGINEERS AS LUMBERMEN

A great deal of wood is needed in modern army construction work. These men of the Forestry Corps, R.E., are here starting to fell a pine tree. Many lumbermen are from the Dominions and are expert in the use of axes. Their strength and skill are of great value to Britain

ammunition, 173,627 tons of petrol, 468,155 tons of stores, 73,335 vehicles.

The Railway units consist of experts in the construction, maintenance and operation of railways, and their equipment comprises the latest mechanical means for rapid earthworks, etc. With the vast quantities of stores which a modern army requires, all depots are, if possible, given full railway facilities with sidings to all parts. In the case of even one ammunition dump, this may necessitate the building of many miles of line.

The work of railway construction in France, carried out by the Railway Con-struction Companies, R.E., comprised laying 110 miles of broad gauge track and 500 "turn outs" in depots and marshalling yards behind the lines.

As with road bridges, so with railway bridges; demolitions on a large scale are probable and rapid repair and replacement is essential. This necessitates the holding of a large quantity of bridge and permanent way materials by a special Transportation Store Company. The actual operating, which includes the signalling, is also done by Operating and Railway Signal Companies. In the war of 1914-18 the development of inland water transport (canals) was large and when possible this method is utilized to take the load off the roads and railways.

Though the Egyptian State Railways are working to their full capacity, help from transportation units is essential to cope with the vast volume of traffic in North Africa. Where necessary a section is handed over to the railway units.

It is not often realized how wide is the scope of the labours of the R.E. Road construction and road cratering, bridge building and bridge demolition, the laying of anti-tank mines and obstacles or the removal of them, the erection of repair shops, stores and accommodation, the provision of supplies of electric light and water, drainage matters, aerodrome construction, ammunition depots, timber felling, bomb disposal, the army postal services, docking, railway and canal facilities—all these (and more) are undertaken by this vast engineering organization. And—let it be remembered—all the time they are *fighting men*, trained and ready to go into instant action.

The vast work done by the R.E. may, in fact, be said to cover all that which, in peace time, is the special interest of the Institutions of Civil, Electrical, Mechanical and Constructional Engineers. Of the R.E., Kipling's description is, in fact, still true: "We are the men who do something all round."

ROYAL ENGINEERS AS ARMY POSTMEN

The distribution of mails to the Army is an R.E. responsibility. Formed largely from J.P.O. staff, these men are highly efficient and work almost unsung upon an exacting task

INFANTRY ERECTING BARBED WIRE

Although mechanical vehicles can overcome wire obstructions, such defences are still a mena
to attacking infantry. Barbed wire and minefields are the chief instruments of close defen

CHAPTER 7

Infantry Organization

Home and overseas battalions. Terms of service in peace time. Make-up of a rifle battalion. Adjutant's duties. Intelligence officer. R.S.M. Signal officer and methods of signalling. Specialist platoons. Stretcher bearers

IF most Army reforms date from wars which showed up faults (and where else test a war machine?) the outstanding name in Army reform and one which concerns the Infantry very closely, is Cardwell (1813-86). For, among other reforms, he introduced the system which equalized the numbers of regular regiments at home and abroad, and introduced brigade districts, the germ of the county connection.

Then home and overseas regiments were linked together so that the home regiment was the training ground for the overseas regiment. The next step was for the linked regiments to lose their numbers and for the brigade districts to be turned into regimental districts. Thus there came into being the modern Corps of Infantry, based on their county depot, with one battalion at home and one overseas.

LINKED BATTALIONS

The depot takes in the raw recruit, and sends him, trained as an individual, to the home battalion (it may be first or second battalion). After a year or two, when he has learned to take his place as a member of the section and platoon fighting team, he is probably drafted overseas to the battalion in India, or elsewhere. This overseas battalion is maintained within fifty or so of its "war establishment," so that it can go on active service at the shortest possible notice.

Beside this system, the Territorial Army battalions are quite different. Their recruits do not come through the depot, and their only interest in the depot is in its capacity as the parent and guardian of that indefinable and invaluable quality, *esprit de corps*. The territorials are just as proud of their history as the regulars.

The greatest difference between today and a hundred years ago that would strike a soldier, could he fight in both times, would be the different parts played in the actual battle by the higher commanders. A century ago the commander was able to appear at the head of his troops, and by his own example and force of personality inspire them to deeds of bravery and devotion. Nowadays, the majority of fighting men probably see no commander higher than a captain or, perhaps, a major in charge of their company once the battle has begun. More often than not the vital phase of the little operation will be fought with the section corporal to guide and spur his few men on. Though machines play an important part, the British view is that it is the man behind the machine that is the deciding factor. This "final" factor is the reason for Army discipline, that driving force which holds a unit together in a tight corner.

It has already been shown that the regiment is a generic term covering a varying number of battalions, all bearing a county name. The regiment consists of two battalions and a depot in peace time. The functions of the overseas battalion is to provide permanent protection for our vital points throughout the Empire. The

MAKE-UP OF A RIFLE BATTALION

Battalion H.Q.

Headquarters Coy.	A. Coy.	B. Coy.	C. Coy.	D. Coy.
Platoon 1	Coy. H.Q.	Coy. H.Q.	Coy. H.Q.	Coy. H.Q.
Platoon 2	Platoon 7	Platoon 10	Platoon 13	Platoon 16
Platoon 3	Platoon 8	Platoon 11	Platoon 14	Platoon 17
Platoon 4	Platoon 9	Platoon 12	Platoon 15	Platoon 18
Platoon 5				
Platoon 6				

Fig. 1.

Dominions look after their own protection in peace, and British Army units are not stationed in them. This overseas battalion may be required to protect the locality in which it is stationed, say Gibraltar, or it may be used, as in India, either for internal security ("second line police-men") or to try to ward off any attack by a first-class power—say, by Japan in the Far East.

This is why the overseas battalion is kept up to its war establishment even during peace time. The men for this battalion are provided from time to time by the home battalion.

Apart from this function the home battalion also forms the skeleton round which a B.E.F. is formed. To understand this it is necessary to know that the terms of service in the Corps of Infantry are seven years with the colours and five on the reserve. That is, a soldier's ordinary peace time contract is for a total of twelve years, the first seven of which he spends in actual soldiering with his regiment, either in the home battalion or overseas. After he has completed his seven years, he is transferred to the Army Reserve. That means he walks out of the regi-mental depot gate again as a "civvy," free to take up any employment he chooses, but with the definite liability that, should a war or other national emergency be declared, he must return to serve again

in the Army whenever he is required

Thus, when war is declared, there is a five-year reserve of well-trained men, the majority of whom will make non-commissioned officers and instructors for the conscript armies that are to come along It is well known that Britain adopted conscription before the Second World War came, but its four months served as but little more than a try-out for the system. No large numbers had been trained by September, 1939, even had there been weapons and ammunition with which to equip them.

Let us now examine the make-up of a modern infantry rifle battalion. The dia-grammatic illustration, Fig. 1, shows that it consists of a battalion headquarters, a headquarters company, and four rifle companies. The officer in command of the unit is ranked as a lieutenant-colonel and the company commanders are usually either majors or captains.

Battalion headquarters (Bn. H.Q.) con-sists of only what the commanding officer (C.O.) requires round him to carry out his function of command. In battle he is relieved of most administrative matters by his second-in-command, a major, and the regimental sergeant-major, a warrant officer (class 1). But the second-in-command (2 i/c) must be prepared to take over active command should the C.O. be absent or become a casualty. I

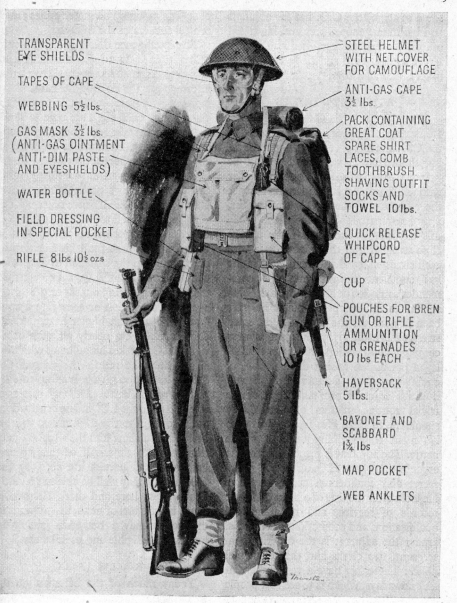

TRANSPARENT
EYE SHIELDS

TAPES OF CAPE

WEBBING 5½ lbs.

GAS MASK 3½ lbs.
(ANTI-GAS OINTMENT
ANTI-DIM PASTE
AND EYESHIELDS)

WATER BOTTLE

FIELD DRESSING
IN SPECIAL POCKET

RIFLE 8 lbs 10½ ozs

STEEL HELMET
WITH NET COVER
FOR CAMOUFLAGE

ANTI-GAS CAPE
3½ lbs.

PACK CONTAINING
GREAT COAT
SPARE SHIRT
LACES, COMB
TOOTHBRUSH
SHAVING OUTFIT
SOCKS AND
TOWEL 10 lbs.

QUICK RELEASE
WHIPCORD
OF CAPE

CUP

POUCHES FOR BREN
GUN OR RIFLE
AMMUNITION
OR GRENADES
10 lbs EACH

HAVERSACK
5 lbs.

BAYONET AND
SCABBARD
1¾ lbs

MAP POCKET

WEB ANKLETS

EQUIPMENT OF A BRITISH SOLDIER

*In wartime, battle-dress is the soldier's uniform. The carrying of soldiers and equip-
ment in motor trucks enables a modern infantryman, though laden, to go into action untired*

s usually the 2 i/c who stays behind in
control at rear H.Q. when the C.O. goes
forward to open up new H.Q., and
similarly, in retirement, the 2 i/c goes

back to select and organize the next
prepared defensive position in rear.
   At Bn. H.Q. (the army thrives on
abbreviations, and it is useful to pick up

some of them) the C.O. has his adjutant and his intelligence officer and his signal officer. As no one can continue indefinitely without food and sleep, these three officers aim at being interchangeable.

ADJUTANT'S DUTIES

The adjutant is the C.O.'s staff officer. He is responsible for keeping a record of the C.O.'s verbal orders, and for confirming them later in writing. He must be prepared to assist the battalion commander with anything, and in the latter's absence the adjutant, as the C.O.'s staff officer, must be prepared to give decisions. To do this successfully he must make a very close study of how the colonel deals with each situation, so that he can feel that he has sufficient insight into his commander's mind to be able to give a decision similar to the colonel's should he have been present. At the same time he must strenuously avoid giving the impression to company commanders that he is a privileged person, exercising the functions of command. After a time a loyal and intuitive adjutant can take a lot of the trivial routine matters off the C.O.'s shoulders, to leave him free to deal with his main responsibility of fighting the battle. The adjutant is responsible for the organization of the H.Q. office, and for all secret and confidential correspondence. He looks after the lists of officers and their records of service, and maintains the qualifications and promotions of N.C.O.s. Under the adjutant is the orderly room sergeant, two clerks and the regimental police. These last have a very important task nowadays, which is to see that people entering headquarters are authorised to pass, and to ensure that vehicles of dispatch riders and visiting officers are left in the car park, some one hundred or more yards away. A conglomeration of different vehicles is easy to spot from the air and may be taken to denote the presence of H.Q. When on the move the police are mounted on motor cycles; they control and direct the column.

The intelligence officer is a regimental officer trained to supply the C.O. and company commanders with all the latest information. To do this he has two or more maps covered with talc, on which chinagraph pencil signs are used to show the latest whereabouts of our own troops and the enemy. He must be prepared at any time, and at short notice, to provide the C.O. with a reasoned and considered forecast of the enemy's probable moves and intentions. The intelligence officer (I.O. usually stays glued to Bn. H.Q., which is where all messages and reports go, so that he can at any time fulfil his function of expounding on the situation to date. The C.O. is away from H.Q. a lot, whether reconnoitring during attack, or preparing a defensive position or attending a conference at the next higher headquarters, Brigade H.Q. On nearly all such occasions the C.O. takes his adjutant with him —and when he returns he expects the I.O. to be able to give him an up-to-date picture of the battle. All "in" messages received go to the I.O. and he usually does not take them to the C.O. unless urgent, preferring to show him the situation map from time to time. All officers visiting battalion headquarters are seen by the I.O., as they may well be able to add little bits of news here and there. All intelligence is little bits of news, insignificant in themselves maybe but often joining up into one intelligible and useful story.

R.S.M.'S WORK

Today much of the battalion intelligence officer's information comes forward from divisional and corps headquarters in the rear, where much useful information is gleaned by various methods which are not available to the I.O. with the unit.

The regimental sergeant-major is jack-of-all-trades, without whom battalion headquarters would either be chaos or

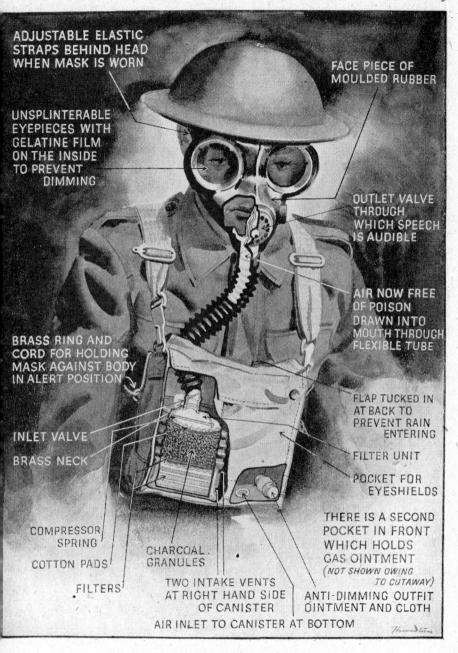

ADJUSTABLE ELASTIC STRAPS BEHIND HEAD WHEN MASK IS WORN

UNSPLINTERABLE EYEPIECES WITH GELATINE FILM ON THE INSIDE TO PREVENT DIMMING

FACE PIECE OF MOULDED RUBBER

OUTLET VALVE THROUGH WHICH SPEECH IS AUDIBLE

AIR NOW FREE OF POISON DRAWN INTO MOUTH THROUGH FLEXIBLE TUBE

BRASS RING AND CORD FOR HOLDING MASK AGAINST BODY IN ALERT POSITION

FLAP TUCKED IN AT BACK TO PREVENT RAIN ENTERING

FILTER UNIT

INLET VALVE

BRASS NECK

POCKET FOR EYESHIELDS

THERE IS A SECOND POCKET IN FRONT WHICH HOLDS GAS OINTMENT (NOT SHOWN OWING TO CUTAWAY)

COMPRESSOR SPRING

COTTON PADS

CHARCOAL GRANULES

FILTERS

TWO INTAKE VENTS AT RIGHT HAND SIDE OF CANISTER

ANTI-DIMMING OUTFIT OINTMENT AND CLOTH

AIR INLET TO CANISTER AT BOTTOM

BRITISH SERVICE RESPIRATOR

Defence against gas is an essential part of training in warfare. The Service respirator gives complete immunity from gases. Air is drawn into the mouthpiece through chemicals and so purified. The glass eyepieces are kept clear by the use of the anti-dimming ointment provided

would take twice as long to establish. The C.O. usually intimates the approximate area of his H.Q. and leaves his signal officer to choose the exact locality. The regimental sergeant-major (always spoken to as "Mr. So-and-so" by all officers, and "Sir" by every one else) then brings up the H.Q. troops and proceeds to organize and lay out H.Q., and arrange for its protection from both the air and the ground.

nition reserves to be established, so that bodies of troops temporarily cut off from H.Q. shall not run out of ammunition. The R.S.M. finds out how the ammunition situation is faring with companies by maintaining close liaison with the company sergeant-majors. He also usually takes more than a passing interest in the provision of rations or hot meals to the companies, and in the feeding of H.Q.

ANTI-AIRCRAFT POST IN THE DESERT

The Bren light machine gun is used with either a bipod or a tripod. Mounted on a tripod, it can be very effective against low-flying aircraft, particularly in such desert post

The R.S.M. is directly responsible for the issue of reserve ammunition to the companies in the fight. He has to arrange with the quartermaster that there is enough ammunition available at H.Q. to satisfy immediate demands. The theory of all ammunition supply is that the fighting troops must never have to send for it: it must arrive from behind, as it is spent. In these days, when enemy sub-units may raid deep into our rear areas, it is more than ever important for small local ammu-

Apart from his jobs during the fighting the regimental sergeant-major is the senior "other rank" in the battalion. Units are divided into "officers" and "other ranks." Officers are commissioned officers; other ranks include warrant officers (R.S.M., R.Q.M.S., C.S.M.) non-commissioned officers (C.Q.M.S. sergeant, lance-corporal, etc.) and privates (or gunners, fusiliers, riflemen signalmen, drummers). The R.S.M. is a warrant officer, class 1, wears a badge on his sleeve as shown on p. 39, and a Sam Browne belt except when in battle dress. He has a very important job in his function of maintaining discipline amongst the non-commissioned officers, and his views on their promotion usually weigh heavily with the C.O. and his company commanders. At the same time he does his best to make himself a father confessor to young lance-corporals on their first appointment, or to lance-sergeants whenever they "get their third stripe."

BATTALION SIGNALS

The drill of a battalion is the result of the work put in by the adjutant and the R.S.M., and on their respective personalities much of the unit discipline depends. More will be said about the need for strict discipline in war, but here it will only be mentioned that discipline is taught and practised during drill parades.

When the unit is out from the battle zone the R.S.M. can be of great help to the newly joined second lieutenant. He probably has more regimental service than any one in the unit, apart possibly from the C.O., and one or two "old sweats" like the sanitary corporal or cook sergeant. He has regimental tradition running fiercely through his arteries: his one object is to have his battalion the finest in the station, and his men noted as the best turned-out in the town. His value and influence is hard to assess, but it is higher than that of an ensign or subaltern in charge of a platoon.

Next at battalion headquarters let us consider the signal officer. It has been said that fire power is the dominant factor of war, with information next. The signal officer and his platoon are concerned with the passing of information. Information about the enemy is vital to every commander, and it is the job of the signal platoon to pass that information as quickly as possible from the troops in contact with the enemy (companies) to battalion headquarters. Equally important is it that flanking units should know what is going on, and the channels of communication are used in the opposite direction for the C.O. to give out, quickly and clearly, his orders to his troops.

The responsibility for establishing methods of communication is from higher to lower, that is, from brigade to battalion, from battalion to company. As a general rule regimental signallers are not provided below company headquarters, but if resources will run to it a detached platoon on an important flank may have a "terminal" (two or three men) allotted to it as a temporary measure.

Among the principal means of communication inside the battalion are the field telephone ("Don five"), the Fullerphone, and cable. The characteristics of cable in the field are that it takes some time to establish because of the time to lay the cable. This is an aspect of communications worthy of much improvement. The time taken to get cable out, inside the battalion, hardly keeps pace with modern war. It is very vulnerable to shell-fire, and to the tracks of armoured fighting vehicles. On the other hand, the hills and trees do not get in the way, as happens with a lamp or a flag. The main attraction is that officers can talk personally without any necessity to understand the Morse code. With good training it is possible for a message to be sent out from headquarters to four, five or even more different people at the same time.

FIELD EXCHANGES

The big disadvantage of the "Don five" telephone is that the enemy can pick up the signals if he is within 4,000 yards of the instruments at work. This is not possible with the Fullerphone.

There are two small exchanges for use at advanced and rear headquarters. They work very much like the small private exchanges one sees in most business

Troops are here seen advancing through a smoke screen with a Bren Carrier in support. Tommy guns and light machine guns are also much used in street warfare

houses today. The signal officer usually insists that the exchange is put into the circuit right from the beginning, even though it seems likely that only one or two lines at the most are going to go out. If the exchange is not put in from the start it is very difficult to impose on the existing circuits without dislocation.

TYPES OF SIGNALLING

If there is not time to establish line telegraphy and telephony there is a choice between visual methods (lamp, flag or heliograph), motor cycle orderly or foot orderlies (runners). Owing to the lack of "personal touch" in these methods much use is made today of liaison officers and motor contact officers.

The lamp used has a range in daylight of two miles, or eight with a telescope trained on the distant station. The great advantage of the lamp is that it can be quickly established, without the necessity of running out cables between the two stations. The two obvious objections are first, that the shape of the ground affects its usefulness, as hills, trees and buildings have an annoying habit of getting in the way ; and second, when used to signal forwards the enemy is likely to pick up the signals and thus learn the probable whereabouts of headquarters. A not-so-obvious objection is that as only the Morse code is used, the personal touch between the C.O. and his subordinates is lost.

Morse flag is hardly ever used in the field as it is too easily spotted by the enemy. It is, however, most useful for teaching the Morse code to a new class, and for instilling into them various matters of procedure. "Signal procedure" means the rules whereby stations call up one another and deal with different parts of messages to prevent or rectify mistakes.

Semaphore flag is sometimes used over very short distances, and, given small flags, readable messages over 500 or 600 . yards can be transmitted while kneeling down behind a bush or other cover. With ordinary practice quite a high rate of sending and reading can be achieved. It is a most useful form of signalling to encourage within a company, when one remembers that men from the signal platoon do not normally work lower than company headquarters. The alternative is the foot orderly, or runner. So he would usually rather wave flags than run!

The heliograph has very similar characteristics to the lamp, but it relies on the sun and a mirror for the source of light. It is thus entirely dependent on the weather, and therefore not much used in Western Europe. In the East it is invaluable, and can be used up to twenty miles easily, and farther as a stunt. Operators require a higher standard of training than with the lamp, as, owing to the movement of the sun, the mirror has to be continually adjusted to meet changing conditions.

The signal officer usually trains all runners in the battalion, so that, in addition to just carrying written messages, they can remember a verbal message, give a reasonable report from observations en route, and carry out elementary repairs to telephone lines.

Dogs and pigeons are not part of the means available within a battalion, but the signallers do require to know how to handle a pigeon, and such details as the fact that they roost at night and don't fly —elementary perhaps, but country foll sometimes are rare in infantry units.

SPECIALIST PLATOONS

Other platoons in the headquarters company are specially designed and equipped for anti-aircraft defence, three-inch mortar support, laying anti-tank mines and defence against gas, in addition to doing carpentering and other general handyman's jobs. There are also special administrative troops with that well-sung man the quartermaster and a mechanical transport officer. Between them and their staff they supply the battalion with its needs and keep the wheels of the mechanical transport turning. The "quarterbloke" is commissioned from the ranks in peace, graduating via C.Q.M.S., C.S.M., R.Q.M.S., and perhaps R.S.M. He has to know every legal way of obtaining all his battalion is entitled to; he also knows one or two other special ways of getting things!

BREN CARRIERS

There are also some Bren carriers at headquarters. They are more fully described in the succeeding chapter. Suffice it to say here that the name "Bren Carrier" is a very adequate two-word description of the platoon's function— namely, mobile firepower, the ability to carry Bren light automatics across bullet-swept areas. *They are not tanks.*

The battalion stretcher bearers are part of headquarters. A proportion of them is usually allotted to each company. There is a medical officer from the Royal Army Medical Corps attached to each battalion. With a medical orderly and some of the stretcher bearers the medical officer (M.O.) establishes the regimental aid post. To this aid post (R.A.P.) the stretcher bearers carry the wounded. The first field dressing carried by all ranks, officers and other ranks, will have already been put on to the wound. (All men are taught how to adjust this.) The M.O. at the R.A.P. sees that the dressing is correctly applied and attends to sending the wounded back.

Also attached to battalion headquarters is the Padre, his denomination depending on the unit, perhaps Presbyterian with a Scottish unit, or Church of England with English units. He attends to the spiritual welfare of his battalion, and is usually a moving force in the unit's entertainment when out of the fighting zone. As far as possible he tries to make his religious services non-denominational.

The brunt of the fighting in the battalion falls on the companies, platoons and sections. There are four identical rifle companies in a battalion, each divided into company headquarters and three platoons. The platoon organization itself comprises a headquarters and three sections, each of a corporal, a lance-corporal and nine privates.

The company is commanded by a major or a captain. At company headquarters he has his deputy, the second-in-command of the company, the company sergeant-major (counterpart of the R.S.M.), and the company quartermaster-sergeant (representative of the quartermaster in the company).

It is well known that animal transport has now been completely replaced by motor transport. Apart from the Bren carriers, which are an innovation, each platoon has its own truck on which are carried the men's packs, blankets and digging tools and other miscellaneous stores. The fighting is still done on foot, but the amount of kit which the platoon truck carries over many difficult places allows the soldier to engage the enemy with vastly heavier armament and in a fresher state. Although the Bren, mortar and anti-tank rifle are quite reasonable man-loads they are generally carried in the platoon truck until the battle begins.

SELF-CONTAINED UNIT

With the mention of the picks and shovels carried in a platoon one is driven to consider how self-contained and independent is the modern infantry battalion. They can fight, dig, cook, march, lay mines, erect wire, tend their wounded, signal, mend boots, drive and maintain their vehicles, and swear, and lots more besides. This is the unit which every lieutenant-colonel is proud to command and train. He knows all the infantryman's shortcomings and advantages in battle, and knows, in addition, how to look after them when out of the fighting zone.

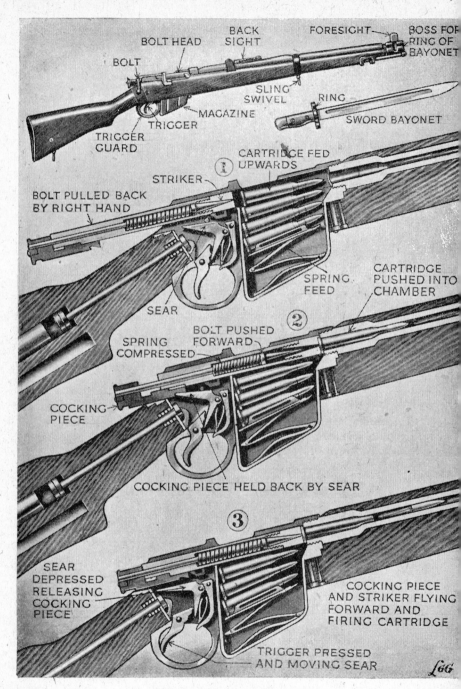

BRITISH LEE-ENFIELD RIFLE

1. The bolt drawn back for loading. 2. Rifle cocked, cartridge in chamber. 3. Rifle when fired

CHAPTER 8

Infantry Weapons

The bayonet. Lee-Enfield rifle. Rifling and mechanism. Bren light machine gun. Anti-tank rifle. Two-inch mortar. Grenades. Thompson gun. Three-inch mortar. Bren carriers. Mechanization

As war is a business of killing, all infantry weapons are designed to kill the enemy, or so to threaten him with death that he either surrenders on the spot or takes such cover that he is unable to interfere with the advance of our troops. The object of modern war as a whole is to destroy the enemy's will to continue the fight. The object of infantry is either to drive the enemy off the ground he holds or else to close with him and deal with him with the bayonet.

As the bayonet is the first weapon to be mentioned and the most elementary, we will deal with it first. Incidentally, it is the weapon most hated by the Germans. It is the only death-dealer which can be seen just before it is felt, and faced with cold steel the German is a coward. His courage is based on the use of overwhelming force, and he shrinks from equal struggles. A well-trained man can do a great deal of damage with a bayonet on the end of a rifle, and can also parry the enemy's thrust and kill him.

A NEW RIFLE

From the bayonet one turns naturally to the rifle. For the second time the British Army went to war with a rifle which had, in fact, been superseded by a newer weapon. In 1914 a different rifle had passed its trials successfully, but it was decided that it was too risky to put another rifle into production when war seemed so imminent. From the time a rifle passes its test to the time it is in full production is a matter of a year or more. It would have taken eighteen months to equip the B.E.F. with a new rifle. Even after eighteen months the men would have taken time to become used to the new weapon. Again, before the Second World War, a new rifle had been tried out and approved, but not mass produced.

EFFECT OF RIFLING

So we still have the 1914 pattern, short magazine Lee-Enfield as our main fighting rifle. The next approved rifle was in actual fact produced and known as the 1917 pattern, or No. 3 rifle. It is the one issued to thousands of Home Guards throughout the country, who were under the delusion for some time that they had been issued with an obsolete weapon, but really they have a more up-to-date one than the S.M.L.E.

The barrel of any service weapon is "rifled"; that is, the inside (the bore) is not smooth but has grooves cut in it. These grooves have a slight twist throughout the whole length. When the bullet is forced by the explosion through the barrel it leaves with a twist which holds it on an even keel. Were the bullet not spinning it would topple about, and be easily blown off its course by the wind. Those who play rugger will remember, when punting against a wind, one tried to get a screw on the ball so as to keep it straight. The rifling in a barrel produces a similar effect, and it exists from the smallest pistol up to the biggest gun.

The 1914 S.M.L.E. is of ·303 inch calibre; that is, the inside diameter of the barrel—irrespective of grooves—is three hundred and three-thousandths of an inch. The magazine will hold ten rounds of rimmed ammunition; Britain is the last country to retain such ammunition. It is a very accurate weapon in the hands of an expert. There are many Bisley shots who can put ten consecutive shots into a 12-inch diameter circle at 300 yards, the size of a man's head. The mechanism is simple and reliable and, in the rigorous conditions of war, it is probably less affected by weather and mud than any rifle of other countries. It is also possible to maintain a fairly high rate of fire, fifteen aimed shots in a minute being quite within the capacity of well-trained troops. C.S.M. Mapp of the Small Arms School used regularly to demonstrate thirty rounds in a minute all in the bull or inner circle at 300 yards.

The present bullet only flies straight for 200 yards, after which it starts to drop because of the force of gravity. To counteract this the tip of the rifle has to be raised slightly, so as to overcome the drop. This is done by altering the height of the backsight. Therefore, at over 200 yards, the range to the target has to be estimated and the correct elevation put on the backsight.

BREN LIGHT MACHINE GUN

The principal weapon of the infantry today is the Bren light machine gun. The Bren is of Czechoslovak origin, and in its first form was made at Brno. With British modifications it was made at Enfield. Hence the BR of Brno, and the EN of Enfield, gave the name Bren. It is a "gas-operated automatic." That is, some of the gases from the explosion which dispatches the bullet are trapped at the front of the barrel to drive the working parts back against a spring and so cock the gun. The spring carries the working parts forward and fires the next round. It can be

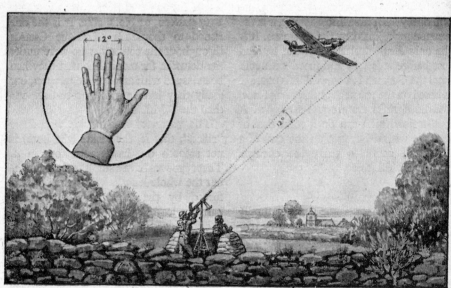

HOW TO AIM AT AIRCRAFT FROM THE GROUND

In the Army, machine guns use a standard "lead" of twelve degrees by which to "aim off" in the direction of flight of the aeroplane. This is a simple and fairly accurate method. The time available in which to aim at a plane from the ground is usually a mere matter of seconds

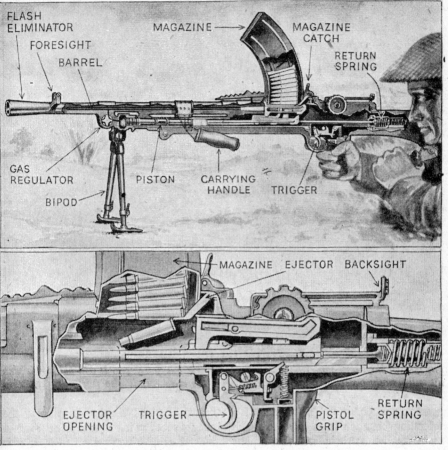

FLASH ELIMINATOR
FORESIGHT
BARREL
MAGAZINE
MAGAZINE CATCH
RETURN SPRING
GAS REGULATOR
BIPOD
PISTON
CARRYING HANDLE
TRIGGER

MAGAZINE EJECTOR BACKSIGHT
EJECTOR OPENING
TRIGGER
PISTOL GRIP
RETURN SPRING

BREN LIGHT MACHINE GUN

This gas-operated automatic is the principal infantry weapon of the Army. Air cooled, it fires 120 rounds a minute and is light to carry. It can be used with either a bipod or a tripod

used as a bipod gun. The tripod used to be adaptable for anti-aircraft work, but this has now been done away with, as sufficiently effective L.M.G. (light machine gun) fire can be developed from the hip. It can also be effectively mounted in vehicles.

It is air cooled (in contrast to the older Vickers machine gun, which is water cooled). To prevent damage from overheating, two quickly changeable barrels are provided for each gun; ·303-inch rimmed ammunition, identical with the

rifle, is fed from a magazine holding thirty rounds. The normal rate of fire is 150 rounds per minute, but, because of the time taken to change magazines and to avoid wasting ammunition, the rate of fire is kept down to 120 rounds a minute. One thousand yards is an effective range.

The main characteristics are the ability to keep up an accurate and high rate of fire, and extreme simplicity and reliability. This high rate of fire is one of the main requirements of the modern battlefield. It has been said that "bullets hold

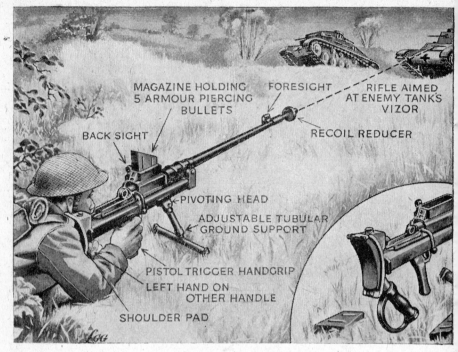

MAGAZINE HOLDING
5 ARMOUR PIERCING
BULLETS

FORESIGHT

RIFLE AIMED
AT ENEMY TANK'S
VIZOR

BACK SIGHT

RECOIL REDUCER

PIVOTING HEAD

ADJUSTABLE TUBULAR
GROUND SUPPORT

PISTOL TRIGGER HANDGRIP

LEFT HAND ON
OTHER HANDLE

SHOULDER PAD

BRITISH ANTI-TANK RIFLE

The ·5-inch Boys anti-tank rifle is very accurate at about 300 yards. It will not stop a tank but will usually penetrate the armour and injure the crew. It is also fairly light to carry

ground, not bodies." The object of a defending battalion is to have so much lead flying across their front that no one can live there. The attackers aim at knocking out with fire the guns or crews which are putting down this screen, so as to enable them to move forward to capture the ground occupied by the defence. Fire power rules the modern battlefield.

Because of the ability of the machine gun, by its high rate of fire, to neutralize so much ground, the attackers always endeavour to discover early in the battle where the defenders' machine guns are, so that they can be dealt with either by the attacking artillery or by the infantry's own mortars. The Germans have also perfected the use of the dive bomber to knock out machine guns. One can easily see that the better a Bren can be concealed the less chance there is of the enemy spotting it and bringing the fire of mortar or dive bomber on to it. If it is spotted and fired on, the gun has to be moved to an alternative position.

There is one light machine gun per section. In attack this is used to give covering fire against the enemy who may hold up the attack. The Bren can be maintained in action by one man for a short time, provided enough magazines are dumped at the gun position. Either the gun is left behind to engage the enemy from the front, while the rest of the section stalks round the enemy's flank, or else the Bren moves round to a flank to give covering fire while the section assaults frontally.

The tripod is not used in attack, but in defence; it has the advantage of allowing the gun to be fired on a fixed line. This means that the gun is clamped on to the tripod to fire in a certain fixed direction at a fixed elevation. By co-ordinating these fixed lines it is possible for a battalion commander to arrange for that impassable screen of bullets around his posts which we mentioned before. As the tripods are firmly embedded into the ground the gun can be fired at night or in smoke, and it is not necessary to see what is being shot at. As soon as the alarm is given the gunner merely presses the trigger and knows that his bullets will fall in a certain place.

The tripod can also be used for traversing, that is, tapping it three or four degrees at a burst to right or left ; and with expert gunners two or three different fixed lines can be given, provided they do not vary too much in elevation or direction. By moving a lever the Bren can be used to fire single rounds, so deceiving the enemy into thinking that only rifles are opposed to him.

For anti-aircraft, a reasonably strong man can fire the Bren from the shoulder or hip, either standing or, preferably, kneeling. Tracer ammunition, that is ammunition with a phosphorus illuminant in the base which lights up in flight, is provided. A useful proportion is —one tracer, one ball, one tracer, one ball, one tracer, one armour piercing and repeat. In the air the effect is similar to a jet of water, and the method of directing the stream of bullets is similar. In practice no sight in the ordinary sense is taken, but the gaze is focused on enemy aircraft,

BRITISH BREN CARRIER

The purpose of this vehicle is to carry Bren light machine guns rapidly to any required place. Highly mobile, it is not a tank and is vulnerable to plunging fire. Apart from the Bren gun it has a small anti-tank gun, is able to communicate by wireless and is fast across country

and the gun moved about until the tracer is seen to be entering the machine. In the Army, rifles and machine guns use a standard lead of twelve degrees or a fixed amount by which to aim off in the direction of flight. Airmen with their many deflection shots would not agree with this, but it is moderately accurate and has the

It is intended to pierce armour up to 500 yards and inflict casualties on the crew. Only a very lucky shot in some vital part of the engine will stop the tank. Our own weapon has been proved to be very satisfactory, so much so that the enemy are reputed to be copying it. It has the great merits of simplicity, and a man fully

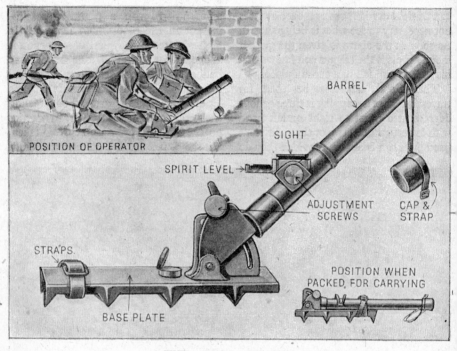

THE 2-INCH MORTAR

This is a valuable light weapon used in platoons. It folds up neatly and is very useful for searching out the enemy behind cover. It can also be used for laying protective smoke screens

very great merit of simplicity. Twelve degrees is given by the distance between the outstretched forefinger and little finger held at arm's length (see p. 174).

The anti-aircraft personnel are equipped with Brens. Small arms fire is effective against aircraft up to 3,000 feet. Above this height infantry must rely on A.A. artillery for their protection.

In considering the legitimate anti-tank rifle next, one must point out immediately that it does not knock out the tank.

trained in the rifle can be taught to handle the anti-tank rifle in two hours. Being small it is easy to conceal and one man can carry it quite a distance and maintain it in action. The calibre of the anti-tank rifle is half an inch. It was invented by a British officer named Captain Boys.

The other weapon available to the platoon commander is the 2-inch mortar. It can be kept in action by two men, and carried by them one or two miles.

The mortar throws the bomb high up

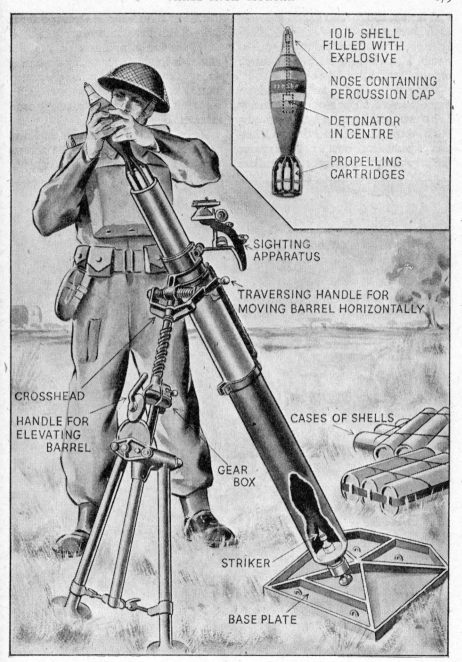

10lb SHELL FILLED WITH EXPLOSIVE

NOSE CONTAINING PERCUSSION CAP

DETONATOR IN CENTRE

PROPELLING CARTRIDGES

SIGHTING APPARATUS

TRAVERSING HANDLE FOR MOVING BARREL HORIZONTALLY

CROSSHEAD

HANDLE FOR ELEVATING BARREL

CASES OF SHELLS

GEAR BOX

STRIKER

BASE PLATE

THE 3-INCH MORTAR

This larger mortar is a battalion weapon. Its bomb is much heavier and the mortar itself weighs about 120 lb. The bomb is fired by dropping it on a striker at the bottom of the barrel into the air, and for this reason it is very useful where the enemy are well established behind bullet-proof cover, such as a wall. Then the mortar bomb can search out the enemy behind the cover.

It is also very useful for putting down a smoke screen, either to blind the enemy at his own position or to hide a move by our own troops. Before an attack a battalion commander normally can arrange for the supporting artillery and medium machine guns to neutralize enemy defence posts which have been located. This is called the fire plan. The main use of a mortar is in attack for taking on enemy strong posts which were not previously located when the fire plan was made. Thus it is nicknamed the "company commander's pocket pistol."

The platoon has several high explosive grenades. The grenade can be thrown thirty to forty yards and is very useful just

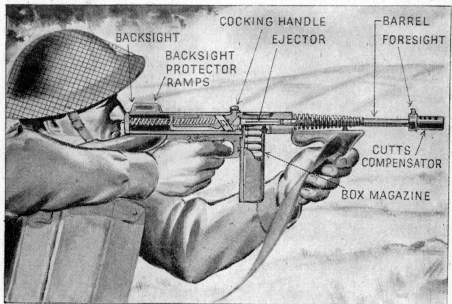

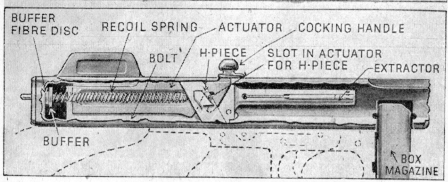

THE THOMPSON (OR "TOMMY") GUN

This sub-machine gun is an essential assault weapon and much used on patrol. It fires 750 ·45-inch bullets per minute. At short range it is deadly and its mechanism is very simple

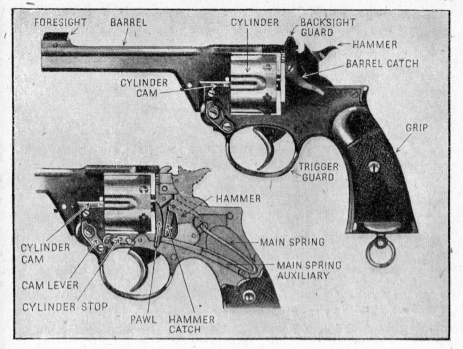

FORESIGHT   BARREL   CYLINDER   BACKSIGHT
                                     GUARD
                                          ←HAMMER
                                          BARREL CATCH
CYLINDER
CAM
                                          GRIP
                                     TRIGGER
                                     GUARD
HAMMER
CYLINDER
CAM
                              MAIN SPRING
CAM LEVER   MAIN SPRING
                              AUXILIARY
CYLINDER STOP
          PAWL   HAMMER
                 CATCH

THE BRITISH ARMY'S HAND-GUN : THE ·38 PISTOL

This is the most up-to-date British revolver, though it is termed a "pistol." It has very great stopping power at between five and twenty yards' range, and the rate of fire is high

before closing on the enemy with the bayonet or in clearing buildings and trenches. The rifle and machine gun bullet inflicts a fairly clean, simple wound, but the mortar and grenade break up into irregular, jagged lumps, with accordingly complicated wounds.

Finally in the platoon there is one sub-machine gun. At present this is the American Thompson gun at £45 apiece! They fire ·45-inch rimless ammunition similar to that fired in automatic pistols, and their rate is very high (750 rounds a minute) The larger bullet has a great stopping power, and the short barrel means that it can be swung quickly from one target to another. The disadvantage of the short barrel is that it becomes inaccurate over certain distances.

There is a mistaken impression that the *effective* range is short; the "Tommy"

gun will certainly *kill* at medium range. It is essentially a close-range assault weapon, for patrolling, etc. If the platoon commander himself does not carry the sub-machine gun it will be used by the leading assaulting section commander.

All officers and drivers are armed with ·38-inch pistols. The characteristics of the "hand-gun" are its great stopping power and high rate of fire (one round per second is the standard with the pistol).

There is no time to aim, at any rate the first two shots. If you look at a mark on the wall and point at it without accurately aligning the arm and finger it will be found to be pretty well on the mark. This pistol is used at from five to twenty-five yards, and at these short ranges it does not matter if the bullet fails to enter a vital part. It will stop an opponent hit anywhere in the bones apart from the arms.

A rifle bullet, say through the shoulder, would not stop a man ten yards away.

These then are the platoon weapons—the rifle and bayonet, the Bren light machine gun, the anti-tank rifle, the 2-inch mortar, the sub-machine gun, the three kinds of grenade and the officer's pistol. The main fighting in the battalion is generally done with these particular platoon weapons.

In addition the battalion commander has at his disposal 3-inch mortars, Bren carriers, anti-tank rifles and anti-aircraft light machine guns.

DETACHMENT OF MORTARS

The 3-inch mortar is very similar to the 2-inch model, but it fires a much heavier bomb with a corresponding increase in destructive power. The range is also much greater. To achieve these increases in performance the component parts have to be increased in weight, and the 3-inch mortar as set up for action weighs 120 lb. Though carried, where possible, in its own 15-cwt. truck, in battle much manhandling is called for, and for this reason the team which operates a mortar (called a "detachment of mortars") has to be fit and strong.

Unlike the 2-inch mortar, which is fired with a trigger and striker, the 3-inch mortar has no trigger, but only a fixed striker pin at the base of the barrel. The bomb has a percussion cap at the bottom, and is fired when it drops down the barrel, the cap hitting the striker, which causes the explosion to send the bomb on its way to the enemy position. With practice a high rate of fire can be maintained over a short period, but it is uneconomical to keep up rapid fire, because of the problem of keeping ammunition supplied to the mortar when this is in action.

That is one of the major problems of modern war. The mechanical efficiency of large numbers of automatic and other weapons means that an enormous quantity of ammunition is expended in a very short time, so to keep the guns served with ammunition puts a heavy strain on the quartermaster, the R.S.M. and on the services in the rear of the battlefield.

Bren carriers have already been mentioned as forming a part of the head-quarters company, when it was stated that the name, Bren carrier, denotes its function, which is to carry Bren light machine guns rapidly over bullet-swept ground.

The sides of the carrier are proof against rifle fire, but the top of the vehicle is uncovered and it is therefore very vulnerable when coming down fairly steep slopes or to plunging fire. Plunging fire means that the bullet or shell is descending at a steep angle, either because it is tossed up high by the gun or mortar, or because it is fired at a long range, and therefore dropping steeply.

Being a track-laying vehicle the cross-country performance is very good, and it has a very fair turn of speed at the same time (twenty-five to thirty miles per hour). On the other hand, the short track (length touching the ground) means that all but the narrowest trenches will stop it. It is, of course, stopped by all obstacles which will hold up a tank.

SOLO MACHINES

The vulnerability of the Bren and its crew when coming into action from the carrier has already been mentioned. In order to get early warning of the enemy and so prevent surprise, the platoon has arrangements to get information. The motor cycle sidecar outfits have a poor cross-country performance, but they do enable light machine guns to be moved about quickly. They can thus take over a position held by a Bren from a carrier, and so enable the latter to resume its mobility. The solo machines have an improved cross-country performance, in that they can be manhandled across certain obstacles. It is probable, however, that they will later be superseded by small cars of much greater stability.

Mobility is one of the chief attributes of the carrier platoon, and for this reason an ordinary infantry section will often take over a machine gun position from the carriers, so enabling these to move on again as required.

The implications of mechanization are dealt with in another chapter. The effect has been to reduce the load carried by the ordinary soldier in action and so increase his radius of action. It is also interesting to know that the change from horse to motor has resulted in a reduction of the rail trucks in the supply train from base to railhead. Apart from the considerations of the tactical advantages, it would have been suicidal to retain the horse, when this animal was quickly disappearing from industry and agriculture at home; ships, too, to bring them from abroad had also fallen off in demand in recent years.

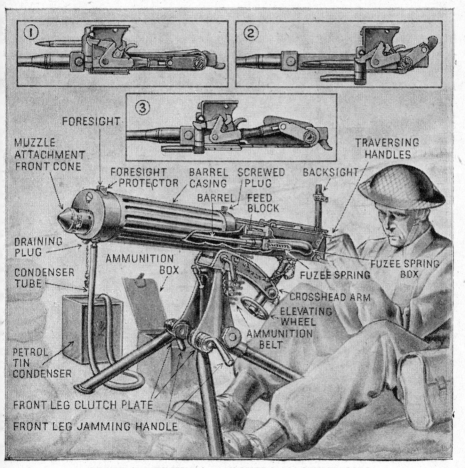

BRITISH MEDIUM .303 VICKERS MACHINE GUN

This recoil-operated gun is fed by an ammunition belt and is water cooled. Insets: 1, lock in forward position, live round in chamber; 2, lock back, new round in alignment with chamber and old round dropping out; 3, lock moving forward, new round nearly ready for firing

FUTURE OFFICERS ON THE MARCH

Any men suitable are carefully trained to be officers in Britain's growing Army. The course at an O.C.T.U. is a severe test of the leadership and initiative vital in modern warfare

CHAPTER 9

Infantry Training and Tactics

Principles of war. Individual and collective training. Discipline. Close-order drill. Unarmed combat. Weapon and anti-gas training. Route marching. Choosing officers and N.C.O.s. Camouflage. Individual stalk. Patrolling. Specialist companies. Signalling. Mine laying. Bren carriers. O.C.T.U.s. Appreciation of a situation. Planning an action. T.E.W.T.s. Sequence of orders. A.A. defence. Protection on the ground

IT has been truly said that "There is no such thing as a bad regiment—only bad officers." Today nearly all officers in a battalion have been through the ranks, either as cadets at Sandhurst before the war, or as private soldiers with a unit, prior to going to an officer cadet training unit. The logical sequence therefore is to consider the stages of training a man towards becoming an officer.

It is easier to understand what the Army sets out to do in its training, by mentioning first of all what are called "The Principles of War." In this way it can be seen from the start what the finished article—the whole British Army—and the infantry in particular sets out to achieve. The training and tactics of the infantry all strive for the attainment of these objects.

PRINCIPLES OF WAR

The Principles of War are eight, and first and foremost is put the *Maintenance of the Object*, by which is meant that doggedness and determination which allows nothing to interfere with the intention to complete the particular task in hand. The Army draws a clear distinction between "object" and "objective." The "object" is the aim of a commander, what he sets out to achieve. It may be the object is to capture a certain bridge, or to deny a certain village to the enemy. The "objective" is something on the ground which the troops are to capture.

Second is *Offensive Action*. In war, victory is not handed out on a plate, the enemy must be sought out and destroyed. This can only be done if all ranks are determined to attack the enemy as hard and as often as possible, when sooner or later he is bound to "crack."

The third principle of war is *Surprise*, which has been defined as the most powerful weapon in war. We all know from everyday experience how our efficiency deteriorates when suddenly faced with the unexpected. The British tanks surprised the Germans at Cambrai in 1917. President Roosevelt surprised Hitler when he substituted the Lease and Lend Bill for the Neutrality Act. The youngest lance-corporal must be continually thinking: How can I surprise my enemy?

The natural corollary to surprising the enemy is the fourth principle of war—*Security*, which is protection against surprise. The more troops know and find out about the enemy and his dispositions the less likely are they to be surprised. In the old days a commander could ensure his security by putting out a protective screen to the front and flanks. Today, protection has to be all round and from the air.

The next three principles hang together: they are *Economy of Force, Mobility* and *Concentration*. By economy of force is meant using only as many men and materials as are needed to achieve the immediate object, thus saving as many units as possible for battles elsewhere. Accordingly a larger number of troops are available for another part of the battlefield, or to rest or refit. An easily understood example of the principle of economy of force is the retention in the British Isles of just enough troops to be certain of defeating the maximum number of men which the enemy can land in this country, so releasing the greatest possible number for other theatres of war overseas.

TRAINING IN WAR PRINCIPLES

Having economized in one place, one wants to concentrate elsewhere. To do this, mobility, the sixth principle, is needed. This merely means the ability to move rapidly from one part of the battlefield to another. On the grand scale, one has only to consider the speed with which the enemy can move his troops from one end of Europe to the other, compared with the time taken for Britain to send out men and machines to Egypt by sea.

Economy and mobility are both needed to permit of successful concentration, the seventh principle, which means nothing more than the ability to face the enemy in the vital battlefield with superior forces, both in number and quality. This is why the Germans always start a battle with overwhelming numbers. There is a sacrilegious saying, that "God is on the side of the big battalions." It may be true that one British soldier is a match for three Germans, but when they start a battle with four times as many men—the fourth German will kill the Britisher. The fear of ignoring this principle is why the Germans have such a hatred of waging war on two fronts.

The eighth and final principle is *Co-operation*, by which is meant the team work of the Army as a whole, the support which each branch gives to the other. In the battalion it means the correct use of all the weapons and sub-units. For co-operation to be successful, commanders must be fully alive to the capabilities and shortcomings of all the men and weapons at their command.

The occasions when all these principles can be put into effect at the same time will indeed be few. In certain situations one

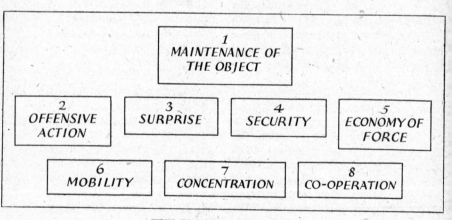

THE PRINCIPLES OF WAR
Warfare is governed by certain well-defined principles, which should be adapted to each situation according to the circumstances of the moment. To ignore any invites disaster

TESTING THE SIGHTS OF A RIFLE

When testing sights one man sights along his bayonet on to his opposite number's rifle, while the other man sights on to the bayonet. Any serious inaccuracy is easy to detect and correct

principle will weigh heavier than another. Nevertheless they cannot ever be completely flouted, or disaster will ensue. Risks have to be taken, but the test of leadership is the ability to distinguish the right situation, which gives added weight to one principle, to the reduced importance of another. It is towards putting these principles into effect that the modern British soldier is trained.

All training is divided into two main categories, individual and collective. The duration of the former varies from eight weeks for the rifle soldier to sixteen weeks for the signaller or Bren carrier personnel.

Although this chapter confines itself to the entirely military aspect of the soldier's training, the Army Council is continually stressing the moral side of warfare. The proper attitude to the winning of a war must originate in the mind: the job is to wind up the mainspring in every soldier's mind so that he sees only one object, a determination to hit the enemy hard wherever and whenever he is met. The British view is essentially that the value of any mechanical weapon lies finally in the determination of the man behind it rather than in the weapon itself. All training of the individual lays stress on this.

Right from the time the new arrival walks through the gates of his infantry

training centre, he starts to absorb what in 1941 the then Chief of the Imperial General Staff, Field Marshal Sir John Dill, defined as "the very life breath of a modern British Army"—discipline. At the beginning of the present war there were hints from certain Press correspondents that some of the British Army discipline might be relaxed. In particular they objected to the stringent regulation, that every soldier will salute every commissioned officer when he passes. Whether or not the Army Council were stirred an inch by these uninformed murmurings, events of the last ten days of May, 1940, culminating in Dunkirk proved to the authorities that the old discipline was just what any army needed to hold it together in a tight corner.

SENSIBLE DISCIPLINE

British discipline of today is not the blind obedience of the charge of the Light Brigade, but the sensible discipline which holds men together in a crisis. Far from demanding unquestioning obedience to orders, it is regarded as definitely wrong to carry out an order if some new factor has arisen, about which the commander did not know when he issued the order. He must be immediately consulted or else the order must be sensibly or wisely altered

The most democratic will submit to discipline as long as its necessity is pointed out to them. For instance, who can object to the salute when it is explained that it dates from the days of chivalry, when knights showed their open hands to each other to demonstrate that their hand contained no missile? The practice of giving "eyes right," far from being a mark of servitude, dates from the days when the freemen were privileged to look their master in the eyes, whereas the serfs had to pass humbly by with downcast glance.

The basis of all discipline is close-order drill. Here the recruit first learns to obey orders instantly, and begins to sink his individuality in the squad at drill. The

PRACTISING BAYONET FIGHTING

Though strict orthodoxy is not observed in an actual bayonet encounter, certain basic movements are essential. (A) The High Port. (B) The On Guard. (C) The Thrust. (D) The Withdraw. Training in bayonet fighting is today usefully reinforced by practice in unarmed combat

PRACTICE IN SCOUTING

Every infantryman is trained to perform an individual stalk. Later stalking, or scouting, by sections forms the basis of their patrol training. The use of ground and natural cover is vital

value is that the recruit subjects himself automatically to discipline without realizing it, while knowing that any slovenliness in turnout or drill will be spotted by his instructor. Even with seasoned troops, short spells of ten or fifteen minutes are invaluable for maintaining that standard of discipline which goes to make the British soldier the finest in the world.

After his drill, the recruit's early weeks will be occupied with fifty minutes' physical training every day. This and a high standard of feeding goes to give recruits an average increase in weight of ten pounds. The exercises are designed mainly to increase a man's suppleness and agility, while improving his general strength and endurance to carry out his job in the field. It is fully acknowledged

in the British Army that the German soldier, after his labour camp training, is physically very fit, and there is no intention of allowing that advantage to remain. If their men can march thirty miles in a day, ours will be trained to do thirty-five. And mortars and anti-tank rifles are heavy lumps of metal which men's muscles must be trained to carry. In order that our men may never find themselves at a disadvantage, they are also taught unarmed combat by the P.T. instructor. This is a combination of wrestling, boxing and general scragging, the essential being speed of assessing the situation and speed in executing some throw or blow, even though the enemy is armed and you are at first caught at a disadvantage.

Along with his drill and P.T., a recruit

is put on early to learn how to use the rifle with which he is personally armed, but soon learns how to handle the rifle battalion's principal weapon, the Bren light machine gun.

As far as possible all army instructions follow a standard sequence, namely explanation, demonstration, execution and practice. That is to say, the instructor first of all states by word of mouth what he proposes to teach the squad: then he gives a demonstration of the movement correctly done: next the squad is made to carry out the movement themselves and faults are corrected: finally, by practice, the whole lesson becomes one cohesive whole. During the demonstration the N.C.O. or officer points out the reasons for the various things he asks the recruit to do. The correction of faults is an art in itself. The object is to get the man, by question and answer, to see for himself what he is doing wrong. It may be necessary to demonstrate the fault, but *an instructor should never have to touch a man to put him right*. If he does touch him to correct a fault, he is a bad instructor.

Quite early in his career the recruit is introduced to fieldcraft. This subject would be far better described as scouting. Lessons cover such matters as cover and camouflage, the best ground for fire positions, how to select a view point, how to observe, how to use ground to assist movement, how to keep direction and how to work at night, ending up with the individual stalk.

THE INDIVIDUAL STALK

All the time our recruit is learning how to march (he must be up to fifteen miles in battle order by twelve weeks), how to put his kit together and look after himself, and something of the past tradition of the regiment to which he belongs. In addition, efforts are made, entirely on a non-party basis, to help the recruit to understand the aims for which Britain is fighting. The

potential officer or N.C.O. begins to stand out from the others after four or five weeks, and about the same time the men go on to the range for the first time. They will by now have learnt how to lay a correct aim and how to release the trigger without disturbing that aim unduly. The first "shoot" is usually indoors on a miniature range (twenty-five yards long with .22 ammunition, fired through S.M.L.E. rifles with specially reduced bore). The targets are reduced to the representative size of a service target at 200 yards. The first shoot is not done with full-scale ammunition, because there is quite an appreciable kick from a rifle which might put a recruit off so much that it would be difficult to coax him out of the habit of flinching as he pressed the trigger.

ANTI-GAS TRAINING

The recruit is early taught how to protect himself against gas. The subjects in which instruction is given are the elementary details of the war gases—how to recognize them, their effects and the protective measures which give immunity. Then the various items of anti-gas equipment are explained, such as the respirator, eyeshields, anti-gas cape, the ointment, and gas detectors. These are items of personal equipment provided to every soldier. In addition vehicles have certain anti-gas equipment, and the unit is supplied with items such as gas alarms, gas warning signs, pathways for crossing limited contaminated areas (100 yards per battalion), anti-gas union cloth for gas-proofing buildings, and certain decontamination stores, all of which a man must know how to use. The various ways in which gas can be spread are explained (air bombs, air spray mortars, etc.), and lessons are devoted to the decontamination of personnel, weapons, vehicles, food and ground. The considerations affecting the use of gas as a weapon of war are explained, so that men may appreciate when

INFANTRY SECTION IN ATTACK

When attacking an enemy position it is usual to occupy their attention by frontal fire from Bren guns and mortars. Under cover of this fire the remainder of a section tries to work round to a flank and so get to close range. Above, Bren guns and a mortar are providing the covering fire ; below, the infantry are seen getting into position. Finally they will move to the assault with the bayonet and light automatic weapons. In favourable conditions a smoke screen may be laid at the last moment by the mortar to cover the last stages of the infantry's advance

it is likely to be used. They are also taught
what tactical action to take when it is first
met during a battle.

A recruit must have an elementary
knowledge of field engineering, and the
items taught include how to dig trenches,
how to erect barbed wire, how to improve,
with camouflage, the natural concealment
provided on the ground, and how to lay
and hide an anti-tank mine.

It has already been mentioned that an
infantry soldier's training in marching
begins early. In spite of the mechanization of many other arms, the infantry have
to do their fighting on foot, and most of
their approach marches will also be on
foot. To do fifteen and twenty miles a day
with a rifle and equipment and then to
fight a battle at the end of it requires a
high standard of march discipline. The
old "column of fours" disappeared shortly

before the war, and columns of threes are
now used, each column in a platoon
representing a section with the commander at its head. Thus a section can
"peel off" quickly to a threatened flank,
without leaving a gap in the column as
used to occur when a section left the old
column of fours. Usually two columns
are one side of the road and one the other,
so that all available overhead cover from
air attack can be used. Three miles per
hour is the rate of marching and, if the
tactical situation permits, there is a ten-
minute halt every clock hour when men
fall out and take off their equipment.

The above is a brief description of the
subjects taught to every infantry recruit.
At the end of six weeks he is on the way to
becoming physically fit, he can shoot with
a rifle, Bren light machine gun and anti-
tank rifle. He can throw a grenade, use his

TWO-POUNDER ANTI-TANK GUN

*This small mobile gun proved very effective against enemy tanks. The wheels are removed and
a special splayed trail takes their place. This forms a very solid and secure gun platform*

CADETS LEARNING TACTICS ON A SAND TABLE

In a model countryside, officers of the future fight mimic battles, discuss questions of supply, fields of fire and "dead ground," and learn to deal with a variety of tactical situations

bayonet and handle the two-inch mortar; he knows how to cope with hostile aircraft, and what to do if gas is reported. He can do foot and arms drill, and is trained in fieldcraft up to the standard of the individual stalk; he has worked in the dark, and can dig a trench and put up a barbed wire obstacle. He can march nine miles in full kit. Above all, he understands the meaning and effect of discipline.

At this stage, potential officers and N.C.O.s are chosen. The officers are being continually watched during their last four to eight weeks of individual training and they then go in front of a regimental board, which, if they pass successfully, hands them on to a command board. From here they go on to their officer cadet training unit (O.C.T.U.). The N.C.O.s are also chosen at this stage and are appointed lance-corporals.

From here the training divides into that for specialists, or a continuance of infantry training for sections and platoons.

The specialists are very carefully selected by the officer commanding the specialist company, in consultation with the infantry company commanders. They have to choose signallers, three-inch

mortar men, transport drivers and men fitted to drive Bren carriers.

The ordinary riflemen carry on with their weapon training which covers such subjects as advanced handling and section work, judging distance and fire orders. In fieldcraft they have to be taught how a section works; that is, how the men start to work as a team. To understand this they must appreciate the organization and equipment of a section. This is usually done at a demonstration of an infantry section at full war strength and with all their equipment and weapons laid out for the recruit to see. Here is stressed the point that the light machine gun is a team weapon, in that the ammunition is distributed throughout the section. Also, that the section can be armed with a variety of different weapons for special occasions. At the same time it is easy to point out how the limited quantity of stores and ammunition with the section curtails the amount of ammunition which they can expend. Fieldcraft is really at this stage a form of elementary tactics, and the first job to be learned is the formations which a section adopts in battle, and the signals to change from one formation to another. As far as possible a section commander's orders are the briefest compatible with intelligibility. Having learnt the formations and the signals, the soldier now learns how a section moves across ground while keeping cover and adopting the best fire positions from which to shoot at the enemy en route to the objective. In the individual stage it will be remembered that the recruit carried out an individual stalk. Now they have to know how to do a section stalk. As a lesson this is done in much the same way, except that one section is put on the defensive position, while the other attacks it from 700 to 1,000 yards away.

PATROL'S JOB

If this is carried out satisfactorily the section now moves on to what is the most important job a rifleman is called on to do, namely patrolling. This is important, because patrolling covers all the lessons of fieldcraft and training and team work which the recruit has been taught. A patrol is usually sent out to answer certain questions, for instance: "Is the enemy in possession of the bridge over a certain river?" or "Has he destroyed it?"

It might help here to digress for a moment and consider the sequence of thought which goes on in the mind of an N.C.O. ordered to take out a patrol. First he says to himself: "Where are the enemy? Who are they? and How are they getting on?" That is to say, he considers to himself whether he is up against seasoned troops or demoralized native levies. Then he considers whether there will be any other patrol of our own troops out and makes quite certain that he is clear about the orders which he has been given. "Have I enough time to do the job? Why is the patrol going out? What is the ground like over which it must move?" The answers to these questions will tell him the strength which he should take out for the job in hand. He will want to make

a reconnaissance, and will by now have decided where is the best point from which to do the reconnaissance. He will be thinking how can time be saved, where should the patrol assemble, and is there any chance of getting them a meal before they go out?

When doing his reconnaissance the main thing he will remember is that he must keep the time spent on it down to a minimum, so as to give the troops who have to do the job the maximum time for preparation. In viewing the ground he will consider such things as: "Where will the sun be when we go out? Which side of the hedge will be in the shade? How many scouts do I need? and Which will be the vulnerable flank?" He will also consider what is the objective, how he can surprise the enemy, and what special weapons are needed.

Having made up his little plan, the patrol leader now assembles the men and issues his orders. Among other things he ensures that there is a "get-away man," who can, if the section is surprised by the enemy, make certain of getting back with the information to the commander. The route to be followed must be absolutely clear in the mind of every member of the patrol, they must have no doubt at all about the job in hand. Finally, every one must of necessity know the password.

FIELD FIRING

The phases of a patrol's work divide themselves into the advance to the objective, using protection on the way; secondly, the observation of the enemy at the position, or whatever the task may be; then the withdrawal from the objective and, finally, the report to the officer who sent out the patrol.

During his early individual training the recruit carried out firing with his rifle and machine gun on the open range, where obvious targets were put up in the butt and he fired from known ranges. Now luring his collective training he carries out field firing, where small, well disguised targets may appear anywhere, so that the distance to them requires to be estimated and where his fire forms part of a controlled plan, under orders from the section commander.

Men of the rifle companies at the infantry training centre receive instruction in advanced anti-aircraft training and in tank hunting and destruction. The

volves a high standard of morale, coupled with an appreciation of the true ineffectiveness of the dive bomber and enemy machine gun. This aspect of attack from the air was unfortunately neglected and misunderstood by the British in the early stages of the war. There was far too great an impression that the crackle of machine gun fire from the air meant in the mind of every individual for hundreds of yards around that he personally had been

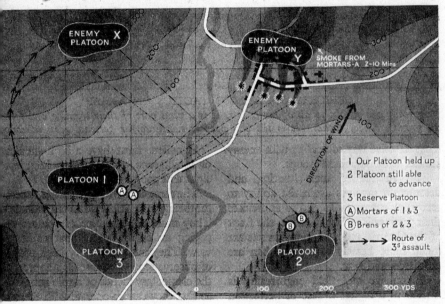

INFANTRY PLATOONS ATTACK ENEMY PLATOONS X AND Y

No. 1 platoon is held up by cross-fire from Y. The Bren guns of platoons 2 and 3 fire (from B) into enemy platoon X, while the mortars of Nos. 1 and 3 platoons (from A) drop a smoke-screen in front of Y. In the meantime, platoon No. 3 carries out a flank attack on enemy platoon X. At the last moment, the mortars at A switch from Y to X to intensify the supporting fire. The capture of position X will at once threaten the enemy position at Y

theory is, that the specialist weapons, such as anti-tank guns and anti-aircraft artillery, may not always be available. The infantryman must therefore be able to protect himself and attack the enemy without the support of the very desirable specialist weapons.

The modern training in the British Army is all against going to ground when enemy aircraft appear. Not to do so in-

singled out for attack by the aircraft. In actual fact the damage done by enemy aerial machine-gunning is infinitesimal, though the moral effect can undoubtedly be very disconcerting. Similarly, dive bombing has been proved time and again a singularly inaccurate method of attack against troops who have been able to dig small slit trenches. Included in his anti-aircraft training the soldier is taught the

OFFICERS DISCUSSING TACTICS ON A MAP

Map reading is taught to all officer cadets. It is a vital part of their training and form
the groundwork of tactics. It is the best possible substitute for personal reconnaissance

most effective way of dealing with enemy
attacks with parachute troops.

The subject of tank hunting and
destruction involves again the ability to
recognize enemy tanks and to appreciate
their weak points. For instance, the front
of the German tanks and gun turrets are
much more heavily armoured than are
the flanks and rear.

Camouflage and field engineering is
carried to a higher degree of perfection
during the rifle company period of a
recruit's training, and he learns how to
use the Bangalore torpedo for destroying
enemy wire and mine fields (*see* p. 243).

In the specialist company the recruit,
who has now carried out his individual
training as a rifleman soldier, learns to
carry out the several duties assigned to the
headquarter company of the rifle battalion.
The care in their selection of the personnel
for the specialist company has already
been stressed. The signallers are taught
the Morse code by buzzer and lamp; and
how to lay cable so that it will stand the
strain of shell-fire, and enemy and
friendly armoured fighting vehicles.

Signallers must have a high standard
of intelligence, good writing, keen eye
sight and good hearing.

The three-inch mortar men are selected
for their physical fitness and individuality
They must not await orders before en
gaging an enemy target that comes in
view. They must have very keen power
of observation, and must also appreciate
the elementary tactics of a rifle company
so that they can co-operate with them to
the best advantage. They must be able to
come into action as quickly as possible
because this is the moment when the
mortar is most vulnerable. To do this
their drill for unloading the mortar from
the truck and mounting its component
parts must be assiduously practised.

Personnel for the Bren carriers are
chosen for their initiative and offensive
spirit. They must be imbued with the idea
of seeking out the enemy and firing on
him with the greatest possible speed.

Their training consists of instruction in
tactical driving, by which they learn to
use the ground to their best advantage,
and learn to keep the carrier under cover

or as long as possible. In order to be able to control the Bren carrier effectively through the din of battle, they must learn the signals and how to act on them immediately. The Bren crews are taught how to maintain their vehicles, and carry out running repairs. Finally, they should be expert map readers.

The training of the ordinary wheeled transport drivers can be summed up in two words—driving and maintenance, with the accent all the way on maintenance. Any one can learn to drive a vehicle, and very little practice is needed to teach them to keep station in a long column distributed with 200 yards or so between the vehicles. What is not so easy is to persuade the drivers that they are primarily responsible for keeping the wheels turning. In the old days it was a point of honour that care and attention was lavished on the horses. The same love is difficult to inspire in an inanimate thing like a platoon truck. Nevertheless, it has been cynically said that a broken-down vehicle is the slowest thing on the battlefield, a battlefield where today speed is the only criterion. For maintenance to be successful, it is essential that the drivers should have an understanding of how the

OPENING AN ENEMY LAND MINE

The work of sappers rendering safe enemy land mines is highly dangerous. This mine near Derna in North Africa has been opened and the springs and explosive apparatus can be clearly seen. When a heavy weight presses upon the springs, contact is made and the charge fired

engine works, and should have a ready routine for carrying out the inspection and greasing of all moving parts.

The training of officers and N.C.O.s begins with the cadres, held in a unit. The sole object of cadres, or for that matter of local courses of army schools of instruction, is to produce an instructor, that is, someone who can hand on the knowledge which he himself possesses. For the greatest benefit to be derived from cadres, courses and schools, the student must arrive at the course himself up to the standard of a trained man so that the maximum time can be devoted to turning him into an instructor. On all courses, most of the time is used on mutual instruction and lecturettes. That is to say, each student in turn comes out and teaches the lesson to the rest of the class.

BATTLE ON A TABLE

The instructor then shows him where he went wrong and where his methods of instruction are at fault. Lecturettes are invaluable for giving an instructor the idea of how to talk to a dozen or so men without appearing ill at ease and lacking in self-confidence.

Models form an invaluable contribution to any form of instruction and the sand table forms a useful example of the adaptation of models to Army requirements. Here a stretch of country is accurately laid out on the model which is mounted at eye level. The roads, hedges and woods all appear as on the ground, and with the aid of wooden toys, matchsticks, and the like, it is possible to carry out a mimic battle and question the squad round the sand table how they would deal with various situations.

Demonstrations also form a valuable means of instruction. These can be either rehearsed or unrehearsed. With the unrehearsed demonstration, one squad is asked to carry out a job without previous warning or practice, while the others

watch and make notes. Then the demonstrators are called back and discussion follows as to what was well done and what was wrongly done and why. Then the two roles are changed and the watchers become demonstrators, while the demonstrators become the critics.

At local courses and at War Office schools, such as the Small Arms School, the technique of instruction and the production of instructors is carried to its highest stage. From the reports of these courses and from their general bearing and character, officer cadets are selected for training at O.C.T.U.s. Here, the main job is to produce a leader—which requires force of character, enthusiasm and a deep knowledge of the subject without which the necessary self-confidence will be lacking. The main jobs of the young platoon commander in battle are to be able to appreciate the situation and to be able to give out reasoned and intelligent orders from the appreciation.

An "appreciation of the situation" is defined in the military textbooks as "a military review of the situation, based on all available information, culminating in a statement of measures recommended to meet it." It is easy to see that with the lives of thirty or more men depending on their decisions, officers from the most junior upwards must be able to size up each military situation as it arises quickly and accurately. To do this successfully, much military knowledge, training and practice is needed, and this the O.C.T.U. fully provides during a strenuous course.

FACED BY CRISIS

Today many people carry out short "appreciations," as, for instance, when wondering whether to take the car somewhere. The distance is considered, the petrol consumption of the car, and the number of coupons still available. Other points may be the urgency of the visit, the suitability of public services and the veather. The choice may eventually lie between a non-coupon public service voyage, and the last drop of "juice" in one's own car: a decision is made and arrangements put in hand—to go by train.

This may perhaps serve to illustrate, by an everyday example, what is meant by a military appreciation. It is the process of thought which flashes through the mind

is required to enable the officer solving the problem to see what really is the object. In the case of the junior officer the object will probably be fairly apparent from the order given from above.

Although there are many factors which may seldom arise, certain points must always be considered. These are relative strengths, time and space, and ground.

CUTTING BARBED WIRE ENTANGLEMENTS

Wire is still a dangerous obstacle to infantry in attack. If it cannot be smashed by artillery re or Bangalore torpedoes, it must be cut by hand. This is both difficult and dangerous

of a well-trained officer when faced by a crisis, leading to a decision about the form of action. It is divided into four parts, namely, the object, the factors which affect the attainment of the object, the course open to both sides, and the plan.

The object is the immediate aim in view, what one is setting out to achieve. This must always be kept in sight, and a certain degree of perspicacity and training

By relative strength is meant the number of men, tanks and guns as between one's own command and the latest reliable reports of the enemy, with the inevitable deduction of the effect on the attainment of the object, and the type of armaments, and the plan needed to beat the enemy.

In considering time and space, weight has to be given to the distances between oneself and the enemy, and the time each will take to reach certain vital points. The deduction may be that unless one moves with great speed, an overwhelming enemy column may have time to reach the battlefield before the object has been attained. Therefore it might seem wiser to attack quickly, without possible artillery support while the numerical advantage is still ours, rather than wait until the gunners are ready, at the risk of the approaching enemy column appearing on the field.

TWO MAIN RULES

The study of the ground will show what ground appears to favour the use of tanks and what ground seems likely to afford cover to infantry. Or one commanding feature may seem to be the clue to the whole battlefield, leading to the conclusion that it might be worth while concentrating most of the attacking force against that one particular tactical point.

Apart from these main factors others

may arise such as the weather, the time o the year, the characteristics of the enemy and in particular the personality of the opposing commander, the enemy's moral and many other special features.

Two main rules emerge in considering factors—only those which have a definit bearing on the attainment of the objec need be considered, and the principles o war—surprise, mobility and security— must be borne in mind. At this stage on must avoid the temptation of making up one's mind prematurely about the plan

From this mental catalogue it should b clear that only two or three courses li open. Each should be considered seriousl and separately, with its advantages and disadvantages. One should then con sider what the enemy is likely to do, and in so doing, it is essential to credit him with as much intelligence as oneself. One's ow courses are considered first, in order t avoid mentally surrendering the initiativ

PRACTICE IN THE THROWING OF GRENADES

Much training is needed if grenades are to be accurately thrown. The position shown abou gives a good trajectory and enables the thrower to fall clear of the exploded fragmen

INFANTRY ADVANCING BEHIND SMOKE

Smoke is much used as artificial camouflage in modern warfare. Tanks sometimes make their own smoke to give them cover. There are also smoke grenades and bombs for the use of infantry

to the enemy. Finally, a decision must be made as to the wisest course to pursue.

This conclusion as to the best course of action to attain the object and so defeat the enemy leads naturally to the plan. Just before making the plan it is well to ask three questions: (1) Has the object been kept in view? (2) How can the weapons be used to the best advantage? (3) How can the plan be kept simple and at the same time vigorous?

TACTICAL EXERCISE

The plan gives, in plain language, the measures decided upon to beat the enemy, with details of the fire plan, but avoiding administrative details, unless they affect the plan to a great extent.

Appreciations vary between the vast affair made up by an army commander and the short mental process carried out by a junior commander in battle. They may be written or not, but in both cases the same sequence of thought is followed. It is always advisable for a commander to put the plan down on paper, just in case he should be hit, then the next to command has something to go on.

It will be realized that reasonable and

logical appreciations require experience and practice. At an O.C.T.U. the instructors provide the benefit of their experience, and practice is given on all kinds of exercises, varying from the individual written effort done indoors to the outside syndicate effort usually associated with "Tewts." T.E.W.T. is an Army hybrid word, known to every officer and most N.C.O.s, and it means a "tactical exercise with troops." Various word pictures are painted by the directing staff to the syndicate students depicting different situations. The syndicates are then given time to reconnoitre, consider the problem and arrive at a majority conclusion. One member of the syndicate gives out the answer, which the D.S. then discusses, and finally the D.S. gives out one solution which they have decided to adopt. Great stress is laid on the fact that it is just *one* solution. There may be three or four other solutions to the same problem, just as likely to succeed. As long, however, as a syndicate appears to have drawn reasonable conclusions from all the relevant factors and not flouted too many of the principles of war, the directing staff will accept most alternative solutions.

Then another "narrative" is given out which paints a further picture and sets another problem, but here the D.S. have to be dictatorial. In order to make up the T.E.W.T. (which takes many hours and days), the D.S. solution to the last problem *must be accepted* in considering the next problem. Otherwise one might have the students' solution with the troops in one place, and the D.S. problem based on troops in quite a different area. So it goes on, according to the time available. Much discussion is provoked, many heresies can be put right, and at the end, the senior member of the D.S. stresses the lesson it was intended to teach and emphasizes the more general faults.

Provided a young officer can be taught how to appreciate a situation, the next stage is to teach him how to issue operation orders. These again follow a logical and very rigid sequence. Apart from the common-sense value of the sequence of orders, it is also a help to those receiving them, in that they know what to expect next. But most of all it is essential that every man should go into battle absolutely clear in his mind about his own job in the immediate fight. This imposes certain very definite duties on the officer in command who gives out the orders. He must have appreciated the situation as carefully and sensibly as time permits. He should point out landmarks before he starts, and he must keep his plan simple and issue his orders clearly and well, so impressing his will on his juniors, without interfering with their power of initiative.

OPERATION ORDERS

Orders are given in the following sequence:

1. *Information.*—(*a*) About the enemy; (*b*) about our own troops.
2. *Intention.*—Followed by a brief appreciation if time allows.
3. *Method.*
4. *Administration.*

5. *Intercommunication.*
6. *"Any questions?"*

Before giving out his orders a commander will call up his subordinates, possibly one at a time to prevent exposure, and show them the landmarks to which he is going to refer in his operation orders.

THE COMING FIGHT

When giving the latest information about the enemy, the commander will rely partly on what his own and flanking fighting units have discovered in action against the enemy, and partly on information which will come forward from higher formation headquarters as a result of aerial photography, interrogation of prisoners and reports from agents. Information about one's own troops will consist mainly of the broad outline of what flanking units are going to do in the battle, and how they are going to support the infantry during the attack.

The intention paragraph is curt and pithy—"We will capture that copse," "We will drive the enemy off the ridge," or "We will deny this knoll to the enemy." The intention must be absolutely clear.

After the intention paragraph, and should time allow, it is usual to give a short appreciation. In actual fact there very seldom will be time for an appreciation, and it must not be included at the expense of giving sufficient time to the troops to prepare for the coming fight. The battle cannot start immediately the platoon commander has issued his orders. It is still necessary for the section commanders to explain to the men all about the battle, and guns and stores will have to be unloaded from the platoon truck and distributed. Nevertheless, if there is time, a short appreciation is invaluable for giving subordinates an insight into the commander's mind, so that they understand how he came to take the decisions which he now gives out in the form of orders. Then the subordinates are better able to deal with an unexpected situation during the battle in the way they feel their commander would have ordered them to do had he been present.

The method paragraph will give the details of how it is proposed to carry out the plan and intention. The main points which a platoon commander's orders must emphasize are, how the necessary fire power will be provided, and in what direction the troops are to advance over the ground using the available cover.

The administrative paragraph may tend covers details of where headquarters will be, and where messages and reports are to be sent, what any Verey light signals to be used will signify, and what will be the password. Watches are synchronized, and finally, all present are given an opportunity to ask any questions. This is probably the last chance which subordinates will have to make quite certain that they are clear, before the battle starts, exactly what their job is for the next two hours or more. Equally a commander is quite prepared to answer the questions put, in

BREN CARRIERS ADVANCING TO THE ATTACK

These carriers are not tanks but are vehicles designed to carry Bren guns rapidly from place to place. Normally the Brens are dismounted from the carriers when about to go into action

to get too long, covering, as it has to today, such numerous problems as the types of weapons to be used, ammunition, smoke, anti-tank, tools, mines, food, water, greatcoats, transport, medical, sanitary, etc. In an actual operation order, the administrative details are confined to those actually affecting the operation in hand, and other matters are dealt with in separate administrative instructions. Furthermore, many of the subjects can be dealt with by Standing Orders.

The intercommunication paragraph order to give his subordinates an insight into his own mind and so ensure that the best possible teamwork will be produced.

Space forbids discussing in detail other subjects covered at an O.C.T.U. To appreciate a situation correctly, an infantry officer must understand the advantages and disadvantages of the various constituent parts of the infantry battalion, and must also understand the primary characteristics of the supporting arms. Some of the other subjects in which he will receive instruction are: Men's welfare, discipline, supply in the field, pay (at home and on service), replacement of clothing and equipment, mechanized transport, salvage, wounded, hygiene and sanitation, camps, bivouacs and billets, censorship, training programmes, etc.

Only the more outstanding features of the tactics within a battalion are discussed in this chapter, but it will be realized that today most operations are combined affairs, and the infantry soldier will usually find support in varying degrees from artillery, army tanks, and aircraft.

seeing the enemy machines crash, but they are likely to do sufficient damage to involve repairs on return to the aerodrome.

The points which are emphasized in training troops to deal with enemy aircraft are to be able to recognize friend from foe early, to withhold their fire till the last moment against dive bombers, and to concentrate their fire on the machines nearest.

In the case of columns of mechanical transport on the move the best protection lies in a wide dispersion on the road, and in keeping moving until actually brought

TAKING COVER FROM ENEMY SHELLING

These British infantrymen in the African desert are lying flat while enemy shells fall. In such bare country, the best hope of safety is in keeping as near to the ground as possible

During an approach march, the infantry will be protected by other units in front of them, most probably the divisional reconnaissance battalion. Their own main concern will be to protect themselves against attack from the air. Concealment is the best protection, but this is not sought after to such an extent as to slow down the march. If aerial bombing does develop, infantry disperse into small groups, and open controlled fire immediately with all weapons against all enemy planes within range (1,000 yards). They will not often have the satisfaction of

to a halt. Even up to a density of twenty vehicles to the mile it is reasonably safe to keep going (that is, eighty to ninety yards between vehicles). L.M.G.s can be mounted on vehicles to fire while on the move and the A.A. platoon can develop quite a formidable fire. Arrangements will probably be made to picket dangerous defiles with anti-aircraft artillery.

Apart from A.A. protection, all commanders are responsible at all times for their own protection against ground attack by the enemy. This is done by adapting formations on the ground which will in themselves protect the force from being surprised. Even when no enemy have been reported to be within thirty miles, it will be realized that today armoured cars and tanks can attack the flanks of an infantry column in an hour. In due course the enemy will be met, and the forward infantry come under fire.

The supporting L.M.G.s and mortars must be well forward and ready for action. The attack usually takes one of two forms. Either the Brens and mortars start to shoot up the enemy from the front, while the assaulting troops work round a flank, or the Bren works round to fire from the flank, when the assault takes place frontally. The danger of infiltering the Bren forward to take the enemy from a flank is that it, in turn, may be ambushed. The advantage is that flanking fire is more effective than frontal. The two-inch mortar, once registered, can fire over the heads of the attackers because of its high trajectory. They fire by observation and must stop when our own troops get within sixty to eighty yards of the position. They can also use smoke to blind the enemy, or to cover a move of our own—or, on occasion, to "pull his leg!"

ATTACK—AND AFTER

When the opposition stiffens, the forward company will eventually be held up. It then becomes necessary for the battalion commander to launch an attack. The principles and sequence are much the same—a reconnaissance and study of reports to find out where the enemy are weakest and where the key to the position seems to lie, a quick appreciation and plan, the arrangements for fire support, and the issue of orders.

Once the enemy are driven off the position, the junior commander must think quickly of various things, such as posting sentries and sending out patrols to maintain touch with the enemy, preparing to beat off a counter-attack, help-ing flanking units who may not yet have got forward, identifying prisoners and sending them back, studying ground ahead, replenishing ammunition supply.

SPECIALIZED TREATMENT

There are certain types of country which require specialized treatment, such as warfare in the desert, where the scope of operations is probably limited by the administrative services, or fighting in mountainous country such as the North-West Frontier of India, where the heights have to be cleared and picketed before it is safe for the column to move up the stony watercourse below. Fighting may perhaps be in closely wooded country, where observation is very restricted, posts are closer together and infiltration easier; on the other hand, control is very difficult. Many woods are tank-proof, but they are also easily located and accurately marked on the majority of maps.

Village fighting has some points worth mentioning. Villages should not be allowed to hold up an advance, and are best left to reserves to deal with, provided a small covering force is left. If the enemy is well established, it is a difficult job to drive him out, and it should not be attempted until an overwhelming artillery or bomber concentration is available. Infantry will finally be needed for the tricky business of a house-to-house search. In defence, houses can be made very strong by clever siting of anti-tank guns, mines and booby traps.

Night attacks are jobs almost entirely confined to the infantry. To be successful they require much detailed preparation and a high standard of training and discipline, so that the operation can be carried through in silence. At night the infantryman really comes into his own. Tanks go into harbour and aeroplanes cannot see him—and the British soldier knows how much the Germans hate the best of all weapons for night fighting, the bayonet.

DESPATCH RIDERS OF THE ROYAL CORPS OF SIGNALS

The despatch riders of the Royal Signals do vital work. They relieve congestion on other methods of communication and replace them when interrupted. Their task is both exhausting and dangerous. Messages must be delivered, however many unexpected difficulties may arise

CHAPTER 10

The Royal Corps of Signals

Communication problems. Corps' wide responsibilities. Four main methods.
The two extremes. Simple and complex apparatus. Limitations of wireless.
Mobile operations. Centres of communication. Organization in the field.
Training in peace and war. Co-operation with the General Post Office

SINCE men began to fight, a commander has had two basic needs: the first is to get information, without which he cannot make a plan; the second is to convey his plan to his subordinates. In earlier times his eye surveyed the battlefield and brought him information: his voice carried his orders through the din. Special signals as well were charged with special meaning—beacons on the hill tops, smoke puffs on the moor, drums in the forest. This business of getting in news and sending out orders has always been vital, but up to our own times it has been simple. In the childhood of men now living, armies consisted of horse, foot and smooth bore artillery, fighting in close order: generals commanded from the saddle, with gallopers to carry their orders and bring back information.

VITAL INFORMATION

The essential problem remains the same today, but in a single generation its setting has changed completely, and is changing still with growing momentum. To gain information a commander uses aircraft, armoured cars and light tanks, covering the vast areas of modern war; and these agents are useless without means to send back what they have learnt. His subordinates at grips with the enemy may be separated from him by tens or by hundreds of miles, and he must know how they are faring before he can intervene with his reserves. In short, he needs signal communications before he can begin to exercise his functions of command. He needs them as well because an army is a highly complex living organism, which is paralysed without a nerve system of inter-communication, extending from its bases to its most advanced elements and making it a living whole.

The problem of signal communications began to take on its present dimensions in the war of 1914-18, when 110,000 men of the Royal Engineers were employed upon it on the Western Front alone, and the commanders' cry was always for more. After the war so large a child could no longer remain with the parent corps, which has sired so many warlike sciences, and in 1920 the Royal Corps of Signals was called into being, to concern itself solely with the study and practice of signal communications. In the short period since that date the problem has grown greatly both in size and complexity. On the one hand, evolution in weapons, transport, tactical methods and strategical conceptions makes ever-increasing claims on a commander, who demands in turn an ever-improving system of signal communications. On the other hand, the applied science of telecommunication, with which military technical methods must keep in step, has changed beyond recognition since the last war, and its evolution continues apace in modern war.

The Royal Signals are today a young corps with twenty-one years of separate existence, proud in the distinction of having the Princess Royal for Colonel-in-Chief, and with roots stretching back into the old traditions of their origins. A study of the last published Army Estimates shows that the corps before the war was a lusty child comparable in size with the Royal Engineers, who begot it. Its functions are to provide a commander with the means to receive information; to exercise control; to keep touch with other commanders with whom he co-operates and to conduct expeditiously the daily business by which his force lives and moves.

The corps provides wireless communi-cations from the War Office to commanders of the Empire's garrisons and armies throughout the world; and, in a theatre of operations, its sphere extends from the base to the headquarters of infantry battalions, batteries of Royal Artillery, regiments of the Royal Armoured Corps and equivalent units of other arms. Below these regimental headquarters, signal communications within the units are maintained by their own regimental personnel, but it is the duty of the Royal Signals to help and advise. The corps provides the ground communication, other than wireless, of the Royal Air Force overseas co-operating with the Army in the field.

To fulfil its task the corps uses every means which science places in its hand.

ARMY SIGNALLERS LAYING LINES

Line is one of the main forms of army communication. By means of a stick the line is placed to the side of the road by a man in another lorry. Farther behind the front thicker cable is used

CLOSE-UP VIEW OF A MECHANICAL CABLE LAYER

The line is paid out over the back of the lorry by an engine. The speed of the turning of of the drum is regulated by the operator and the line is kept clear of the back of the lorry. Such methods are, however, not entirely satisfactory in view of the speed of modern war

Its activities fall under the four main headings of communication by lines, by wireless, by visual means and by despatch riders. Each method has its sphere of usefulness, its strength and weakness for service in the field, which must be summarized before we can see how the signal officer builds them into a flexible system suited to his commander's plans.

Connection by line allows messages to be sent more quickly and in more volume than by any other means. It is comparatively secret and it allows for discussion by telephone. On the lines of communication and at the headquarters of higher formations such as armies and corps, it is indeed the only method which could carry the volume of traffic necessary for the day to day administration and maintenance of a force. Within divisions and lower formations, lines still give the best form of communication where the speed of operations allows them to be laid, again on account of their traffic capacity, secrecy and telephone facilities. Their main drawbacks are three: first, that they take time to lay; and, once laid, a change of plan may find them laid in the wrong place: second, they use much material and transport : third, they are cut by shell fire in forward areas and by bombing in any part of the theatre of war. In spite of these weaknesses, lines form the basis of the Army's signal system and absorb the greater part of the energies of the Royal Corps of Signals.

Types of line communication vary with the purpose in view. At one end of the scale we may find two men crawling with a drum of light cable to a battalion headquarters in battle. At the other end we may find a strong working party and highly qualified craftsmen installing armoured multi-core cables to connect general headquarters, or headquarters of armies or establishments on the lines of communications, to the main telephone and telegraph network of the country where they operate. The apparatus may range from a simple field telephone outfit to all the complicated equipment of modern multi-channel, long distance methods adapted from the latest civil practice. Between these extremes there is a gradually increasing scale of traffic capacity, and therefore of solidity in construction, as we go back from the battle front. Light field cable gives place to heavier armoured cable in the higher formations. Overhead open wires are likely to be less and less used under the threat of bombing. Where conditions allow their use, however, they will range from light field construction in corps areas, quickly put up and easily repaired, to solid permanent routes in the rearward zones.

SEARCH FOR COMPROMISE

In arriving at the best type of line construction for the higher formations, behind the area where field cable meets the needs, there is a constant search for compromise between weight of line material on the one hand, and simplicity of terminal apparatus on the other. The simplest apparatus needs a separate pair of wires for each telegraph connection; but between the higher headquarters this would involve cables of so many wires as to be out of the question for use in the field. On the other hand, a single pair of wires may be made to carry a number of connections simultaneously, by the use of sufficiently complicated and delicate apparatus at each end, which is again unsuited to the stress of active service. There is a further compromise imposed by the fact that current can be carried over the

necessary distance either by the simple method of using sufficiently thick wires, which would involve very heavy cables and has been abandoned in civil practice; or by using thin wires and introducing certain technical complications to maintain the necessary strength of current throughout the line—complications which may be unsuitable for use in the field.

LISTENING ENEMY

Wireless communication avoids all the drawbacks of line. It takes little time to establish; it overleaps physical obstacles; it involves comparatively little material or transport and it cannot be cut by shell fire or bombing between its points. There was a time, in fact, soon after the war of 1914-18 when it was acclaimed as the solution of the army's intercommunications troubles. But, like other developments of applied science, it brings its own troubles with it. The first of these is inherent in its own usefulness, for the more it is exploited the more does mutual interference increase and the more hampered does its use become. The allotment of wireless frequencies, to avoid chaos, throughout a force which numbers its sets by thousands, presents a difficulty which rises in a sharp curve as the numbers increase; and when all is done the interference from enemy and neutral sources is, of course, unpredictable.

This method has, however, a greater drawback than the congestion caused by its own exploitation. The enemy can hear it. He can, in addition, locate the area from which transmission is taking place, and can use this knowledge in building up his picture of his opponent's dispositions. This is not the place to discuss the measures and counter-measures, the devices of attack and defence in the matter of wireless interception and position finding in the field. It is enough to say that they engage a considerable part of the energies of the Royal Corps of Signals.

A further limitation in using wireless is its small traffic capacity compared with line: no wireless system has yet been developed which could carry a tenth of the administrative telegraph and telephone traffic of a major headquarters in the field.

The supreme value of this method is that it gives communication where no other means will serve. It allows aircraft to co-operate with ground troops. It in adapting equipment to its purposes. That used in the field varies from a set carried complete on one man's back for short distance work in forward areas, to long range sets at the higher headquarters, embodying the latest devices of radio engineering. These devices aim in general at reducing weight and bulk and increasing the speed of transmission, the number of telegraph or telephone chan-

A "DON V" PORTABLE WIRELESS SET

*This wireless set is carried on a man's back and is most useful for work in forward areas.
Its disadvantage is that it is often possible for a nearby enemy to overhear conversations*

allows mechanized cavalry patrols to send in their information and tanks to be controlled in battle. It provides communication for artillery and infantry in forward areas of battle, where field cables cannot be laid or maintained. It gives the higher command a means of keeping in touch with the situation and retaining control when their lines are bombed.

The art of wireless design progresses daily and it offers wide scope for ingenuity nels carried by a single wireless connection, and security from interception.

There is a third method of telegraphy—visual signalling. This owes its survival on the modern battlefield to the introduction, in the war of 1914-18, of the small portable electric signalling lamp. Though the smaller wireless sets are reducing its value, there are still many occasions for its use over short distances in the forward areas. It remains indispensable in the specialized technique of mountain warfare on the north-west frontier of India.

There remains despatch riding, which acts as a cement binding the whole fabric of signal communication, co-operating with the various forms of telegraphy, replacing them when broken down and relieving them of congestion by carrying returns and other administrative matter which is yet too urgent to go by the Army Postal Service. It is indeed the only way to carry certain orders and reports which do not lend themselves to telegraphic form. The despatch rider must be a man of courage, resource and endurance, able to find his way across any country in any weather and to keep his machine going under all conditions. He may be found in the back area on a routine daily run with a heavy pack crammed with despatches, or carrying a single urgent message in battle. For a long message or a short distance he

may be quicker than the telegraph: he can go when all telegraphic methods fail, and in the stress and confusion of action he often provides the only possible means of communication. The limitation of this method lies in the fact that it is more exhausting to carry a message than to telegraph it, and men and machines may be worked to a standstill.

Carrier pigeons provide a specialized form of despatch-carrying which is invaluable in its own sphere of activity. That sphere is not in a theatre of mobile operations, but in an area where lofts can be established and birds can be taken out to fixed points, from which to carry messages back to their lofts. They are essentially an emergency method, to carry a few vital messages when other means fail or are not available. Typical instances of this use would be to send news from an isolated observation post of the enemy's

A SIGNAL "TERMINAL" IN TRAINING

A small group (or terminal) of signallers can be of great use in the field. A portable aerial is set up and the messages received are handed to a despatch rider for rapid delivery

A LIGHT WIRELESS TRUCK

This is a type of light wireless truck much used by the Royal Armoured Corps. It is highly mobile and enables communication to be kept between fighting vehicles in fast-moving warfare

approach, to send a report back from a small raiding party on a special mission or from a defence post which may be cut off and must hold out where it stands.

With these four elements of communications—line, wireless, visual and despatch carrying—the signal officer builds up his system. He will use lines wherever they can be laid and maintained. He will use wireless to communicate with detached forces, with highly mobile troops and with aircraft, to keep touch between columns moving separately but acting together, and wherever line communication is impossible. He will use it to double-bank his lines and so provide an insurance against their interruption by shell fire or bombing. He will use visual signalling for short distance communication not under the enemy's immediate observation, and he will use despatch riding throughout to reinforce all his other means of maintaining contact.

At the headquarters of each formation is established a signal office, which is its centre of communication. Here all messages for transmission are handed in by the staff, and all incoming messages are received for delivery to their destination. Here are the telegraph instruments, the telephone switchboard and the testing apparatus by which a watch is kept on the state of the lines. Here linemen receive their instructions before leaving to mend a fault or to carry out routine maintenance. The signal office is the point of arrival and departure for despatch riders. Records are kept there showing the position and movements of every formation or unit to which a despatch may be sent, and the routing for telegrams to any part of the force: the upkeep of these is no light matter at the headquarters of a large formation with constantly changing make-up, engaged in fluid and often confused operations. Technical records are maintained and a brief register of messages is kept to ensure that none is overlooked, that any delay is noted and that any message on which a question arises can be checked and traced to its destination. At a major headquarters, where complex apparatus is installed and the daily messages are numbered by thousands, the signal office is a highly developed technical organization employing a large number of men in specialized duties. With a fighting unit, at the other extreme, it may be limited to a signal clerk, who receives and records messages for transmission, a couple of operators to send them, an orderly to deliver those which arrive from outside and a despatch rider in waiting. The aim throughout is to resist the ever pressing tendency to complication and to seek speed and simplicity.

SIGNAL OFFICE LOCATION

Let us picture the setting up of an infantry brigade headquarters signal office in battle. The men and equipment should be on the spot in time to establish communication before the brigade headquarters move there. A special party has been held in reserve for the purpose. The signal officer arrives accompanied by a staff officer of the brigade, and together they settle the layout of the headquarters and the position of the signal office. A signal clerk takes his seat with his message register, despatch riders stand by for duty and a signal office in nucleus is thus in being, for messages can be sent. Sites are chosen for wireless sets working to battalions of the brigade, to divisional headquarters and to neighbouring brigades or other elements co-operating by land, air and sea. These sites are determined by certain rules for concealment, distance from brigade headquarters and convenience of access: the wireless detachments go to them and establish communication, and a second phase in the growth

of the signal office is thus completed.

Meanwhile line parties have set out, laying cable to battalions and to a flanking brigade, and a mechanized cable layer drives up at speed, bringing a line from divisional headquarters. A small telephone switchboard is installed for the brigade commander and his staff. Diagrams are compiled and the signal office, on its technical side, is complete. The signal section assumes whatever part may be allotted to it in the defence of brigade headquarters against tanks and aircraft, and, throughout all the coming and going, precautions are taken against leaving telltale tracks to be noted by the enemy aircraft on reconnaissance.

That, at any rate, is the way in which a signal office seeks to come into being, but time and the enemy may intervene in a hundred ways. Movement may be so rapid that the Signals can only accompany brigade headquarters and communicate by despatch rider or wireless as they move: lines may be cut as fast as they are laid: linemen and despatch riders may be killed or wounded: wireless may be jammed: or, perhaps the hardest blow of all, an unpredictable eddy of battle may force the brigade commander to have his new headquarters somewhere else when all the work is done.

After this account of the work of the corps, it is time to look at its organization in the field. Each formation has its signal unit, at the disposal of the formation commander for communication within its command. These units are entitled divisional signals, armoured divisional signals, corps signals, army signals and so on, according to the formation which they serve. Each such unit is the equivalent of a battalion, commanded by a lieutenant-colonel and divided into companies. Companies in turn are composed of sections, of which some have specialized technical functions such as line sections, operating sections, wireless sections, or maintenance sections. Other sections combine in themselves all the necessary technical roles and serve the smaller formations : they are called infantry brigade signal sections, artillery regiment signal sections, and so on.

It is clear that a number of signal units, each working independently for its own other commands. The Signal Officer-in-Chief is normally a major-general, and Chief Signal Officers are usually either brigadiers or colonels.

The Signal Officer-in-Chief is the head of the corps in the field. He issues his own technical instructions to Chief Signal Officers, and he advises the Commander-

TELEPHONE COMMUNICATION AT A COMMAND POST

The link between the O.P. and a gun battery is a vital life-line and is the responsibility of a battery N.C.O. The Royal Signals provide the men between batteries and regimental H.Q.

formation commander in his own area, would make a formless pattern without plan or cohesion, and that a chain of technical control is needed to give unity and direction to the whole. This is secured by the appointment of a Signal Officer-in-Chief at general headquarters, and of Chief Signal Officers at the headquarters of armies, corps and certain in-Chief or the Chief of the General Staff on matters of signals policy and on orders concerning signal communications, which are sent out to subordinate commanders by G.H.Q. Through his own authority in the technical sphere and his advice to his commander in the sphere of policy and tactical employment, he exercises the necessary control of signals throughout the force. Chief Signal Officers follow suit in their degree, so the same tactical and technical doctrines permeate the force from top to bottom. The higher signals direction for the British Armies in the field, the overseas garrisons, the forces allotted to home defence and the training establishments, is provided at the War Office by the Director of Signals, a major-general on the staff of the C.I.G.S.

Like the rest of the Army, the Royal Signals spend the greater part of their existence in preparing for war in time of peace, and no account of the corps would be complete which omitted their peace time life and training. Before the Second World War the regular officers, with those of the Royal Artillery and Royal Engineers, were drawn from cadets of the Royal Military Academy at Woolwich, with a proportion from the universities.

The first eighteen months of their commissioned service were spent at the School of Signals at Catterick on a course designed to give them a technical and tactical grounding for their duties in the field. On the technical side this course aimed at scientific education rather than at technical training in its narrower sense. The passing-out standard necessary to qualify for corps pay was equivalent to that required by the Institution of Electrical Engineers in the educational test for associate membership.

Fortified by eighteen months at Woolwich and eighteen at the School of Signals, the young officer is in a position to profit by practical experience in the signal unit to which he is posted. He may find himself in charge of a signal office with its many sided activities or in command of a line or a wireless section, or he may be

RADIO TELEPHONE TO H.Q.

SECTIONAL AERIAL MAST

RADIO FROM ARMY CO-OPERATIONAL AIRCRAFT

A.A. DEFENCE

LEAD IN

EXHAUST FROM ENGINE

LEAD IN

R/T TRANSMITTING SET

AMPLIFIERS
W/T RECEIVER
WATER TANK

RADIATOR

AUXILIARY ENGINE

SWITCHBOARD

GENERATOR

CHAINS FOR SAND

A MOBILE WIRELESS VAN OF DIVISIONAL SIGNALS

These vehicles help to maintain communications between mobile ground units. They also keep in touch with their supporting aircraft. Their sets have a radius up to about 100 miles

entrusted with a brigade or artillery regiment signal section and have to organize the communications of his commander in battle. Success or failure on his part touches not only his men and himself but affects closely the wide issue of success or failure in operations.

And so with the call on the other ranks. The men of a signal unit, when the formation which they serve is deployed in battle, are working at various tasks in parties distributed over the length and breadth of the formation's area, completing the interlocking parts of a widespread signal plan. An operator must make no mistake in a message, whatever may be his circumstances of discomfort, fatigue or danger: if he works a wireless set, he must observe a strict discipline in transmission to prevent the enemy from learning all about him. A lineman on patrol must do his work honestly, whatever the deterrents imposed by Nature or the enemy. A despatch rider must get his message through: if he finds the enemy where he expected to find the headquarters which he seeks, he must use such wit and courage as God and his Army training have given him; but he must get through. Such tasks are carried out alone and unmarked, with no N.C.O. at hand to hearten the reluctant or to correct omissions. They demand discipline of the highest kind, with a technical skill which prevails over every circumstance.

LINKS WITH G.P.O.

To reach this standard, recruits for the corps have first to pass a test for education and intelligence and then to go through a course at a signal training centre: this includes a recruit's basic training, followed by technical training in the trade selected—operator, lineman, despatch rider, instrument mechanic, electrician, fitter or draughtsman.

The corps maintains close links with the General Post Office. Certain problems

CARRIER PIGEON POST
This is a specialized form of despatch and is particularly useful in mobile operations or when a defence post is entirely cut off

of development are tackled together: regular officers and other ranks attend G.P.O. courses of instruction: a large number of G.P.O. officials are members of Supplementary Reserve and Territorial Army units of the corps and attend courses of training with the Regular Army. Among the higher formations and on the lines of communication the corps employs methods which conform closely to civil practice, and the work is done by supplementary reserve units officered and manned in great part by the members of the staff of the G.P.O.

A characteristic on which the corps prides itself is the comradeship between its regular and non-regular branches. The regular and territorial army units took shape together in the war of 1914-18, and they joined the new corps together when it was formed in 1920. There was no question of newly formed territorial army units being added to a long established and hitherto entirely self-sufficient corps.

HAULING A BREN CARRIER OUT OF TROUBLE

The break-down lorries of the Royal Army Ordnance Corps are very powerful. A Bren carrier is no light weight, yet this one is being hauled out of a ditch by a cable and winch on the lorry

CHAPTER 11

The Army Ordnance Service

Military and civil personnel. Clothing, general and warlike stores. Ordnance officers. Ordnance mechanical engineers. Training and grading of other ranks. The workshop branch: armourers, armament artificers, artisans. Director-general of Army equipment. Director-general of Army requirements. Functions of depots. Mechanical transport. Workshops on wheels and L.A.D.s. Base ordnance workshop. Field parks. Mobile laundry and bath units. Salvage service. Returned stores

THE Army Ordnance Service of today includes both military and civilian personnel. The military element is the Royal Army Ordnance Corps, which retains in its badge the coat of arms of the ancient Board of Ordnance, and its motto—*Sua Tela Tonanti*—which may be translated "To the Thunderer His Weapons."

The work of the Ordnance Service is no longer confined to the limitations suggested by its motto; it may be likened in fact to a vast departmental store, with a great variety of branches wherever a force of the Army is situated.

TECHNICAL NEEDS

At the head of the Service is the Director General of Army Equipment, who is responsible to the Quartermaster General of the Forces, for the *maintenance* of the army with ordnance stores. This term, like many others, has a special connotation in the Army. Briefly, it may be said to mean the provision of stores required to cover the needs of the Army for a defined period ahead. It involves estimating needs, arranging for production with the Ministry of Supply, inspecting stores on their arrival at depots, checking, storing and repairing them, and maintaining their efficiency until issued. In many cases, such as weapons,

ammunition, instruments and fighting vehicles, it also involves seeing that they are kept in good condition after issue, by systematic periodical inspection and repair. This maintenance after issue is the primary function and problem of the engineering branch.

Ordnance stores are grouped under three main headings :—

1. *Clothing*, which includes battle-dress and full dress, anti-gas clothing and "necessaries"—the military term for underclothing, table and toilet gear, and hundreds of miscellaneous items.

2. *General Stores*, which are generally of a non-technical nature, such as accoutrements, anti-gas equipment, bicycles, tools and workshop equipment, ironmongery and metals, tents and camp equipment, field-cooking appliances, and all sorts of furnishings and stores used in the equipping of barracks, hospitals and War Department buildings generally.

3. *Warlike Stores*, a very extensive class comprising every nature of weapon used in the Army and the ammunition required for them; explosives of all kinds; field engineering and bridging equipment; searchlights and other electrical stores; signalling equipment; all mechanically propelled fighting, technical and general service vehicles (except for the vehicles used by the R.A.S.C.), including all types

of tanks, armoured cars and scout-cars.

The chief function of the civilian section of the Army Ordnance Service is to maintain the continuity of the organization when the military element, that is the Royal Army Ordnance Corps, is transferred elsewhere. In peace time the Corps is trained for immediate service in the field on the outbreak of war. On mobilization, units proceed to the war zone, leaving behind experienced key personnel of the R.A.O.C. assisted by civilians, until reinforced by reservists and newly trained men. The civilians are mostly recruited from ex-Service men from all the three Services. The R.A.O.C. is composed of two main branches: the administrative and stores side, the officers in which are styled ordnance officers, and the mechanical maintenance side, where the officers are called ordnance mechanical engineers.

Normally ordnance officers are obtained from regular officers of other arms and the Royal Marines. Ordnance mechanical engineers are qualified engineers selected by the War Office to undergo special training in the more technical matters pertaining to armaments and mechanical transport. Both the ordnance officers and the ordnance mechanical engineers are assisted by a large number of officers promoted from the warrant officers of the Corps, men whose long practical experience is of much value in the more detailed duties of such a vast organization.

Shortly after the outbreak of the war an O.C.T.U. was formed, and the bulk of the war emergency officers were later obtained from this source. The selection and training of cadets is very thorough

A BRITISH MOBILE RAILWAY WORKSHOP

These workshops were used by the B.E.F. in France. They are used to do heavy repairs in the forward areas and not at the base depot. In mobile warfare they are a great asset, if available

REPAIRING AN ANTI-TANK RIFLE AT AN ARMY FORGE

*With the mechanization of modern armies the shoeing of horses at a forge has given place
to the repair and adjustment by the R.A.O.C. of the delicate machinery of various arms*

and designed to turn them out primarily as officers and leaders of men, and secondly as ordnance officers.

Much the same procedure is followed with the O.M.E.s, except that the needs of war preclude the long and thorough training an O.M.E. receives in normal times. Thus the wartime O.M.E. specializes in only one particular branch of ordnance mechanical engineering. Some become coast defence engineers, some are instructed in field equipment, others in wireless; while others are trained as A.A. equipment specialists.

The training of other ranks is carried out in a number of training battalions. The first essential, however, is to turn out the recruits as soldiers. The basic training given in the R.A.O.C. includes instruction in the rifle, bayonet, machine gun and anti-tank rifle, and men are made to realize that they are soldiers first and cogs of great importance in the maintenance wheel afterwards.

During their preliminary training the men are graded into the branch of the Corps to which it seems their capabilities best suit them, the store branch or the workshop branch. The store branch includes clerks, storemen and ammunition examiners, while the workshop branch is divided into three sections: armourers, armament artificers and artisans. The armourers are responsible for the inspection of all types of small arms and machine guns; and the armament artificers specialize in armament equipments, i.e., guns, mountings, instruments, fighting vehicles and general mechanical transport; and the artisans comprise all the well-known trades, such as blacksmiths, fitters, carpenters, etc., not included in the other sections.

No other corps in the Army is so universally distributed as the R.A.O.C., for in addition to those serving at Corps installations, officers and other ranks are attached to formations, and N.C.O.s and men are attached to almost every fighting unit in the Service, as armourers, armament artificers, fitters, shoemakers, etc.

MANIFOLD PROBLEMS

Many of the foremost experts in both the military and engineering world have been brought into the present organization of the R.A.O.C. to deal with the manifold problems which present themselves each day. At the head of the organization, which like the other arms and services is controlled by the Army Council from the War Office, is the Director-General of Army Equipment. As his right-hand men, he has four directors, responsible for ordnance services, warlike stores, mechanical maintenance and kinematography respectively, and two inspectors of Army Ordnance Services and Army Ordnance Workshop Services, who see that the policy of the War Office is carried out, in the supply and repair services respectively.

The Ministry of Supply is responsible for producing the equipment and stores required by the Army, and the Director-General of Army Requirements ensures that supplies from the ministry meet the demands of the Army Council.

Distributed over England are central ordnance depots, and their sub-depots, administered directly by the War Office, each of them holding large quantities of stores of a particular nature.

These depots receive supplies from the manufacturers, and store and maintain them until they are required for distribution to the various command ordnance depots throughout the country, although in many instances supplies are sent direct to units. They are also entirely responsible for supplying the base ordnance depots in a theatre of war.

With an Army numbered in millions, and with tens of thousands of our allies to be equipped as well, to say that a central ordnance depot may be likened to a wholesale warehouse is an understatement. Let us take a look at one or two of these great depots.

The oldest of them dates back to 1803, and is concerned with the supply of rifles, swords and bayonets, pistols and machine guns. Consequently, its activities have been most prominent during the wars of the last century, with intervals of comparative quietude in its rural setting. Probably its most outstanding piece of work was connected with the inauguration of the Home Guard which came into being after the evacuation of the B.E.F. from France, when invasion of our islands appeared to be imminent.

To provide this force with their weapons, this depot was called upon to exert every effort to issue these arms quickly. They rose to the occasion and played a great part in equipping such a large force in unprecedented time.

RAPID EXPANSION

In contrast to the oldest depot the newest and largest of the C.O.D.s was only in its embryo stage at the outbreak of war. With the rapid expansion of the Army it was imperative for its construction to be proceeded with immediately, but owing to its isolated position it was difficult to obtain labour.

There is wonder still among those who saw this depot grow and begin to function as the Germans swept over France to the Channel Ports; wonder that the labour was found, the depot (so vitally needed) sufficiently completed to handle the hundreds of tons of stores that at one time blocked the railroads for miles.

Now sheds are completed covering 3,000,000 square feet, eight main sheds full of thousands of items of all stores; 72,000 square feet of office space; four and a half miles of well-built roads, along

handles engineer and signal stores—wireless sets, bridging equipment, cables, telephones, etc.

Hundreds of civilian and military clerks work side by side, under the control of R.A.O.C. officers, to provision and account for the receipt and issue of these stores. In the storage sheds civilian and military storemen select, pack, and

MOBILE BREN CARRIER WORKSHOP

The rapid repair of mechanical vehicles is important today. In addition to mobile workshop lorries, easily erected workshops (shown above) enable work to be done close at hand

which runs a constant flow of stores-transport in and out through the gates of the perimeter fence, which itself stretches for more than four miles.

And how do such places serve Britain's new Army? This depot is two in one. One half receives from contractors and issues to the units all armament equipment—from the two-pounder anti-tank gun up to the large coastal defence guns, with all their spares and fire control instruments. The other part of the depot

despatch according to instructions. Every item (and there are nearly 100,000) is accounted for in detail, though at this particular depot the traffic turn-round has now reached between 8,000 and 10,000 railway wagons a month, with some 6,000 tons of stores to be handled every week of the year.

The work of receipt and issue is highly organized, the issues being regulated in carefully balanced batches representing about an hour's work for each storehouse

DIAGRAMS & DOCUMENTS

7½ K.W. SWITCHBOA

3½ K.W. BATTERY CHARGING BOARD

PETROL TANK

2 CARGO LIGHTS

LATHE CHUCK

ELECTRICAL TEST SET

1 FIXED 4½" VICE

2 ADJUSTABLE BENCH LIGHTS

A MOVABLE WORKSHOP: "M" TYP.

The tempo of modern warfare has made a speedy repair organization an essential matter
Wholesale mechanization has compelled vast repair arrangements to be made. Particularl

FITTER OPERATING
GRINDING & POLISHING
MACHINE

SWINDEN SWIVEL VICE

VALVE REFACING MACHINE

5 K.W. MAIN GENERATING PLANT

FITTER OPERATING ⅝ CAPACITY
ELECTRIC BENCH DRILL

OXYGEN
ACETYLENE
BOTTLES
AND HOLDERS

ARMY MOBILE REPAIR LORRY

*vital are the mobile lorry-workshops which help to keep the armoured divisions in action.
They have a lathe, drilling and grinding machines, and are better equipped than many garages*

function in turn. Several of these hourly batches are passed for action daily, their progress being systematically watched to ensure a rapid and even flow of work.

When this particular depot began to function, though less than half built, the 500 wagons that jammed the railroads were cleared by a handful of Ordnance Corps men who had newly returned from France, and cleared in less than forty-eight hours. Order had come out of early chaos, a supreme co-operative effort in the shortest possible time.

EVERYTHING MOBILE

At another depot everything pertaining to mechanical transport is dealt with.

It used to be said that the Army moved on its stomach. To a large extent this is still true, but it is now no less a truism to say that the Army moves on its wheels. In the modern Army mechanical transport is every bit as important as guns and ammunition. The tank is the spearhead of the attack and everything—even the workshops and the general's office—must be mobile. The work of supplying and maintaining the army vehicles for action is therefore of increasing importance.

For the Army, as for the private consumer, there must be an intermediate link with the factory. For the private car owner there are garages and distributing firms; for the Army there is the Royal Army Ordnance Corps.

In the Army, whether at home or overseas, every vehicle and every spare part of every vehicle (other than R.A.S.C.) is obtained through the ordnance. Their work extends right from the factory to the front line. Whenever the Army goes into battle the ordnance supplies the spares, and in all major cases the ordnance carries out the repairs.

Long before a new type of vehicle is used by the Forces, skilled technicians estimate the stock of spares to be ordered. These stocks then have to be maintained

at such a level that whatever part of a vehicle may break down at any time in any place, the spares can be provided and the vehicle be back in service with the minimum delay.

All this involves very detailed organization and routine procedure to ensure efficient working. The volume of work involved is illustrated by the fact that in the main depot alone of this C.O.D. the weekly issues have amounted to 177,000 items, ranging from a solitary washer to large quantities of tank tracks.

In addition to all this work of handling vehicles and spares there are workshops for carrying out every kind of major and minor vehicle repair.

The stores held at another depot comprise what are known as "general stores," which may mean anything from a packet of split pins to a fully equipped hospital. They include everything that the Army requires in the way of material equipment, except clothing, ammunition, weapons, vehicles and food. In this depot there are in all some 25,000 different types of stores, the stocks of which in some cases may be numbered in millions. Furniture of all kinds, beds and bedding, tools and machinery for all army trades, trailer fire pumps and other such appliances, camouflage materials, bicycles, tentage and other items are supplied to the Army, and in many cases to Dominion and Allied troops as well.

SPECIAL EQUIPMENT

As the Second World War develops new types of equipment are added—sledges and sleeping bags, alpenstocks, ropes and ice axes for operations in arctic climates; and specially designed equipment for such new formations as the Paratroops and the Commandos. The supply of these stores may lack the excitement and glamour associated with the more spectacular items of equipment such as tanks and guns, but a soldier must be fed and equipped before he can fight.

The clothing of the modern Army is designed on strictly utilitarian lines. The gold braid and finery that form such a picturesque part of uniforms in peace time are banished; but, even so, many varied types ef specialist uniforms must be available in the central ordnance depot concerned with the supply of clothing.

Uniforms must be provided that are suitable for tropical climates and arctic conditions, as well as for our own equable climate. Clothing for Paratroops and other special formations, as well as uniforms for despatch riders, cooks, etc., must also be provided.

If the central ordnance depots are likened to wholesale warehouses, then

LOWERING A BREN CARRIER OFF A TRAILER

The wear and tear on mechanical vehicles is severe. Special trailers and conveyors are provided for broken-down transport. This Bren carrier is being lowered from a trailer by a winch controlled by the two men at the sides. There are also somewhat similar vehicles for the conveyance of "dead" tanks. Others carry "live" ones, so saving their tractors (see p. 265)

command ordnance depots may be compared to large chain-stores. They supply the needs of all troops in a certain area, and there is one or more of them in each command. They hold stocks of practically every nature of stores and clothing although it is sometimes expedient to issue certain stores, such as mechanical transport vehicles, direct from the central ordnance depots to units. At the principal command ordnance depots are large workshops, equipped with modern machinery, where repairs of all kinds to military vehicles, guns and equipment can be executed. These command depots, as their name implies, are administered by deputy directors of ordnance services at each command headquarters. The depots for ammunition are dealt with in the chapter on this subject.

In a theatre of war one of the first essentials is to ensure that adequate supplies will be available for the troops. First a convenient port, some distance from the field of operations, is found, where stores can be safely unloaded. The stores are then moved inland to the main source of supply to the troops—the base ordnance depot.

BASE ORDNANCE DEPOT

For the most part the B.O.D. draws its stores from the central ordnance depots at home, and it is organized into three sub-depots, one dealing with motor transport vehicles and their spare parts, another with clothing and general stores, and a third with all armaments, engineer and signal stores.

A returned stores depot is also included to deal with the vast collections of stores returned from the front in all conditions, the activities of which are dealt with later.

Advantage is taken of every suitable building that can be used as a storehouse, in the town selected for the depot. At a later stage in the campaign special buildings may be constructed, if neces-

sary, and even duplicate and triplicate bases established. In modern warfare this enforced dispersal of the warehouses is in some ways an advantage, as it minimizes the possibility of damage from enemy bombing; although it may be a handicap from an administrative view.

REPLACEMENTS AND STORES

In addition to supplying new fighting units which have been formed with everything they need, the B.O.D.s must also be prepared to replace equipment worn out or put out of action—guns, rifles, tanks, tents, cookers, clothing—in a word, they must see that the Army in the field lacks nothing to make it fighting fit. They must also see that the stores required reach the front line speedily. In practice, stores are taken by rail to as near the front line as possible, to a point known as a supply railhead, and from here they are taken by lorry, and finally handed over to the unit.

The quality of its fighting men apart, the measure of an army's strength is never the *number* of tanks, transport vehicles, field artillery equipments, or machine guns it possesses. The Army's real power depends on how many serviceable vehicles, guns and automatic weapons it can put into action, and *keep* in action throughout engagements.

The German attacks on Russia provided a striking example of the dependence of machines on maintenance. The fierce onslaughts of the Panzer divisions is mass mechanical warfare on a giant scale, but it should be noted that it can be maintained for only comparatively short periods, for the tanks are largely brought to a standstill, not because of supply difficulties only, but because they need mechanical overhaul and repair.

The R.A.O.C. must be ready to repair any portion of the equipment it issues, from a fighting tank to a pair of binoculars, from a howitzer to a steel helmet.

Right up with the front-line troops there are small workshop units known as light aid detachments (L.A.D.). One of these compact workshops is allotted to each mechanized regiment or similar-sized unit. The L.A.D. is virtually a workshop on wheels. It consists of a few skilled artificers carried in vehicles, one for breakdown jobs and another equipped to handle minor repairs. These need skilled hands but no heavy equipment.

The duties of the L.A.D. include recovery, that is, the collection of vehicles ditched by accident, or immobilized by enemy action or mechanical trouble. These derelicts are not repaired by the L.A.D., but withdrawn so that they may be towed farther to the rear for repair in a suitably equipped workshop.

Farther behind the lines is the formation ordnance workshop. It is mobile and self-contained, and situated as far forward as conditions allow. It is equipped with simple machine tools, and its main job is the replacement of complete assemblies—such as engines or gear boxes. Adjacent to each F.O.W. is a Field Park, which carries supplies of spare parts and assemblies for the workshop.

Next come the army ordnance workshop and the army ordnance field parks. These are semi-mobile and are equipped with power-driven tools and a large stock of spare assemblies and parts. They undertake repairs beyond the scope of the formation ordnance workshops, and they also repair the damaged assemblies sent back to them by the F.O.W., returning them eventually to the Formation Field Park for reissue.

REPAIRS AND MANUFACTURE

Finally, there is the base ordnance workshop. This is a large static establishment, fully equipped and capable of undertaking almost any repair work and in some cases original manufacture.

In addition to repair work, the ordnance mechanical maintenance organization is also responsible for the regular inspection of all Army equipment.

In every base, or wherever the normal civil facilities are non-existent, static laundries operated on modern principles are established by the R.A.O.C. To cater for the essential needs of troops in the forward areas, mobile laundry units of the R.A.O.C. are established. Each of these units is a self-contained mobile laundry, equipped with plant to wash the underclothing of 2,000 troops per day. They work in close co-operation with the formation mobile bath units, so that after bathing the men are supplied with a clean set of clothing supplied from the laundry unit, and the clothes they have discarded are removed for washing.

SALVAGE AND RETURNED STORES

To assist in the efforts to recover material, a salvage service has been formed under the quartermaster-general.

The returned stores depot receives ordnance stores of all kinds and in every condition sent back from the forward areas. It is a veritable hive of industry, employing a host of men and women, mostly recruited from local sources. Here the wagons from the front are off-loaded, their contents sorted out into kind and condition, M.T. vehicles being diverted to the returned vehicles park sited near the M.T. section of the base ordnance workshops. A proportion of the returned stores may be fit for immediate reissue, in which case they are sent over to the appropriate issuing sub-depot of the B.O.D. Those capable of being repaired are either made serviceable within the R.S.D. itself or sent to the base ordnance workshops. The unserviceable stores may either be disposed of by sale as they stand or broken up into their original elements of metal and other material. These materials may be either sold locally, or sent home or elsewhere for disposal.

SHELLS FOR A COASTAL GUN

These shells are being checked and wheeled to an underground shell store. The gun is camouflaged from aerial observation. The rings round the shells indicate the type of filling

CHAPTER 12

Ammunition of Today

Artillery ammunition. Projectiles. Smoke, shrapnel and star shells.
Cartridges. Fuzes. Tubes and primers for infantry weapons. Small arms
and mortar ammunition. Grenades. Military engineering appliances.
Demolition explosives. Bangalore torpedoes. Anti-tank mines. Aerial
bombs, types and weight. Storage, inspection, repair and supply

MODERN science has brought about many changes in warfare, but nowhere are they more evident than in the types and quantities of ammunition that must now be available for mechanized warfare. In the war of 1914-18 over five million tons of ammunition were transported to France, and the amount expended in a single day often exceeded the whole of what was consumed during the thirty months of the South African War. In the Second World War the figure was still rising—a division heavily engaged may easily expend 150 or more tons daily — and new types were constantly being introduced, until today there are over 350 types of explosive armament.

The different types of ammunition may be placed in four groups: ammunition designed for use with artillery, with infantry weapons, with engineering appliances, and aerial bombs.

The basic component of every round of ammunition, whether it is projected from gun, mortar, machine gun, rifle, pistol or even aeroplane, is the projectile, bullet or bomb; the other elements are necessary only to propel the projectile and to ensure that it does the greatest possible destruction at the desired moment.

Artillery ammunition embraces all types of ammunition fired from pieces of ordnance, whether in the field, from anti-aircraft or coast defence guns, or from guns mounted in armoured fighting vehicles, for example, tanks. Generally speaking, any "fire" weapon whose projectile weighs more than one pound is regarded as a piece of ordnance, and in the British Service such weapons are known by the numeral weight of their projectiles up to the twenty-five-pounder field gun. Thus, an anti-tank gun firing shells weighing two pounds is known as a two-pounder anti-tank gun. Above twenty-five pounds the size of the piece is distinguished by its calibre or diameter of the bore; for example, a Q.F. 3.7 inch A.A. gun, or a B.L. 9.2 inch howitzer. There is, however, no hard and fast rule.

IGNITING THE CHARGE

Every round of ammunition consists of at least the projectile and its propellant charge. If the projectile is a shell, it requires a fuze to ensure that it bursts on impact or at some desired range in the air. In addition, the propellant charge must be enclosed in a container suitable to the gun from which it is fired and it is then known as a cartridge. This cartridge must have some means of igniting the charge, either by percussion or electric action in a "tube" placed in the breech mechanism of the gun, or by a percussion "primer" inserted in the base of a brass cartridge case. The means adopted to fire the charge and prevent the escape of the explosive gases through the breech of the gun when fired—"obturation" it is called technically—determines whether the gun or howitzer is styled Q.F. (quick firing) or B.L. (breech loading). The term "quick firing" is nowadays rather misleading, for the modern "breech loading" piece (both are, of course, breech loaders) is almost as rapid as a quick-firer in rate of fire.

There are three main types of ordnance a low trajectory, so that, consequently, it has a longer range; its charge is usually made up in a standard weight of propellant, and in some cases the weight of shells is heavier than those used with a howitzer of the same calibre. The howitzer is comparatively short and light with a small chamber, low muzzle velocity, and a high trajectory; consequently it has a shorter range and the projectiles descend at a

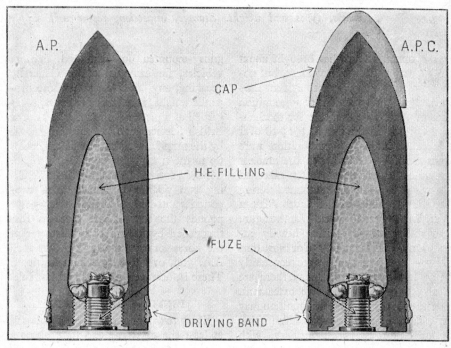

ARMOUR-PIERCING SHELLS

Figs. 1 and 2. *Armour-piercing shell (A.P.) have soft steel caps on their heads (A.P.C.). These act as a cushion between the shell and armour plate, increasing the penetration*

—guns, howitzers and gun-howitzers. Each has a different function, and a different type of ammunition must therefore be used for each.

A brief description of the differences between the gun and the howitzer may here be helpful. The main difference is in the trajectory, or curve of flight of the projectile. The gun is long and heavy, with a large chamber, high muzzle velocity, and steeper angle; its cartridges are made up in removable parts, which enables the propellant charge to be varied when engaging targets at short or long range and at different angles of descent. There are modern pieces of ordnance, which combine the characteristics of both gun and howitzer, known as gun-howitzer.

Guns and howitzers are either B.L. or Q.F. In the British Services the heaviest

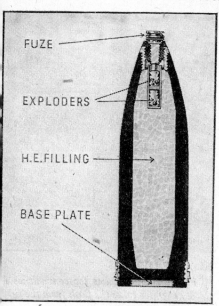

HIGH EXPLOSIVE SHELL

Fig. 3. *Such an H.E. shell, filled with explosive, has many different types of fuze*

Q.F. ordnance in general use is the Q.F. 4.5-inch A.A. gun. The essential difference between B.L. and Q.F. is that in the former the charge is contained in a fabric bag, and in the latter it is enclosed in a brass cartridge case. Obturation in B.L. ordnance is effected by introducing certain gas-sealing features in the breech mechanism; in the Q.F. the brass cartridge case acts as the obturating agent.

On firing a B.L. gun, combustion of the charge also consumes the fabric bag, but to obviate the possibility of any smouldering remains igniting the next round prematurely, the chamber has to be sponged out between rounds. With Q.F. ammunition this is unnecessary, because combustion is effected inside the cartridge case which is automatically ejected.

Q.F. ammunition is sub-divided into fixed and separate. Fixed ammunition has the complete round—fuzed shell, cartridge and primer—assembled together, and is loaded in one operation. With separate

.M.A.—H*

ammunition, the fuzed shell is loaded first, following by the primed cartridge. Fixed Q.F. ammunition makes rapid loading possible and is adopted in all A.A. and anti-tank artillery. In Q.F. howitzers and gun-howitzers the ammunition is separate, the charges regulating the range.

The projectile, as already mentioned, is the most important of the main component parts that make up a round of gun or howitzer ammunition. Nowadays it is almost entirely shell, although a small proportion of solid shot is used with field and anti-tank artillery for penetrating tanks. When armour piercing shot is used against tanks, it is fitted with tracers so that its flight may be observed.

Service shells are divided into seven principal classes:

1. Common
2. Common pointed ⎫
3. Armour piercing ⎬ Filled with some high explosive compound.
4. Semi-armour piercing ⎭

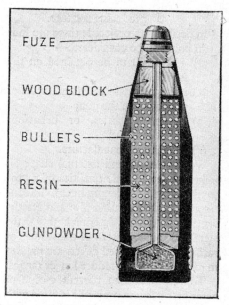

SHRAPNEL SHELL

Fig. 4. *This shell bursts in the air and throws a cone of bullets forward violently with effect*

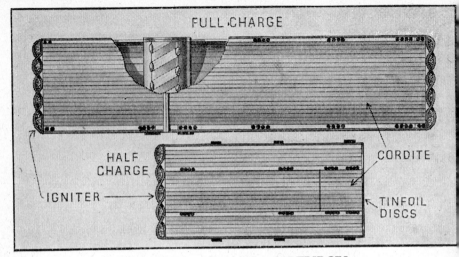

FULL CHARGE

HALF CHARGE

IGNITER

CORDITE

TINFOIL DISCS

BREECH-LOADING (B.L.) CARTRIDGES

Fig. 5. *Cartridges for B.L. guns are made up in one charge, unless for convenience in handling, half charges are used in heavy ordnance. The igniter takes the flash from the tubes.*

5. Shrapnel ⎫ Small powder
6. Star ⎭ bursting charge.

7. Smoke ⎫ Small high explosive bursting charge to release smoke-producing mixture.

In designing a projectile there are four main points to be considered:—

(1) The result to be obtained on the target;
(2) its capability to withstand forces of projection in the gun;
(3) ballistic qualities, or behaviour whilst in flight;
(4) economical manufacture.

Weight, length and external shape all influence the ballistic qualities of a projectile. Weight and length have to be considered in close relationship; and for the same reasons that determine the sharp stem and rounded stern of a fast liner or racing car, streamlined effects are present in modern shell to produce longer ranges.

To rotate, and to prevent escape of gases past it, every projectile is fitted with a driving band made of some soft metal, generally copper, so that it gives the least possible wear to the gun. These bands are pressed into an undercut groove on projectiles near their base, and being larger in diameter than the bore, are forced by the firing of the charge into the spiral grooves of the rifling, thus imparting a spinning motion to the projectile in flight.

All shells are hollow to permit the insertion of the bursting charge. When the shell is filled with high explosive it is obviously most important that it should arrive at its objective intact, so that strength to provide against danger of premature explosion of the gun is imperative. The strength of a shell is governed by internal design and quality of material, and its external shape is more or less determined by ballistic requirements.

Usually the internal design follows the external contour, keeping approximately the same thickness of metal as at the shoulder. Armour-piercing shells, however, have specially strengthened heads which are practically solid, because of the severe shock of impact with a steel armour plate. All shells should be strong enough not to break upon impact but to burst as a result of explosion, or detonation, initiated by a carefully set fuze.

All pointed shells, that is, armour piercing, semi-armour piercing and common pointed, have their fuzes fitted in the base, whereas all other types of shell are nose fuzed. Most armour piercing and some common pointed shells have soft steel caps attached to their heads to act as a cushion between the nose of the shell and the armour plate and so increase the penetrating power of the shell against armour plate (Figs. 1 and 2).

Practically all shells used with the field army are nose fuzed. The type in general use is the common high explosive shell, known as H.E. These are designed to cause damage to material by the force of their burst, or to personnel and aircraft by fragments. In the former case a delay or non-delay fuze is used, according to the depth of penetration required, and in the latter a direct action or instantaneous fuze is necessary to ensure the burst occurring immediately on impact. The explosive used for filling these shells is either tri-nitro-toluene, sometimes called trotyl (T.N.T.), or amatol, a mixture of trotyl and ammonium nitrate (Fig. 3).

By themselves these explosives are not easily detonated, so that some means of amplifying the impulse given by the explosion of the fuze is necessary, to ensure the complete detonation of the bursting charge. This is effected by the employment of an exploder system, whereby the comparatively weak initial explosion or detonation in the fuze is passed on to the exploder, which augments the impulse sufficiently to detonate the main bursting charge.

Complete detonation of T.N.T. gives a grey-black smoke thrown up in a regular plume into the air. With amatol there is very little smoke, but to assist observation a proportion of such shells has some special smoke-producing material introduced into them.

Most shells fired from A.A. guns are of the H.E. type, fitted with time fuzes designed to burst the shell at a pre-arranged moment in its flight. A proportion of these are provided with tracers which emit a flame from their base whilst in flight, thus enabling the gunner to follow their course, and to make any necessary adjustment of aim. In some modern types of A.A. shell, a device is introduced which destroys the shell at a certain time after discharge, thus fully eliminating it before it can fall to earth.

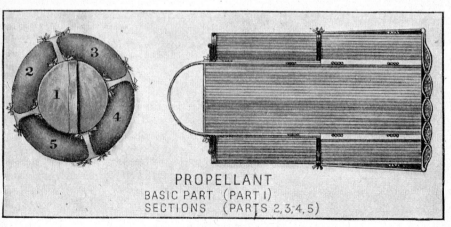

PROPELLANT
BASIC PART (PART 1)
SECTIONS (PARTS 2, 3, 4, 5)

B.L. 12-INCH HOWITZER CARTRIDGE

Fig. 6. *This cartridge has a basic part, with igniter attached, and some detachable sections*

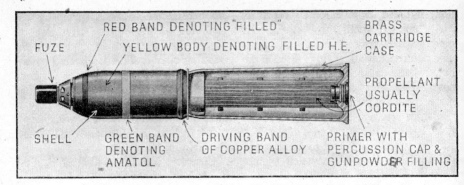

Q.F. FIXED AMMUNITION 18-POUNDER H.E. SHELL

Fig. 7. *Q.F. cartridges are used either with fixed or separate ammunition. With fixed ammunition the cartridge is attached to the projectile. The driving band engages in the rifling*

Smoke shells are used for the production of smoke screens. The bursting charge of H.E. in the shell is only just sufficient to open it, as the smoke charge must not be scattered too far. The bursting is usually effected in the air by means of a time fuze, the smoke canisters being ignited and ejected towards the ground through the base; other types are actuated by the functioning of a percussion fuze and so burst on the ground. The Germans used smoke shell in France, particularly to screen their operations when forcing a passage across difficult rivers.

SHRAPNEL BULLETS

Shrapnel shells are intended primarily for use against personnel in the open. The body of the shell is made of forged steel as thin as possible, consistent with standing the pressure set up on discharge, so that it may contain as many bullets as possible. The small bursting charge of gunpowder is held in a tip container fitted in the base of the shell (Fig. 4).

Above the container is a steel disc resting on a shoulder formed on the interior of the shell to prevent damage to the burster-container when the bullets are set back on the shock of discharge. One end of a central tube screws into the disc and fits tightly into the mouth of

the burster container. The other end is connected to the fuze socket in the nose of the shell. Surrounding this tube is a large number of spherical leaden bullets, embedded in resin, poured in a molten state and allowed to set. The resin prevents the movement of the bullets and also provides more smoke for observation purposes. The head of the shell is secured to the body either by screws or rivets.

Fuzes used with shrapnel are designed to burst the shell either in the air by time arrangement or by percussion on impact. The flash from the magazine of the fuze passes down the central tube and fires the bursting charge, which blows off the head and ejects the bullets in the form of a cone owing to the forward velocity of the shell and its spin. The ideal aimed at is to burst the shrapnel well in front of the target, so that the bullets are thrown forward in a cone of dispersion which will ensure their producing as many casualties as possible.

The purpose of star shell is to illuminate a particular area or target. The body is of steel, fitted with a small gunpowder burster in the head, below which is fitted the star; this consists of a steel case filled with star composition. The rear end of the shell is closed by a steel base, and attached to the star case and neatly folded underneath it is a fabric parachute.

The bursting of the shell is actuated by a time fuze in the nose, which fires the bursting charge. This both ignites the star composition and forces out the base plate, thus ejecting the parachute and the ignited star. The parachute opens out and falls slowly towards the ground with the illuminated star suspended from it.

Propellants may be in either stick form, such as cordite, or in granular, such as ballistite, nitrocellulose (N.C.T.), etc., generally cordite in the British Service.

The size of diameter of the sticks determines the rate of burning, since for a given weight a number of small sticks will offer more burning surface than a few large ones. To increase the burning surface, tubular sticks are sometimes used, and by regulating the thickness and length of the sticks, the same pro-

pellant can be used for all weapons, from a revolver to a big gun.

The main properties desirable in a propellant are that it should—

(1) Burn regularly;

(2) be smokeless and leave no smouldering fragments;

(3) be free from flash;

(4) ignite easily; most do not and thus require gunpowder igniters.

(5) cause no erosion or excessive wearing of the bore;

(6) be stable in storage and transit, insensitive to shock and friction and unaffected by moisture and temperature.

Generally speaking charges are determined for a maximum muzzle velocity (that is, speed in feet per second at which the projectile leaves the muzzle of the gun) with a certain size of cordite, which will

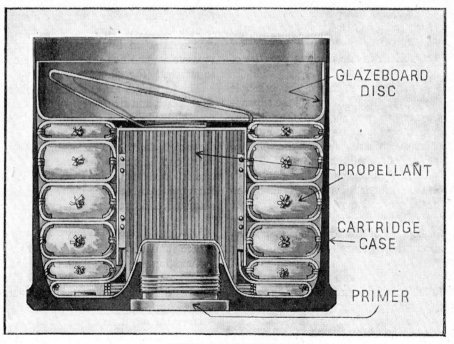

GLAZEBOARD DISC

PROPELLANT

CARTRIDGE CASE

PRIMER

A 3.7-INCH Q.F. CARTRIDGE

Fig. 8. *The propellant charge in a Q.F. cartridge is ignited by a primer, screwed into the centre of the rear end of the cartridge case. There is a percussion cap sealed in its rear face*

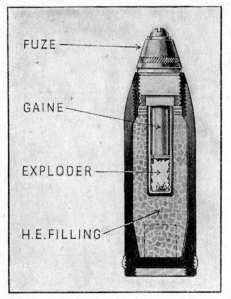

FUZE

GAINE

EXPLODER

H.E.FILLING

SHELL OF Q.F. 3.7-INCH HOWITZER,
H.E.

Fig. 9. *Some fuzes lack the quality of detonation in themselves and a gaine is used, particularly in H.E. shells, to achieve this* not exceed the safe working pressure of the gun to be used.

In designing a charge the principle aimed at is that when ignited the expanding gases will gradually push the projectile until the maximum pressure is attained as it leaves the muzzle; and the whole of the propellant will be consumed.

Certain expedients are introduced into cartridges for reducing muzzle flash, and for the prevention of depositing of copper in the bore, known as "coppering," due to stripping of driving bands. Coppering affects the accuracy of the shooting.

A B.L. cartridge is simply a bundle of propellant fitted into a cylindrical bag of suitable material, provided at one or both ends with an igniter of fine grain gunpowder between shalloon discs. The cartridge is loaded into the gun with the igniter nearest the breech, so that it readily takes the flash coming from the tube placed in the breech mechanism.

Cartridges for B.L. guns are usually made up in one charge, but in heavier ordnance, for convenience of handling, they are made up in two or more charges (Fig. 5).

With a howitzer, large angles of descent may be required at short as well as long ranges; therefore the cartridge is made up of a basic part with igniter attached, together with two or more additional sections, in such a way that its weight can be readily reduced by detaching any sections not required. The basic part is usually made up in inverted mushroom shape, the additional sections forming rings surrounding the stalk, or in segments attached to it. The weights of the sections are selected in such a way as to provide for all ranges (Fig. 6).

In Q.F. cartridges the charge is carried inside a brass case, and is fired by a primer screwed centrally in its base.

Q.F. cartridges are used either with fixed ammunition, or separate ammunition; with fixed ammunition the cartridge case is attached to the projectile; with separate ammunition the projectile is not so attached (Fig. 7).

The cartridges for Q.F. howitzers are all separate, and are made up with a basic part and additional sections similar to those for B.L. howitzers. The mouth of the case is closed by a removable leatherboard cup. The cases for these cartridges can be used many times, so that their recovery from the front for refilling is a matter of considerable importance (Fig. 8).

FUZE TYPES

The function of a fuze is to detonate the bursting charge of a shell, either upon impact or graze, or at any particular instant during flight. Thus fuzes are divided into :—

1. Percussion fuzes.

2. Time, and time and percussion.

There are two types of percussion fuzes. The first type are direct action fuzes which function as a result of a direct blow on the nose, a hammer or needle being forced on to a detonator. The second type are graze fuzes, the detonation of which depends on the forward movement of an internal graze pellet relatively to the body of the fuze. The first type is instantaneous in action, but in the second there is a slight comparative element of delay. As direct action fuzes depend on a direct blow they are eminently suitable for use in steep angles of descent and against solid material; they are, however, ineffective in a glancing blow: for example, when fired from a gun with a flat trajectory. On the other hand, the graze fuze because of retardation is quite effective in a glancing blow. All base percussion fuzes, which are used with pointed shells, are of this type, the slight delay being of some advantage by ensuring that the burst occurs after penetrating armour plate.

The action of time fuzes is initiated by the shock of discharge of the gun, but explosion of the filling does not occur until after a definite time, this time being fixed by the position in which the fuze is set before firing. There are two types of time fuzes; in the first type are those which are dependent for their timing action on the burning of powder composition pressed into rings, one of which is movable to allow of setting. These are known as igniferous time fuzes. The second type depends upon clockwork or other mechanical device for the timing action; these are mechanical time fuzes. Time and percussion fuzes are time fuzes, which carry percussion mechanism.

SAFETY DEVICES

All modern fuzes are made of metal, certain alloys and steels being embodied within them for special purposes.

Arrangements are incorporated in the design of fuzes to ensure safety: 1, for storage and transport; 2, during shock of discharge, and 3, during flight.

Generally speaking, the moving parts of a fuze are securely locked together by a number of devices, which are only unlocked by the combination of forces to

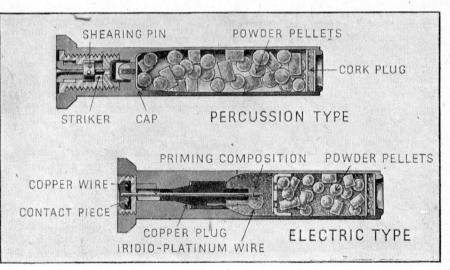

VENT SEALING TUBES

Fig. 10. *Tubes ignite the propellant charges of B.L. guns and howitzers. They seal the escape of gases rearward through the vent. These tubes are worked by percussion or electricity*

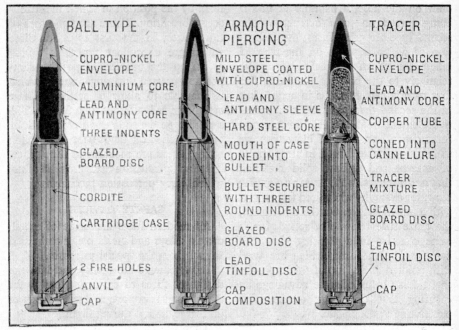

BALL TYPE
- CUPRO-NICKEL ENVELOPE
- ALUMINIUM CORE
- LEAD AND ANTIMONY CORE
- THREE INDENTS
- GLAZED BOARD DISC
- CORDITE
- CARTRIDGE CASE
- 2 FIRE HOLES
- ANVIL
- CAP

ARMOUR PIERCING
- MILD STEEL ENVELOPE COATED WITH CUPRO-NICKEL
- LEAD AND ANTIMONY SLEEVE
- HARD STEEL CORE
- MOUTH OF CASE CONED INTO BULLET
- BULLET SECURED WITH THREE ROUND INDENTS
- GLAZED BOARD DISC
- LEAD TINFOIL DISC
- CAP COMPOSITION

TRACER
- CUPRO-NICKEL ENVELOPE
- LEAD AND ANTIMONY CORE
- COPPER TUBE
- CONED INTO CANNELURE
- TRACER MIXTURE
- GLAZED BOARD DISC
- LEAD TINFOIL DISC
- CAP

TYPES OF SMALL ARMS CARTRIDGES (.303 INCH)

Fig. 11. *S.A.A. includes the cartridge case, percussion cap, propellant charge and bullet. The most used varieties are ball (the ordinary bullet), armour-piercing and tracer ammunition*

which they are subjected when fired from the gun. It is in fact a form of combination lock in which firing from a rifled gun is the key. These mechanical details of locking and arming arrangements vary with different types of fuzes, and embrace such parts as pellets, detonators, safety shutters, springs, etc.

With some fuzes which lack the quality of detonation in themselves, it is necessary to use under them some means of initiating the wave necessary for detonating a H.E. shell. These devices are called "Gaines" and are generally used in H.E. shells fitted with a time fuze (Fig. 9).

Tubes are the means whereby propellant charges of B.L. guns and howitzers are ignited. They are all designed to seal the escape of gases rearward through the vent in which they are fired; an action analogous to that of the Q.F. cartridge in the gun chamber. The vents in some guns

are of some length so that the strength of the flash must therefore be sufficient to function over this distance. They resemble small cartridges, and some types, in fact, are made from small arms ammunition cases. Tubes may be actuated by friction, percussion or by electricity. The friction type functions when a roughened bar is withdrawn sharply by means of a lanyard; percussion tubes fire when struck by a striker operating in the breech mechanism of the gun, and electric tubes by a current passed through the tube and breech mechanism (Fig. 10).

A primer is the normal means of igniting the propellant charge in the Q.F. cartridge. It is screwed down flush into the centre of the rear end of the cartridge case and has a percussion cap sealed in its rear face. It has a magazine filled with gunpowder and a vent sealing device introduced. Primers are fired by a striker perating in the breech mechanism of the gun or howitzer (Figs. 7 and 8).

Briefly it will be seen that a round of gun ammunition functions as follows:—

(1) The tube or primer is struck;

(2) the flash ignites the propelling charge;

(3) gases from the charge force the projectile out of the bore of the gun, the driving band biting into the rifling of the barrel of the gun and giving rotation to the shell;

(4) the fuze "arms," its various safety devices overcome by acceleration and rotation;

(5) on impact, in the case of D.A. fuzes, and at the required height for time fuzes, a flash or wave is passed to an exploder in the shell;

(6) the exploder amplifies the flash or wave and the shell functions.

Up to 1914 the rifle and bayonet were the principal weapons of infantry, but during the war of 1914-18 the machine gun, trench mortar and grenade became more and more important as weapons of the infantry arm, and today machine guns and mortars are their main offensive weapons, the rifle and bayonet being relegated to the position of the soldier's personal weapon. The anti-tank rifle is used generally throughout the army.

Ammunition used with the rifle, heavy, medium and light machine gun, sub-machine gun, revolver and pistol is known generally as small arms ammunition (Fig. 11). This term means the complete round including the cartridge case, percussion cap, propellant charge and bullet, familiar to most people.

There are many varieties and sizes, all of them made to a high degree of accuracy. Cartridges firing ball (the ordinary bullet), armour-piercing, tracer, observing and flame bullets are used in rifles and machine guns, while in pistols

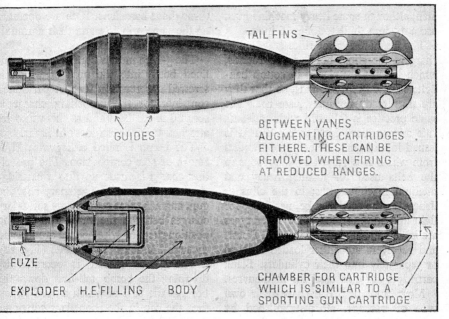

TAIL FINS

GUIDES

BETWEEN VANES AUGMENTING CARTRIDGES FIT HERE. THESE CAN BE REMOVED WHEN FIRING AT REDUCED RANGES.

FUZE

EXPLODER   H.E. FILLING   BODY

CHAMBER FOR CARTRIDGE WHICH IS SIMILAR TO A SPORTING GUN CARTRIDGE

THREE-INCH MORTAR BOMB, H.E.

Fig. 12. *A perforated container for charge is secured to the base, and vanes are attached for steadiness. The propelling charge can be augmented by secondary charges between the vanes*

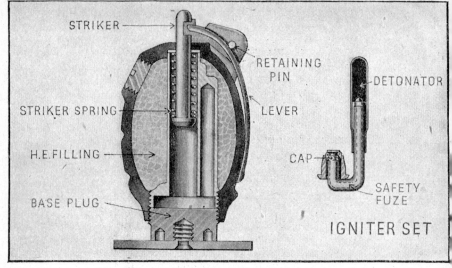

STRIKER

RETAINING PIN

DETONATOR

STRIKER SPRING

LEVER

H.E.FILLING

CAP

BASE PLUG

SAFETY FUZE

IGNITER SET

No. 36.M. GRENADE

Fig. 13. *When the retaining pin of the grenade is released, the striker acts on a percussion cap and a length of safety fuze. After an interval of time the grenade is detonated*

and revolvers ball is used mostly. Sizes vary in diameter from .30 inch to .55 inch, although some heavy machine guns use a 15-mm. bullet, about .6 inch.

The ammunition for rifles is issued in chargers (or clips) holding five rounds, which in turn are placed in cotton bandoliers holding fifty rounds, so that they are thus ready for immediate use. The same practice is followed with anti-tank rifle ammunition. Most other S.A.A. is issued loose in cartons or paper bundles from which it is placed by the troops in the belts used for loading heavy and medium machine guns; in the clips or drums, as the case may be, necessary for light and sub-machine guns; other types are issued already packed in belts. Pistols and revolvers are either loaded in clips or separately into their cylinders. Blank cartridges are also used for manœuvres.

Most kinds of S.A.A. have their own type of package, all distinguished by labels and certain outside features for identification by sense of touch at night.

Two types of mortar are used by infantry: 3-inch and 2-inch diameter bore, the latter being distributed generally throughout battalions. Both are operated on the same principle and their ammunition follows the same lines.

The 3-inch mortar bomb has a streamlined body, into the nose of which is screwed a percussion fuze. A perforated container for the propelling charge is secured to the base and to this vanes are attached to give steadiness in flight.

The bomb is filled either with H.E. smoke or star composition. The propelling charge is made up into a cartridge similar to that for the ordinary sporting gun, augmented as required by secondary charges between the vanes and held in position there by wire hooked around and through the holes of the vanes (Fig. 12).

The 3-inch mortar is operated by dropping the bomb tail-first down the bore, at the base of which a fixed striker fires the cap in the propellant cartridge, which in turn projects the bomb from the mortar. This simple operation enables a high rate of fire to be maintained.

The bombs are packed in special carriers which facilitate transit in the field.

Grenades in some shape or form have been used in armies from remote times; hence the term grenadiers. But from Crimean days they fell into disuse, until the principle was revived again during the war of 1914-18. Originally they were solely anti-personnel bombs, but newer types are used also against tanks.

There are two main types: hand and rifle, the former thrown by hand and the latter fired by means of a blank cartridge from a rifle fitted with a discharger cup attached to the muzzle (Fig. 13).

One means used to detonate a grenade is by a striker mechanism acting on a percussion cap and a length of safety fuze which burns to detonation; this method allows a small interval of time between the throwing or ejection of the grenade and its burst; the Mills bomb is a typical example. Other means are by percussion fuzes acting on impact or graze. The fillings are mostly H.E. or smoke, whilst some types are filled with arrangements of coloured stars or coloured smoke for signalling purposes.

Amongst the activities of the Royal Engineers are included demolitions and the laying and removal of anti-tank mines.

For demolition work generally, the main charge consists either of wet guncotton, ammonal, dynamite, gelignite, or blasting gelatine; T.N.T. and plastic H.E. are also frequently used.

COVERING PATROL

TORPEDO BEING PLACED UNDER WIRE

SLOW BURNING FUSE

COVERING PATROL

PLACING A BANGALORE TORPEDO IN POSITION

Fig. 14. *The Bangalore torpedo is used against wire obstructions. It consists of a pipe filled with explosive. A slow-burning fuze detonates the torpedo at the desired moment*

Wet gun-cotton is nitrocellulose pressed into small slabs containing a percentage of water which renders it safe to handle. These slabs are perforated to take a dry gun-cotton cylindrical primer which has a hole in the middle for the insertion of a detonator. The use of the dry gun-cotton primer is necessary because otherwise it would be difficult to bring the wet gun-cotton to detonation.

BANGALORE TORPEDOES

The uses of demolition explosives in the military sense are many and varied. Mines, tunnelling, destruction of bridges, destroying roads and buildings are only a few instances. The methods employed vary according to the object aimed at, but the detonation of the charges is usually effected by one of the following means:—

1. The use of a length of safety fuse. This is ignited by a match or other means and burns slowly at a regular rate, enabling the demolition party to retire to cover before the detonation of the charge.

2. Firing the detonating charge electrically through lengths of cable, by means of an instrument called a dynamo exploder. This ensures the firing of the charge instantaneously at the desired moment.

3. Firing a number of charges simultaneously by the use of instantaneous detonating fuze, which, in turn, is fired either by safety fuze or electrically.

The detonators used closely resemble those used commercially. They are simply small aluminium tubes half filled with very sensitive detonating composition. The other half of the tube receives the safety fuze on to which the mouth of the detonator is pinched. Electric detonators have an electric firing head crimped in the mouth, with protruding leads to which the firing cable is attached. Because of their extreme sensitiveness, detonators of all kinds are packed carefully and must be handled very gently.

The detonator must be placed in close contact with, or embedded in, the explosive charge to ensure detonation.

For cutting passages through wire entanglements Bangalore torpedoes are used. A Bangalore torpedo consists of pipe filled with explosive and is usually improvised. The pipe should be at least two inches in diameter, and of sufficient length to extend across the width of the entanglement to be cut. Both extremities are plugged and through one of them hole is made for the safety fuze or electric leads, according to the method of firing to be used (Fig. 14).

Two types of anti-tank mines are now used in the British Service. Those in general use are known as contact mines, a heavier type filled and used by the Royal Engineers is known as the R.E. anti-tank mine.

Both types are designed to destroy the mobility of any vehicle or motor cycle which passes over them, and their principle of action is much the same. The mines consist of a steel container filled with H.E., fitted with a detonator which is fired by a striker mechanism actuated by pressure. The mines are buried just below the surface and laid in large numbers arranged in various patterns. The area is known as a minefield.

BOMB TYPES

Mines of much larger capacity, sensitive to weight pressure, are used on beaches as a defence against invasion.

Shrapnel mines are used against troops in the open. They are housed in a mortar placed below ground level, from which they are fired by a small cartridge actuated by a trip wire, and burst about four feet above ground.

In addition to the various natures of ammunition and explosives mentioned, the Army uses a miscellaneous assortment of pyrotechnical stores such as signal cartridges, rockets, lights, portfires, matches, as well as many kinds of smoke generators for use both from tanks and from infantry positions on the ground.

In comparison with other types of projectiles the bomb has been developed in a very short time. In the war of 1914-18 they were in their infancy; today there are bombs for all occasions, and fresh types are being constantly introduced for new developments in aerial warfare.

In all new designs bombs of more than forty pounds in weight have detachable tail units. Packed in cartons or crates they can be transported or stored without fear of damage.

TERMINAL VELOCITY

The distance in advance of its target at which a bomb must be discharged is dependent on the height and speed of the aircraft. A bomb leaves the aircraft with a forward velocity equal to that of the machine. At short range, such as dive bombing attacks, small bombs impact with little more velocity than the speed of the machine. Up to 10,000 feet the bomb accelerates its speed in falling, but from a greater altitude it does not gather greater speed. Above the 10,000 feet line is regarded as "high altitude bombing," and below this height as "low altitude bombing." The speed of travel on impact is known as the "terminal velocity," and is a factor which plays an important part in the general design of a bomb.

Bombs are of various types and weights, according to the purpose for which they are required. They include:—

(1) General purpose bombs, ranging from 40 lb. to 1,900 lb.

(2) Fragmentation bombs of light weight, fitted with instantaneous fuzes, for use against personnel.

(3) Armour-piercing bombs, from 450 lb. to 2,000 lb. in weight, for attacking armour and concrete (Fig. 17), and incendiary bombs.

Most direct action bombs are fuzed in the nose (Fig. 15). Others in which delayed action is required have tail fuzes (Fig. 16), which incorporate the delay element, and some types are designed for fuzing at both ends, to make them suitable for both purposes. The H.E. fillings require an exploder system to ensure complete detonation.

Reconnaissance flares, smoke floats and flame floats resemble bombs in

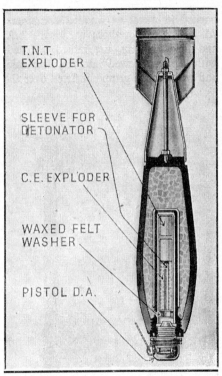

TYPICAL 20-LB. F. or 40-LB. G.P. BOMB

Fig. 15. *General purpose (G.P.) bombs range from 40 lb. to 1,900 lb. Fragmentation (F.) bombs are of light weight, for use against personnel when unprotected by cover*

appearance, and are carried and released in the same way.

The proper assembly of bombs and their various components calls for an intimate knowledge of their design and characteristics, and certain R.A.F. personnel are trained for this purpose.

In the field, the R.A.O.C. are responsible for the storage and issue of R.A.F. bombs and ammunition, being assisted by detachments of the R.A.F.

As the business of an explosive is to explode, ammunition in all its forms must always be treated with the respect due to its potential destructive properties. For protection against the weather, and for purposes of transport, all ammunition, except the heavier types of shells, is packed in metal or wooden containers. All shells, except those used with A.A. and field artillery, are issued unfuzed, with a plug screwed into the fuze hole, and with a rope grummet fitted over the

DELAY EFFECT AT TAIL

ADJUSTABLE DETONATOR HOLDER

MILLBOARD WASHER

DETONATOR

C.E. EXPLODER

T.N.T. EXPLODER

C.E. EXPLODER

DETONATOR

MILLBOARD WASHER

ADAPTOR

PISTOL NOSE

INSTANTANEOUS EFFECT AT NOSE

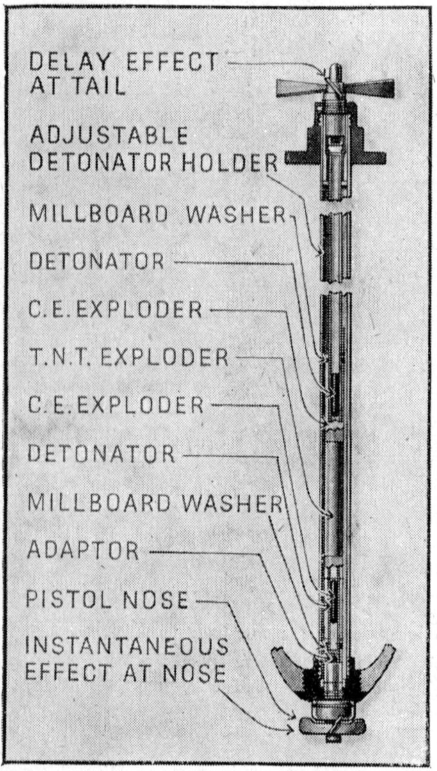

TYPICAL CENTRAL TUBE FUZE

Fig. 16. *Direct action bombs are fuzed in the nose and delayed action ones in the tail. This type is fuzed at both ends and is therefore suitable for either of these purposes*

driving band for its protection in transit. The gunner removes the grummet and plug, and fuzes the shell before loading it into the gun. B.L. cartridges are packed in air-tight cases to protect the gunpowder igniters from moisture; either metal cylinders or metal-lined boxes, the lids or both of which are hermetically sealed, are used for this purpose. The primers or igniters of Q.F. cartridges are protected by the brass cases; protective clips are also used to prevent external damage.

Ammunition packages are painted and stencilled with markings and symbols so that their contents may be readily identified, and as there are several hundred types and varieties of ammunition, a standard system of colours and markings is used. Types of shells are denoted by their body colouring, by different coloured tips, rings round the head and bands round the body. Certain features of design and type are also indicated by stencilled markings on the body; thus, all H.E. shells are coloured yellow, while all smoke shells are green. A red ring round the nose shows that the shell is filled with explosive, and a green band round the body with a fraction stencilled on it indicates that the filling is amatol.

IDENTIFICATION AIDS

In addition to the colours and markings, more detailed information, such as dates of manufacture and lot numbers, are given on ammunition packages. Whenever lots are found to be other than serviceable, it may be necessary to change the components in a particular type of ammunition so that these lots must be easily identifiable. For example, if it is found that a certain lot of time-fuzes are proving unsatisfactory it will be necessary to change all the fuzes. This will mean notifying all stations at home and abroad and sending the necessary replacements.

Modern ammunition needs far greater care than the gunpowder of our ancestors, which could be preserved without diffi-culty, provided that the axiom "keep your powder dry" was observed. Today certain types of explosive gradually deteriorate from the day of manufacture, even under perfect conditions, and it is necessary for proof and inspection tests to be carried out continuously. Climatic conditions affect explosives greatly, and particularly in hot climates frequent inspection and tests are necessary. Careful records are kept of the results of all tests, and of the ammunition stored in all parts of the world.

AMMUNITION INSPECTION

The inspection and repair of ammunition is carried out by inspecting ordnance officers and ammunition examiners. They are attached to every command and area, to every large formation of an expeditionary force and to every ordnance ammunition depot. Any ammunition which they find to be unsatisfactory is returned.

Approximately one-third of the tonnage required to maintain an army in the field consists of ammunition, and during the war of 1914-18, no less than 5,253,338 tons of ammunition were shipped to France between 1914 and 1918. Under modern conditions of warfare it is estimated that about 150 tons of ammunition is required daily for each division heavily engaged, although this figure may probably be exceeded when advances are to be made.

A cardinal principle in the supply of ammunition is that troops must never have to turn back for it. Ample reserves therefore must always be maintained. Batteries and units are supplied by the divisional ammunition companies, R.A.S.C., which in turn draw on the corps transport column, R.A.S.C., whose holdings are replenished from stocks held by R.A.O.C. at ammunition railhead or from advanced ammunition depots. An ammunition railhead is the nearest point

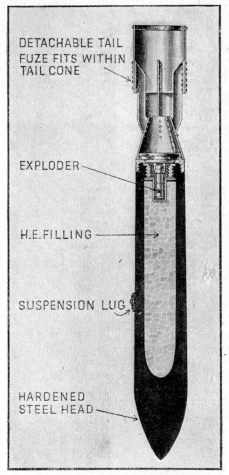

DETACHABLE TAIL
FUZE FITS WITHIN
TAIL CONE

EXPLODER

H.E.FILLING

SUSPENSION LUG

HARDENED
STEEL HEAD

TYPICAL 2,000-LB. A.P. BOMB

Fig. 17. *Armour-piercing bombs have a hardened steel head to ensure a penetrative effect. This huge 2,000-lb. bomb is useful for attacking armour and concrete ground defences*

on the railway to which it is practicable to bring supplies from the base depots.

The efficient maintenance of supply of ammunition absorbs the complete energies of a vast organization embracing the War Office, central ammunition depots at home, the ports and a staff at G.H.Q. in the field and at the various base and other ammunition depots, administered by the R.A.O.C. in various theatres of war.

THE ARMY'S UNIVERSAL PROVIDERS

The R.A.S.C. undertake a multitude of tasks for the Army, chief among them the provision of food and ammunition. This involves a vast organization in all theatres of war. (Top) A British lorry in the Libyan desert is loading up with captured tins of German petrol. (Bottom) Men of the R.A.S.C. unloading boxes of ammunition into lighters at Tobruk harbour

CHAPTER 13

The Royal Army Service Corps

A combatant corps. Maintaining ammunition and food supplies.
Organization. Mechanical transport and supply depots. Skilled bakers
and butchers. Petrol-filling centres and parks. Bulk trains. Pack trains
Divisional supply column. Report centre. Bulk breaking point.
Convoy routine and tactics. Feeding the guns. Training recruits

A T first glance the work involved in supply and transport may seem rather dull and commonplace in contrast with the adventurous life of tanks, armoured cars and artillery. But the R.A.S.C. is a combatant corps, armed, equipped and organized in the same way as the infantry, and receiving the same basic training. Its designed task is that of maintaining the supply services of the troops in the field. To the officers and men of the Royal Army Service Corps, whose job is so tersely described as "S. and T.," there is one very satisfying consolation: the knowledge that their work is vitally important to the life and fighting efficiency of the Army as a whole.

Ammunition for the guns, petrol for tanks, armoured cars and lorries, and food for the men who handle them—these are the three essential commodities which it is the task of the Royal Army Service Corps to supply and transport in ample and regular quantities to the men who do the actual fighting.

HIGHER CONTROL

Head of the Royal Army Service Corps is the Director of Supplies and Transport at the War Office, who is responsible for these two services in the British Army wherever it may be serving. He is a major-general. The director has several deputies, brigadiers in rank, one for each of the static commands at home and overseas and one each for the G.H.Q. of our various field forces. They in turn have assistants (colonels), who are responsible for the R.A.S.C. services in each corps, each of which generally consists of two or three divisions.

DIVISIONAL ORGANIZATION

The divisional R.A.S.C. commander is a lieutenant-colonel, and he has under him three companies, handling supplies, ammunition and petrol respectively, as well as his own headquarters staff. On his efficiency depends the life-blood (petrol), the endurance (food) and striking power (ammunition) of the whole division, and this efficiency has to be maintained under all conditions of climate, locality and actual battle.

Each of the companies is commanded by a major, with captains and subalterns under him running sections of vehicles which are divided into sub-sections in the charge of N.C.O.s. And so we come to the men who really "deliver the goods," the drivers themselves, on whose steadfastness ultimately depends the welfare and strength of the fighting soldiers.

That is the broad outline, but there are also a hundred and one other R.A.S.C. formations and units commanded by officers who vary in rank from brigadiers down to second-lieutenants.

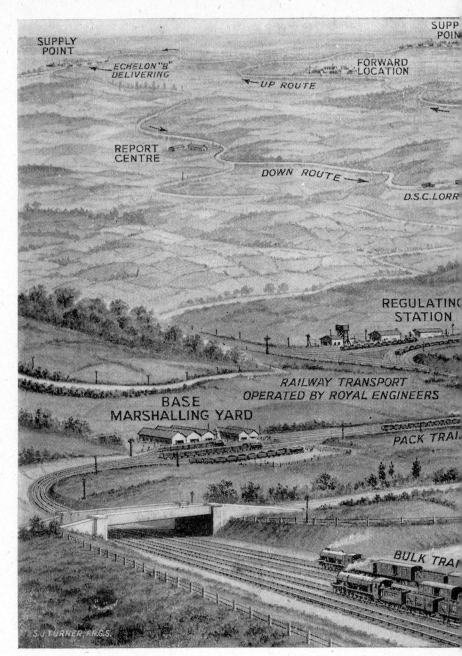

SUPPLY
POINT

ECHELON "B"
DELIVERING

SUPPLY
POIN

FORWARD
LOCATION

UP ROUTE

REPORT
CENTRE

DOWN ROUTE

D.S.C. LORR

REGULATIN
STATION

RAILWAY TRANSPORT
OPERATED BY ROYAL ENGINEERS

BASE
MARSHALLING YARD

PACK TRAI

BULK TRA

S. J. TURNER, F.R.G.S.

STAGES IN THE SUPPLY OF

Supplies begin their journey in bulk trains; these proceed to the base marshalling yard
where they are shunted into pack trains. The pack trains then go to the regulating station
where the ammunition and petrol trucks are sent to different railheads (see pages 256 and
257, 268 and 269). At supply railhead the trucks are rapidly unloaded into the lorries

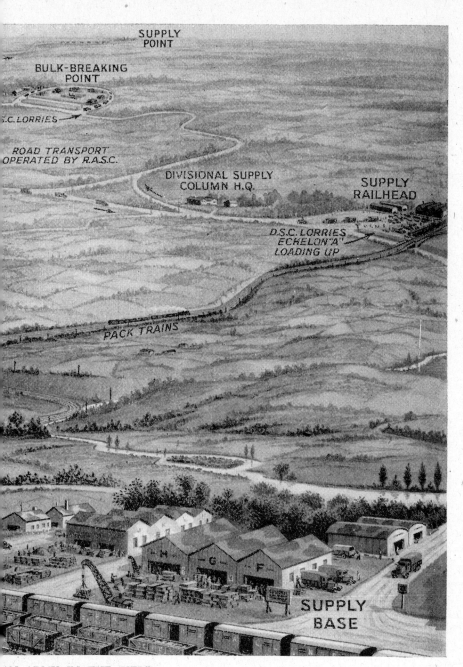

SUPPLY
POINT

BULK-BREAKING
POINT

.C. LORRIES

ROAD TRANSPORT
OPERATED BY R.A.S.C.

DIVISIONAL SUPPLY
COLUMN H.Q.

SUPPLY
RAILHEAD

D.S.C. LORRIES
ECHELON "A"
LOADING UP

PACK TRAINS

H · G · F

SUPPLY
BASE

AN ARMY IN THE FIELD

of the R.A.S.C. Divisional Supply Column. The loaded lorries are taken in a convoy to the bulk breaking point (see page 253), where the bulk supplies are broken up into a day's rations for particular divisional units. The lorries then go forward to the forward locations or the supply points and hand over the stores to units. They return with salvage to railhead

Recruits joining the corps are sent to training brigades, commanded by brigadiers, where in the space of a few months they are transformed into smart, disciplined soldiers, at the same time learning the special work which they will be required to perform. Most of them become drivers, but there is plenty of scope for those who prefer to be butchers, bakers, artificers, clerks or issuers.

MILLIONS OF RATIONS

A big organization is required to provide and keep in running order the vehicles used by all R.A.S.C. units. At home there are mechanical transport depots, which are made up of various departments. The vehicle reception depot receives the vehicles from the motor manufacturer and issues them to the units. The mechanical transport stores depot carries complete stocks of spare parts and equipment. Frequently there is a heavy repair shop too. The same units are found on a smaller scale overseas wherever the Army is operating, and between them they are responsible for a tremendous amount of motor transport.

Then there are the various kinds of supply depots from which the rations of the Army are drawn. There are supply reserve depots, main supply depots, base supply depots, advanced supply depots, field supply depots, command supply depots and detail issue depots—all dealing with millions of rations made up of certain fixed commodities.

At many of them are bakeries and butcheries, where skilled men bake the finest white and brown bread in the world and carry out all the preparation of meat from slaughtering oxen to the trimming of sides of beef. With every active service force there are field bakeries and field butcheries, using the latest mobile equipment that can be operated quickly and conveniently in the often "impossible" conditions of modern warfare.

There are also the different R.A.S.C. units concerned with petrol supplies, stretching in a chain from the ports to the petrol tanks of lorries. There are base petrol depots where the fuel is stored in vast tanks straight from the ships. There are base petrol filling centres where it is put up into the standard four-gallon tins used in the Army. There are bulk petrol companies and corps petrol parks.

Other R.A.S.C. units, outside the main divisional layout, include ambulance car companies, motor ambulance convoys and field ambulances, working in conjunction with the Royal Army Medical Corps; reserve M.T. companies operating fleets of lorries, which are available as a reserve for any purpose ordered by G.H.Q.; troop carrying companies and motor coach companies for the rapid movement of infantry; bridge companies with lorries specially adapted for carrying pontoon bridges; and motorboat companies and pack transport companies for supplying troops that are fighting in places where the use of motor transport is impracticable.

From all this it can be seen that in numbers alone, quite apart from the importance of its work, the R.A.S.C. represents a very considerable part of the British Army. Let us trace now the process by which supplies—food, petrol and ammunition—are obtained and sent out to our fighting troops.

WIDESPREAD BASES

First of all, the base. In war, when expeditionary forces are being maintained in different parts of the world, it does not necessarily follow that all supplies are collected in Britain at huge depots and sent out to the various armies abroad. It is more economical to use sources of supply as near as possible to the expeditionary force.

And so we find a base in every theatre of war, collecting supplies from the home country, from the U.S.A. and from all parts of the Empire. At the base are the various depots for food and petrol that have already been briefly mentioned.

From these great storehouses or dumps the supplies begin their long journey to the front. To begin with they are carried as far as possible by rail to railheads, in other words, the points nearest to the

R.E. transportation service who will be responsible for it until it reaches the appointed railhead.

The bulk trains travel only a short distance to the base marshalling yard. Here they are split up and the trucks are shunted about to form pack trains.

A pack train is made up of several pack sections, each of which consists of the

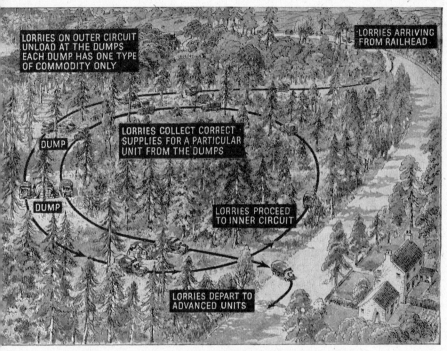

LORRIES ON OUTER CIRCUIT UNLOAD AT THE DUMPS EACH DUMP HAS ONE TYPE OF COMMODITY ONLY

LORRIES ARRIVING FROM RAILHEAD

LORRIES COLLECT CORRECT SUPPLIES FOR A PARTICULAR UNIT FROM THE DUMPS

DUMP

DUMP

LORRIES PROCEED TO INNER CIRCUIT

LORRIES DEPART TO ADVANCED UNITS

SORTING STORES AT A BULK BREAKING POINT

The supply lorries from railhead dump their supplies in separate dumps on the outer circuit.
When empty, they reload from the dumps what is necessary for their particular unit

battle area at which it is feasible to use railways. This railway transport is operated by the Royal Engineers, who also run the ships or barges if coastal or canal transport is available.

The supplies begin their journey in bulk trains containing several commodities, such as petrol and lubricants, ammunition and food supplies. Each truck is sealed by the R.A.S.C. staff at the base depots before it is passed on to the

daily needs of a division or some other formation of troops in the forward area. There are so many trucks of bread, so many of meat, so many of petrol, ammunition and R.E. stores, and others containing groceries, canteen stores, spare parts for lorries, mails, gifts, comforts—in fact, everything a division requires to keep in fighting trim.

The pack train pulls out of the base marshalling yard, but it does not proceed straight to railhead. First of all it has to be dealt with by the regulating station, where the ammunition and petrol trucks are detached and sent on to their respective railheads. As far as possible, separate railheads are arranged for supplies, petrol and ammunition. This is done not only for the sake of convenience, but for safety. Keeping petrol and ammunition apart is a golden rule of the R.A.S.C.

A STEADY FLOW

When the pack train is shunted into the siding of the railhead, everything is ready to unload without delay, so as to keep the trucks on the move and reduce the risk of bombing by the enemy. Petrol, ammunition and supplies are all handled in rather different ways at railhead, so it will be necessary to deal with each in turn. Here we will follow the supplies and ammunition right up to the front line. Petrol we will leave for the present, as it is dealt with in the next chapter of this book.

First, supplies. A small part of the supplies on the pack train are taken to a reserve store near—but not too near—the station. This is used both as a reserve, in case the railway traffic breaks down, and for issuing rations to the troops working at railhead.

Each supply pack is dealt with by the supply column of the division to which it has been consigned. The lorries of this R.A.S.C. divisional supply column have to be divided into two sections or echelons. The reason for this is that one day's supplies arrive at the railhead every day, and the two echelons take it in turns to collect them. While one echelon is *loading up* at the station, the other is *delivering* the supplies, and between them they keep up a steady flow of supplies, day by day. The sequence of events is that the supplies arrive at the station one day, are delivered the next, and are consumed by the troops on the day after.

No attempt is made at railhead to split up the supplies into the smaller quantities required by the individual units of the division. Speed in unloading the trucks is the essential thing at this vulnerable point. Meat, bread and other supplies are all loaded in bulk, in accordance with loading lists prepared before the job is started, and very soon the convoy of lorries is ready to move off, each keeping a safe distance from its neighbour so as to present the most difficult target possible to enemy bombers.

After travelling a few miles the convoy is halted, still widely spaced, and each lorry in turn enters the bulk breaking point. This consists of any site where there is sufficient cover, either of trees or buildings, for the bulk supplies to be broken up without interference from enemy aircraft. Various methods are adopted, one of the most usual being for the lorries to dump their loads on the ground in a horse-shoe pattern. Then each empty lorry proceeds round the dump once more, collecting enough meat, bread, groceries, etc., from each stack to make up a day's rations for one particular unit. There are separate stacks of letters and parcels, ordnance stores, spare parts for vehicles and anything requiring to be forwarded up the line. The lorries are then ready to continue their journey.

MOTOR CYCLIST GUIDES

The next step taken by the vehicles of the divisional supply column depends largely upon the tactical situation. If it is "all quiet" on the front, and the location of the troops can be foreseen with certainty, the lorries take up the supplies straight to the unit lines. On the other hand, if the situation is "fluid," and only the approximate position of the troops is known, then supply points are decided upon by the staff. Motor cyclists from the units meet the lorries there and guide them to where the troops are located.

And so the R.A.S.C. lorry, laden with supplies, at last arrives at the unit lines, with a motor cyclist chugging along in front showing the way. There the issuer on board the lorry hands over the supplies to the quartermaster, who gives him a receipt. The final distribution of the supplies within the unit itself is done by the N.C.O.s and men of the unit itself.

UNFORESEEN HITCH

All this may sound quite straightforward on paper, but there are several points of organization required which are not without interest. One question, for example, is where do the lorry drivers have their own meals if they are continually on the move?

The divisional supply column has its own headquarters, where there is accommodation of some sort for the men and where they can feed. But after the lorries have left railhead for the supply points, the echelon commander sets up his own headquarters at the report centre. This is a point somewhere on the down route, to which the lorries report after they have delivered the supplies. At the report centre are cooks, mechanics, a breakdown lorry and spare lorries. The subalterns in charge of the sections of lorries know that they can obtain assistance from the report centre in case of accidents of all kinds, and they know, too, that they can get in touch with the echelon commander there if the troops have been suddenly moved or some other unforeseen hitch occurs. And there is always a good meal available for the drivers after their long stretch at the wheel. When the last section officer has checked in, the report centre is closed down and the echelon returns to divisional supply column headquarters for a few hours before proceeding to railhead once more to meet another pack train. The cycle is completed.

On the return journey, incidentally, the lorries have brought back to railhead the mail of the units and any other parcels or goods requiring despatch to the base. The lorries never return empty, because there is always some salvage to bring back from the troops—tins, scrap metal, wood and other useful material.

So much for the passage of supplies from the base to railhead and beyond to the troops themselves. But the system is not quite so automatic as it sounds. Obviously, if a fixed amount of food were sent up to divisions and units every day, there would be days on which there would be more than enough for everybody, and other days when belts would have to be tightened—depending upon the actual number of men in the various companies and battalions. This in turn depends upon several factors: casualties caused by battle, sickness and, in quiet times, leave.

And so, to cut possible waste and to make the supply organization as accurate as possible, every company and unit in the British Army has to order every day the food it will consume four days hence.

This is done quite simply in terms of so many rations, according to the number of men in the unit. It would not do to have quartermasters ordering bread, meat, tea, sugar and other foodstuffs separately. Instead, there is a standard Army ration, or sufficient food for one man for one day, which varies in composition according to the time of the year, the locality, the difficulties of sea supply, and so on.

OUNCES BECOME TONS

These "shopping lists" are sent back to the base, and it is on the total number of rations demanded by a division that the amount of meat, bread, groceries, etc., in each pack section of the pack train is worked out. The few ounces of meat required for each man's ration become tons of meat on the divisional pack train.

Just in case the conditions of battle should make it impossible for the normal supply system to continue functioning,

EMERGENCY DUMP

EMERGENCY DUMP

AMMUNITION POINT

CORPS AMMUNITION PARK LORRIES

AMMUNITION RAILHEAD

CORPS AMMUNITION PARK H.Q.

PACK TRAINS

BASE

BULK TRAINS

HOW AMMUNITION IS CONVEYED

Ammunition, its manufacture, inspection and conveyance as far as ammunition railhead is the responsibility of the R.A.O.C. From railhead to the guns it is transported by the R.A.S.C. On its way it passes through two organizations—the corps ammunition park and the divisional ammunition company. The lorries of the corps ammunition park carry it

256

EMERGENCY DUMP

EMERGENCY DUMP

EMERGENCY DUMP

AMMUNITION POINT

IVISIONAL AMMUNITION COMPANY LORRIES

DIVISIONAL AMMUNITION COMPANY H.Q.

AMMUNITION REFILLING POINT

REGULATING STATION

BASE ARSHALLING YARD

PACK TRAINS

S.J.TURNER, F.R.G.S.

FROM THE BASE TO THE FRONT

as far as the ammunition refilling point, where the boxes of ammunition are transferred to the lorries of the divisional ammunition company. If a battle is in progress, these lorries take the ammunition to the ammunition points, a short way behind the guns. If a big advance is being contemplated, emergency dumps are established as far forward as possible every officer and man in the Army carries on him an emergency ration when he goes into action. This is what used to be known in the war of 1914–18 as the "iron ration." It consists of a small block of vitamin food made of chocolate and other nutritive additions, packed in an airtight tin. The important point about this emergency ration is that it is intended for use only when other food is definitely impossible to obtain. The decision to consume it can only be made by an officer, who has to account for his action afterwards.

GUNS' APPETITE

And now we come to the question of ammunition. In the early stages—manufacture, inspection, shipping and passage up the lines of communication—in fact, right up to railhead, this is the responsibility of the Royal Army Ordnance Corps. It is not until the ammunition train arrives at the siding of railhead that the R.A.S.C. takes it over, and its job consists of transporting it up to the guns.

In the same way that the divisional supply column brings up the supplies of the division for one day, so does the divisional ammunition company meet the requirements of the division in the way of ammunition. But there is this fundamental difference. The consumption of food does not fluctuate violently from day to day, but the appetite of the guns varies with the battle situation.

Weeks, even months may go by with nothing more than a few rounds being used during patrol activity. Then, suddenly, an offensive is started by one side or the other and the gunners and infantrymen cry out for ammunition—more and more in ever increasing quantities.

And so the first difference about an ammunition railhead as compared with a supply railhead is that trains do not arrive every day. The second difference is that the divisional ammunition company does not operate as far back as railhead.

Unlike supplies, which are conveyed from railhead to troops entirely by the divisional supply column, ammunition passes through two hands before it reaches the artillery lines. The first stage, from railhead to corps ammunition park, or to a dump, is made in the lorries of the park. There it is kept until the gunners send in a demand for ammunition, by way of the divisional ammunition company. The lorries of the corps ammunition park then move forward to an ammunition refilling point, where the boxes of ammunition are transferred to the lorries of the divisional ammunition company.

The next stage varies according to circumstances. If a battle is being fought, the lorries move up the line to ammunition points a short way behind the guns, where they await the arrival of the R.A.S.C. motor cyclists attached to the gunners. These motor cyclists (the R.A.S.C., by the way, does not have any despatch riders, or D.R.s; they are called motor cyclists in the Corps), are very important people. They bring back the orders for ammunition, and have to conduct the lorries back to the artillery lines.

In less strenuous times the lorries go from the ammunition refilling point to the location of the divisional ammunition company, delivering direct to units as and when motor cyclists arrive from the gunners with demands for ammunition.

THE BATTLE STARTS

The job of the R.A.S.C., then, as regards ammunition, can be summed up as replenishment. A certain stock of ammunition is held at various stages from the gun pits themselves right back to railhead. The lorries and limbers of the batteries are kept full; so, too, are the vehicles of the divisional ammunition company and the corps ammunition park.

Directly a battle starts the ammunition begins to be consumed by the fighting troops at a rapid rate. This drain on the stock must be counterbalanced by continual replenishment, and it is up to the R.A.S.C. to see that there is always ammunition in plenty for the men behind the rifles and guns.

CONSTANT VIGILANCE

Life in the Royal Army Service Corps can sometimes have a spice of danger in it. This was true in the war of 1914-18, when the roads up to the front were targets for enemy shelling—especially when rations and ammunition were on their way up the line. In those days the danger came from recognized sources—gunfire and occasional bombing or machine gunning from the air. Nowadays it is a very different story. There is no front. The old fixed zig-zag lines of trenches, from which infantry sallied forth to drive back the enemy a few hundred yards, have gone for ever. The combined assault of dive bomber and tank has shattered that idea of warfare for all time. Instead, we have sorties by squadrons of tanks which penetrate deep into the territory of the enemy, with the aim of fanning-out and cutting across the lines of communication and supply of the opposing forces.

The result is that the officers and men of the R.A.S.C. have to be prepared for anything and everything as they rumble along the roads in their convoys of camouflaged lorries.

They have to keep their eyes skinned for dive bombers and fighters swooping down to attack them from the air with bombs and raking machine gun fire. So quickly does this sort of attack develop that the drivers have to be trained in sizing up the situation quickly and acting immediately. Sometimes, when the road is lined with trees, it pays to pull up quickly under cover and leave the cabin of the lorry for the shelter of a ditch. At others, when cover is scant, it is better to keep on the move and hope that, being a moving target, you make it more difficult

for the enemy pilot to aim accurately. The experience is made all the more exciting if your lorry happens to be laden with three tons of ammunition!

But it would not do for the drivers of the R.A.S.C. to confine their scanning to the skies. The road ahead must be watched too, for it can reveal all kinds of surprises. Round that next bend, for example, may be encountered a small band of enemy tanks, even though the troops for whom your load is destined may be fighting, undefeated, many miles ahead. This happened to many a Royal Army Service Corps convoy in the Battle of France. Whether or not the convoy could extricate itself from its dangerous predicament depended on the alertness of the lorry drivers and motor cyclists.

What are the weapons with which the R.A.S.C. does its fighting? To begin with, every driver in the corps has a rifle of the normal infantry pattern. This he keeps in special clips in the cab of his lorry, always ready at hand to be used at an instant's notice. Officers have pistols. Every R.A.S.C. unit has also its regulation quota of light machine guns—Bren or Lewis—and anti-tank rifles.

For convoy work the machine guns are mounted on special protection lorries, the crews of which are continuously on the alert to ward off the attacks of dive bombers. Normally the gun is mounted in the back of a lorry, with a swivelling seat for the gunner; occasionally it is situated on the top of the driver's cabin.

CONVOY PROTECTION

Protection, or defence, forms a regular part of the arrangements made by every R.A.S.C. unit, echelon or section at its halting place, whether it is for one night or for a prolonged stay. There are two possible forms in which an attack may develop, by enemy aircraft, or from the ground by marauding tanks or paratroops, and both require special precautions.

Air defence is largely a matter of concealment. Even if the position of the bulk breaking point, ammunition refilling point or supply point is communicated to the enemy by fifth columnists—as used to happen frequently in France—the job of the enemy bomber pilots can be made extremely difficult by paying careful attention to concealment. Vehicles must always be parked under trees, and the addition of a cleverly pegged-out scrim-netting can make a solid three-ton lorry almost invisible from the air.

TELL-TALE TRACKS

Nothing gives away the presence of a mechanized unit better to an airman than wheelmarks across fields—and even the tracks made by men walking through long grass on the same path. And so one of the first jobs of an R.A.S.C. officer when moving into a new location is to work out traffic routes to the various lorry standings which involve making the smallest possible number of new tracks, both by machines and men. If he wants to be particularly careful, he will have the tracks extended to a point where the lorries are actually parked, and he may even decide to make false tracks in neighbouring fields.

All this is defence of the passive kind. The job of an R.A.S.C. unit is to deliver supplies to the troops, not to bring down enemy aircraft with ack-ack fire, and if it can avoid detection it will stand a better chance of carrying out that job. That is why the men who man the unit's machine guns are given strict orders not to open fire until an attack is actually made, no matter how tempting the target may be. Once a gun is fired the position is given away.

In modern mobile warfare, R.A.S.C. units must also be on their guard against the possibility of attack by enemy tanks which have broken through or by parachutists and airborne troops. The first consideration to be remembered by the officer commanding the unit is that the attack may develop from any direction, not necessarily that in which the main armies lie. And so machine guns and anti-tank rifles and rifle parties are put out at all approaches to the point where the unit is located, all of them in concealment. Here again, as in the case of enemy aircraft, it is not the business of the R.A.S.C. to seek battle, but to deliver supplies, and if the enemy should appear and pass by without noticing the vehicle park so much the better.

On the other hand, if an attack by the enemy should occur the men at the Bren and Lewis guns and the anti-tank rifles are ready. They will be helped by men hiding in hedges and ditches, armed with grenades and Molotoff cocktails. This fighting capacity of the R.A.S.C. was proved in many incidents during the Battle of France and Belgium.

Most of the transport work done by the R.A.S.C. nowadays is performed by motor vehicles. Supplies, petrol and ammunition are all conveyed by motor lorry, and so, too, are the infantry whenever this is possible. But conditions will always exist where the motor lorry cannot be used with success, and it is for these theatres of war that the R.A.S.C. retains a nucleus of animal transport companies. There are places on the coast of Britain even, where gun and searchlight crews are supplied by pack animals, so wild is the country thereabouts.

RECRUITS' CREED

A special pack harness is used for this purpose, with two boxes slung on each side of the animal where the saddle is usually placed. The load carried is 180 lb., so that it takes thirty-seven horses to carry the load of a single 3-ton lorry!

It is the creed of the R.A.S.C. that a man must be a soldier first and foremost, and a driver afterwards. This does not mean that his training as a driver is incidental, but it does mean that to be a good soldier-driver a man must have ingrained in him that sense of discipline which can only come from general military training, which, in the early stages, means the drill square.

The "intake" then passes on to the driving school, where it is divided into three categories. In the first are men who have driven vehicles of all types in Civvy

steeds will never let them down. At the end of the course every man is passed out by an officer. The thoroughness of the training can best be judged by the fact that ninety-eight per cent come through the ordeal successfully.

After a short spell at a depot battalion, the driver—now a driver in name as well as fact—is posted to a unit. He does not know what or where it will be. He may

BLOCKING THE ROAD WITH R.A.S.C. LORRIES

Though the business of the R.A.S.C. is that of supply, the corps is a combatant one. Having blocked the road, these men, armed with rifles and automatics, are getting under cover

Street, the men who used to handle buses, motor coaches and long distance goods lorries. Then come those who can drive a car or light van, but who need practice on bigger vehicles. Finally, there are the men who have chosen to become drivers, but who have never driven a vehicle before.

Throughout their training at the driving school the men continue to be drilled, both on the square and with their vehicles. Maintenance, too, forms a daily part of the curriculum, so that—like the A.S.C. men of the war of 1914-18—their

have to carry anything or anybody, from ammunition, petrol or supplies to fully equipped infantrymen going into battle or wounded men returning from it.

But the job will be the same—to deliver the right goods at the right place at the right time. In the war of 1914-18 the men of the Army Service Corps made a splendid name for themselves by never failing the fighting men who depended upon them. The title "Royal" was later conferred on the Army Service Corps by His late Majesty King George V.

ARMY BREAKDOWN LORRY

The maintenance of vehicles is a vital matter. The R.A.S.C. is well equipped with mobile workshops and breakdown lorries, able (as above) to raise whole engines out for repair

CHAPTER 14

Transport in the Army

Load carriers. Bridging lorries. Office trucks. Wireless lorries. Search-
light, air compressor and water vehicles. Workshop section. Tank
recovery and transporter vehicles. Scout cars. Quads. Armoured com-
mand vehicle. Transport organization. Maintenance. Petrol supply.

ONVOYS of khaki camouflaged motor vehicles are a familiar sight on the roads of Britain. To the casual observer they are all "Army lorries," but in actual fact these convoys include a wide variety of types, all with their special uses.

The standard lorry (load carrier) in the Army is the 3-tonner, although there are numbers of 30-cwt. lorries still in use. For lighter loads there are 15-cwt. and 8-cwt. trucks. On these various chassis are built all kinds of different bodies.

The majority of lorries, of course, are what the Army calls "load carriers." They have a metal superstructure with a canvas covering which can be removed if it is desired to use the lorry as an open one. The load they carry can be anything— troops (twenty to a lorry), food, petrol or ammunition, and stores of all kinds. Many of the latest types are constructed so that the engine drives all four wheels, instead of the rear wheels only. This enables them to keep going on very rough or muddy ground indeed. A certain number of them have tipping bodies which are useful for making and repairing roads and aerodromes in support of an advance.

It may be asked what happens when there is a load heavier than three tons which requires shifting from A to B? If the load can be split up, it is just a question of putting extra lorries on to the job, but it sometimes happens that there is a solid piece of machinery, or part of a

heavy gun that has to be moved. Then one of the bigger lorries, with a capacity of six or ten tons, is detailed for the job. For outsize loads there are always the tank recovery vehicles or tank trans-porters, but these are specialized vehicles as distinct from load carriers.

In addition to "universal" load carriers, there are also lorries which are designed to carry a particular load. Many of these are set aside for the exclusive use of the Royal Engineers, although they are manned by the Royal Army Service Corps. In this category are the lorries made to carry the parts of a box girder bridge and pontoon bridges, including folding boats on which to rest the plat-form of the bridge itself.

TRAVELLING OFFICE

There is also a big range of Army vehicles with special bodies. There is, for example, the rakish looking office truck. No matter where a division or brigade is operating, whether it is in barracks or in the field, there is always a certain amount of office work to be done in connection with the personnel and equipment of the unit. Indents and returns have to be rendered about all kinds of subjects from "boots, ankle, pairs" to spare parts for the formation vehicles. And so the Army pro-vides an office on wheels, with a table, chairs and built-in cupboards and drawers, in order that staff officers can work, plan and render returns in comparative comfort—even though headquarters may be miles from the facilities of civilization.

A technical vehicle that is more easily recognized is the wireless lorry, of which there are two types—the light van for short distance intercommunication in the field, and the big six-wheeler with its own generating plant, self-sufficient for radio-telegraphy in the wildest possible country. These wireless vans can generally be spotted by their aerials.

BLOOD TRANSFUSION

There are also lorries constructed as travelling searchlight units, and others built as air compressor plants. One of the most highly specialized motor vehicles in the British Army is the motor blood transfusion lorry, in which blood can be refrigerated and conveyed to the field hospitals to assist in the recovery of casualties who, in previous wars, would very probably have died of wounds.

There are water tanks, squat little vehicles, which are a tremendous boon to troops on the move who bivouac at night at the roadside. And there is the range of technical vehicles which go to make up a travelling workshop or servicing station for all types of mechanical equipment. The normal workshop section in the R.A.S.C., to take an example, consists of three vehicles. First there is the breakdown lorry, with its sturdy derrick for lifting lorries out of hopeless bogs and a winch that can extricate them from the deepest ditch. Being a six-wheeler with knobbly tyres, this breakdown lorry can go practically anywhere itself, and it carries on board a very comprehensive tool kit for repairs.

The second lorry is the workshop lorry itself. This is a beautifully designed vehicle, and within the few square yards of its body-space it carries equipment and plant, including a lathe, of which many garages would be glad.

The section is completed by the stores lorry. This vehicle carries in cunningly devised racks sufficient spare parts and workshop material to enable the section to deal with all but major repairs.

Another vehicle with a special body is the R.A.S.C. bread lorry. In its capacious interior are hundreds of trays and racks, which can be easily scrubbed, with a trap-door in the centre of the body.

Then there are the different types of ambulances, heavy, medium and light, all strongly constructed to operate smoothly on the roughest roads.

Next come the vehicles designed to carry tanks. These are of two kinds, known as recovery and transporter. The recovery wagon is made to handle "dead" tanks, or tanks that are non-runners owing either to a mechanical breakdown or to damage inflicted in battle. It has a winch which hauls the heavy, inert weight of the tank up two runners on to the floor of the lorry. Alternatively, if a crane is available, the tank can be lifted up and deposited on its mobile resting place.

The transporter lorry is designed to carry only "live" tanks. The difference is that it possesses the two runners but not the winch, and tanks are expected to climb up on to its back under their own power. These tank transporters form part of the vehicles of every armoured division, and enable the division to move from one location to another without causing unnecessary wear and tear of the tanks. Instead of them crashing and clattering along main roads for hour after hour, the tanks go by lorry and save their energy for the journeys of actual battle.

RECONNAISSANCE CORPS

Besides all these there are the machines which come into the Army category "A.F.V."—armoured fighting vehicles—although they are not strictly speaking armoured cars, which are described elsewhere in this book (pp. 88 and 90).

The smallest of these is the scout car, which is used by the Reconnaissance Corps. This is an amusing little machine that looks very much the same at both ends, so that you are never quite sure in which direction it is going to move. It is short and squat, but is very nippy and is capable of travelling quickly over rough ground as well as on good roads.

Most people are familiar with the "Quad," the name given to the beetle-backed tractor which is used to tow field guns. With its bullet-proof windscreen

nowadays known as the "Dorchester." Its proper name is "Armoured Command Vehicle" (p. 90), and it is the headquarters of a brigade of an armoured division. It weighs twelve tons and is thickly armoured from stem to stern. Inside it travel the brigadier and his brigade major, intelligence officer and signals officer, with two radio-telephonists, all seated at tables and switchboards. This is the brain and nerve centre of the armoured brigade. From it emanate the orders, verbal by radio and written in

TANK RECOVERY VEHICLE NEAR TOBRUK

The recovery vehicle (as above) hauls "dead" tanks aboard with a winch. There are also transporter vehicles for "live" tanks—on to which they mount under their own power, to save wear and tear on the tractors. Metalled roads are very bad for such heavy vehicles

and heavy armour, it can bring a gun into positions which can only be reached by crossing country exposed to enemy fire. Being driven on all four wheels, and having deeply ridged tyres, it can surge through mud and slime. If the gun becomes bogged after the battery has been in action, the Quad pulls it out by means of the steel hawser of its winch.

And finally, there is that wonderful vehicle which in the early days of the war was nicknamed the "Gin Palace," but is

the form of messages handed out to motor cyclists while on the move, which direct the tanks of the brigade in battle. Flowing back to it, by the same channels, are the reactions and reports of the scout cars and the tank commanders.

The rest of the vehicles of the Army consist of motor cars and motor cycles.

The transport of the British Army comes under three headings: armoured fighting vehicles (known in the Army as "A" vehicles), units' first line vehicles (known in the Army as "B" vehicles) and Royal Army Service Corps vehicles. The first needs no explanation. The Royal Army Ordnance Corps supply and undertake the heavy repairs not only of all armoured fighting vehicles but also of all the "first line" vehicles of the Army. These vehicles belong to the infantry, the artillery and the armoured corps, and are in fact the vehicles of all units except the R.A.S.C. The Royal Army Service Corps supply and keep in running order the "second line" and "third line" vehicles, which belong to the R.A.S.C. units of the line of communication. These make up the divisional ammunition, petrol and supply companies, to which must be added all vehicles used by the staff and the medical services.

The chief difference is that whereas the R.A.S.C. does all the running repair and maintenance work of its vehicles, including driving them, the R.A.O.C. only does the heavy repairs of the first line vehicles. These are driven by the men of the infantry or artillery units to which they belong, and are kept in running order by the artificer sections of those units.

This is how it is done. The various running adjustments and jobs required to keep a vehicle in good fettle are grouped into sixteen "tasks." One of these has to be performed by the driver every day. It does not matter when or where he does it, while his lorry is being loaded and unloaded during his "detail," or on his return to the company location in the evening. The main thing is that he must do it, and he has to sign a written declaration that he has done so. These sixteen tasks cover all the jobs that can be done by a man without specialized

QUAD HAULING A FIELD

These beetle-backed tractors, known as "Quads," are used to tow guns. They are heavily armoured and have bullet-proof windscreens. This enables them to tow guns rapidly acros

knowledge or skill—rather like the advice given to motorists in the instruction books of their cars. It follows that the whole machine is tuned up twice a month.

But the maintenance does not end there. Once a month the car or lorry is inspected from radiator cap to tail light by an N.C.O. The inspection is carried out "by numbers," in true Army fashion. Every part of the vehicle is listed in a special book kept for the purpose, and the N.C.O. goes over them methodically, making notes for the driver about any adjustments necessary. Also once a month, fourteen days before or after the N.C.O.'s inspection, the vehicle is sent to the workshops for a similar examination, and here are carried out the jobs which are beyond the capacity of the driver. Finally, the Army at home have recently introduced a system whereby one day a week is a petrol-less day, on which only essential journeys are carried out. This is known as the "make and mend" day, and is given over entirely to vehicle maintenance.

Altogether, then, an Army vehicle is maintained at a very high pitch of mechanical efficiency. But even so, breakdowns are bound to occur, as well as the need for complete overhauls. The mechanics of the artificer squads, the light aid detachment or the workshop section attached to every unit are always busy. The equipment carried by their three vehicles—workshop lorry, breakdown lorry and stores lorry—enables them to tackle most jobs that an ordinary garage or service station can do. Major repairs, such as reboring the cylinder of an engine and fitting new pistons, are sent back to the heavy repair shops.

Stores and spare parts are obtained by

GUN ACROSS A RIVER

bullet-swept ground without loss. Their enormous tyres can plough through mud and slime; should the gun become bogged, the Quad can usually pull it out with its hawser and winch

PETROL POINT

PETROL POINT

DIVISIONAL PETROL COMPANY LORRIES

PETROL RAILHEAD

RESERVE FOR 25 MILES ADVANCE

CORPS PETROL PARK LORRIES

BASE PETROL FILLING CENTRE

PACK TRAINS

S.J.TURNER,F.R.G.S.

SUPPLYING PETROL TO A

Modern war is a war of machines, and petrol is their life blood. Petrol and oil are kept in huge tanks at an overseas base. From there they go to the base filling centre to be put into tins. The tins are loaded in to pack trains which travel by way of the base marshalling yard and regulating station to petrol railhead. Hence the corps petrol park lorries carry the

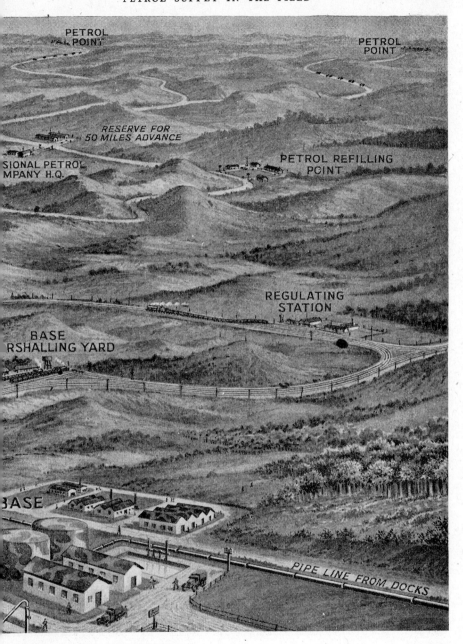

PETROL
POINT

PETROL
POINT

RESERVE FOR
50 MILES ADVANCE

SIONAL PETROL
MPANY H.Q.

PETROL REFILLING
POINT

REGULATING
STATION

BASE
RSHALLING YARD

3ASE

PIPE LINE FROM DOCKS

MODERN ARMY IN THE FIELD

*petrol and oil as far as the petrol refilling point. At this point the lorries of the various
divisional petrol companies take the fuel up the line to the petrol points. Reserves of fuel
are shared by the divisional petrol company, which has stores for an advance of fifty miles,
and by the corps petrol park, which has enough stored for a further twenty-five miles*

NINTH DIVISION

ALL THREE BRIGADES TIMED TO ARRIVE AT 12·15

71ˢᵀ BRIGADE 20 M.I.H.
(MILES IN THE HOUR)
THE LONGEST ROUTE
THEREFORE THE HIGHEST SPEED

70ᵀᴴ BRIGADE 17 M.I.H.
(MILES IN THE HOUR)
THE SHORTEST ROUTE

MOTOR CYCLE PATROL

WIRELESS CAR ON EDGE OF WOOD

MOBILE A·A GUNS IN SPINNEY

WIRELESS VAN

BOFORS GUN UNDER COVER

A·A GUNS IN WOOD

CRATER IN ROAD REPAIRED BY R.E.ˢ

HOW A DIVISION MOVES

In a British division there are between two and three thousand lorries, cars and motor cycles. When a division moves, a "march table" is worked out for it in great detail to avoid road congestion. Each of the three brigades is usually given a different route to the assembly point. Two matters of vital importance in a march table are speed and density. In the Army speed

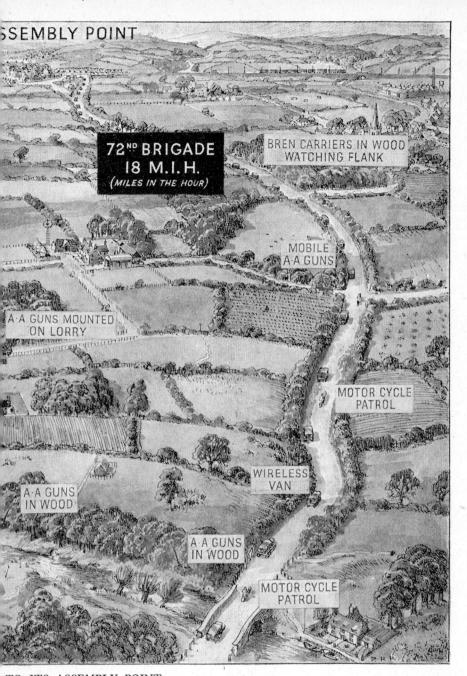

72ND BRIGADE
18 M.I.H.
(MILES IN THE HOUR)

BREN CARRIERS IN WOOD
WATCHING FLANK

MOBILE
A·A GUNS

A·A GUNS MOUNTED
ON LORRY

MOTOR CYCLE
PATROL

WIRELESS
VAN

A·A GUNS
IN WOOD

A·A GUNS
IN WOOD

MOTOR CYCLE
PATROL

TO ITS ASSEMBLY POINT

is not denoted by miles per hour, but the term is miles in the hour. Density is the degree of spacing between vehicles necessary to reduce the risk of aerial attack to a minimum. On the march full precautions are taken against attack, particularly by the use of A.A. guns. Motor cyclists control and guide the traffic; wireless is also much used for interunit communication

the workshop section from the depots of transport stores, which form a regular feature on every line of communication.

Where do all these vehicles—the tanks, armoured cars, lorries, motor cars and motor cycles—obtain their petrol? This is the job of the Royal Army Service Corps, universal providers of the army.

PETROL RESERVE

Let us start at the base, where vast quantities of petrol and oil are kept in great storage tanks. From there it goes to the base petrol filling centre to be put up into tins. These tins are then loaded on to the pack train which proceeds by way of the base marshalling yard and the regulating centre to the station specially chosen as petrol railhead.

The train is unloaded at the siding by the men and lorries of the corps petrol park, who move the petrol as far as the petrol refilling point, which may be anything up to fifty miles from railhead.

At the refilling point the tins of petrol are transferred to the lorries of the various divisional petrol companies. It is their job to take the petrol up the line to the petrol points, a distance which may amount to another fifty miles. The petrol point is where the first line vehicles of the fighting troops collect their quota of petrol tins, and it is therefore situated only a few miles behind the battle area.

In the same way that a stock of ammunition has to be available at all times for the guns, so is a reserve of petrol always held in readiness for a sudden advance by the first line vehicles of the fighting units. This reserve is shared by the divisional petrol company, which carries sufficient for an advance of fifty miles, and by the corps petrol park, which holds enough for a further twenty-five miles.

At this point it would be as well to mention that the fighting troops mentioned here are infantry, for whom an advance of more than seventy-five miles

in one bound would be exceptional. In the case of armoured divisions, which can push forward hundreds of miles within the course of a few days, different arrangements necessarily have to be made.

The tanks themselves, of course, are filled to capacity with petrol before zero hour, and they can travel a considerable distance before needing to refuel. Following in their wake come the lorries of the special R.A.S.C. company whose job is the most "front line" of all in the corps today, being actually ahead of the infantry. These lorries carry petrol, ammunition, wireless batteries and food for the tank crews. Meanwhile, new petrol points are established as far forward as possible, so that the lorries can quickly pick up a fresh load of petrol cans and set off once more behind the advancing tanks.

From the hectic rush of an advancing armoured division, let us turn to the problems involved in the move of an ordinary infantry division behind the battle area. It may not sound a very complicated problem, until it is realized that the modern Army travels on wheels, and that there are approximately 2,500 lorries, cars and motor cycles in a division.

To allow this number of vehicles to proceed from one location to another as they pleased would be to invite chaos, and so there is nothing for it but to work out the whole move in the closest detail. This is done by the staff officers of the division in the form of a march table.

MOVING A DIVISION

The first thing to be decided is the route, and this has to be arranged in consultation with G.H.Q. to avoid clashing with movements of other troops on the same day. In the case of a division, each of the three brigades is usually given a different route. If the division were moved as a whole, with its vehicles travelling at 100 yards intervals, the convoy would be nearly 150 miles long!

The next detail to consider is the starting point. This has to be fixed at a place where all the units of the brigade can be marshalled into the proper order just before reaching it. What happens is that the vehicles of the leading unit leave their camp at a certain time, and as they proceed slowly along the road towards the starting point, the vehicles of the remaining units emerge from lanes, woods and fields and fall in behind.

TRAFFIC GUIDES

And so each brigade—and at various starting points, the whole division—gets ont he move. The men travel in 3-ton lorries or motor coaches. Other lorries carry the stores and supplies. Four-wheel-drive tractors pass by towing the artillery, and Bren carriers rattle along at a surprising speed. Here and there can be seen office trucks, and dotted throughout the columns are motor cars. At intervals are stationed the protection lorries with Bren guns pointed skywards in anticipation of attack by enemy aircraft, and right at the end come the great breakdown lorries of the Light Aid Detachment, Royal Army Ordnance Corps.

But the progress of the convoy is not quite so automatic as it may sound. Ahead of it ride motor cyclists who straddle their machines at every road junction to ensure that the vehicles keep to the proper route and to act as local traffic policemen. Each of these motor cyclists has been taken over the route beforehand and knows his job to the letter. Other motor cyclists in the column itself keep company commanders in touch with their subordinates, and report any breakdowns or casualties.

Two points which are always specified on the march table are speed and density. The Army has its own way of describing speed. Instead of saying that the convoy will travel at so many miles *per* hour, they say it will cover so many miles *in* the hour. In abbreviated form this is m.i.h.

Density is the degree to which the vehicles have to be spaced out so that they do not present too inviting a target to enemy aircraft. Density is always given in terms of so many vehicles to the mile of road, v.t.m. for short.

This generally works out at rather less than 100 yards between vehicles by day, and half that distance at night. The reason for the greater density at night is partly because there is less risk of bombing (the lorries travel without lights when aircraft are about) and also to prevent drivers straying from the route down side-turnings. All army lorries nowadays have a special form of rear lighting which cannot be seen from the air at all. A white light shines on to the back axle casing, which is painted white, and on it is the serial number of the unit. This can be seen by the driver of the following vehicle, who can tell whether he is in the right convoy.

Most divisional moves take several hours to complete, and a halt for food is therefore generally required at some point on the journey. This is arranged by deciding upon a definite time for the column to halt. Haversack rations are produced and after a short interval the column gets on the move once more.

JOURNEY'S END

The procedure at the end of the route is very much the same as that at the starting point. As each unit of the brigade convoy passes a certain point, it is picked up by one of its motor cyclists who knows exactly where it is going to be quartered. And so to right and left the vehicles turn off, being led straight to their "standings." In a few minutes the quartermasters can be supervising the unloading of stores.

In the meantime the divisional petrol company is establishing petrol points where the vehicles of the division can fill up in readiness for another sudden move.

A HOSPITAL SHIP COMES HOME

Modern weapons produce very varied types of wounds. When seriously wounded, men come
home in hospital ships. They are then taken by orderlies of the R.A.M.C. to a home hospital

CHAPTER 15

The Royal Army Medical Corps

Growth of corps. Fitness groups. Hygiene and diet. Route of a casualty.
Gallantry of doctors. R.M.O. Special institutions at home. Organiza-
tion. Motor ambulance convoys. Ambulance trains. Special units in field

IT is not easy to realize that less than a century ago the medical and surgical organization linked with our land forces was not only meagre but in many aspects appallingly deficient. The Crimean War, which began in 1854, was the stern necessity that formed a stepping-stone to the Army Hospital Corps. In 1873 this branch of the Service had bestowed upon it the name Army Medical Corps, but the prefix Royal was not forthcoming until 1898. Having laid its plans mainly to cope with battle casualties, the R.A.M.C. discovered in the South African War that eight out of every ten non-effective combatants were not the victims of enemy action. They had gone down before the onslaught of cholera, typhoid or some other epidemic, visitations that took a much more ghastly toll of human life than did the artillery or snipers of the Boers.

MAINTAINING HEALTH

Thus was born a painful realization of the need to keep an army fighting fit. The present-day purpose of the corps is therefore, in the first instance, to create and maintain the highest standard of health and to grapple by scientific anticipation with any scourges to which numbers of men under arms are prone. It also succours the wounded and ministers effectively to the sick. Victoria Crosses and other richly deserved decorations are won by doctors and stretcher-bearers for saving life under fire and in the teeth of

every conceivable peril. There are, however, no spectacular awards for bringing about, often by preventive measures, the continuous well-being of hundreds of thousands of troops.

The R.A.M.C. obtrudes itself as soon as a man has crossed the threshold into Army service. The candidate who enlists as an enthusiastic volunteer for a military career, or the man who is called up with his group after registering with the Ministry of Labour, is required first of all to face a medical board of five doctors who carry out a thorough examination. Then, after due consultation, they include him in one of four distinct grades. If he is placed in Grade I he can regard himself as being physically fit for anything that may befall, but Grade IV decrees that he cannot be accepted for the Forces in any circumstances. As for the intermediate classes, they point the way only to specified forms of duty with the Colours, strictly in keeping with the soldier's bodily limitations.

An approved man is called to his unit and the day after his enlistment the regimental medical officer (R.M.O.) checks up the preliminary grading. The recruit is placed in one of five military categories. In A he is suitable physically for active service in any theatre of war and can consider himself a potential front line fighting man. The B soldier may be called upon to render service at the base, on lines of communication, or be posted to garrison duties at home or overseas. C recruits are reserved for home service only, whilst Ds are temporarily unfit and the Es permanently so.

A month passes, probably very quickly in what must inevitably prove a strange new world, and then the soldier again comes before the M.O. for a further examination. The results upon him of four packed weeks of regular, disciplined life, vaccination, and inoculation against typhoid and tetanus, are assessed from the doctor's point of view. At the end of this searching test the R.M.O. is empowered to raise the category of a soldier. This is often done, though a man can only be relegated to a lower group by a Medical Board composed of several officers. Throughout his training as a

recruit, the newly joined soldier is interviewed at intervals by the M.O. of his unit and he will certainly be rendered dentally perfect by the dental officer. Further, when the man ceases to be a "rookie" and is ready to take his place with his fully trained colleagues, he is again closely examined.

Many men, drawn into a completely fresh and unknown sphere, are naturally anxious as to what would happen to them in the event of accident or sickness. In such cases the R.A.M.C. has carefully laid plans to meet every eventuality. Thus, the soldier who is but slightly off-colour can spend two or three days at the reception station of his own camp or barracks. If his condition dictates such a step, he is sent to a military hospital

WALKING WOUNDED LEAVING A DESTROYER

In times of stress wounded come home on warships. These soldiers are able to walk up the gangway from a destroyer. Wounded men carry labels relating to their wounds and treatment

BRITISH WOUNDED RETURNING FROM NORWAY

When men are too badly wounded in the legs to walk, orderlies of the R.A.M.C. carry them from the hospital ship to shore. Still more seriously wounded men are placed on stretchers. They are then wheeled to the hospital train on the rubber-tyred trolleys in the foreground. Such a stretcher can be seen moving off in the left of the picture and other stretcher-bearers are waiting in the background ready to go aboard the ship. R.A.M.C. doctors are in attendance

where there will be facilities for specialist treatment. In instances of serious illness relatives are informed. When there is the slightest danger to the patient's life, free travel warrants are granted to two relatives to visit him, these warrants being obtainable at all local police stations.

Provision is also made for a man so ill or a soldier so severely injured by an accident that he is of no further use to the Army. In practice only a Medical Board can mark a man permanently unfit, and upon the Board falls the onus of recommending to the War Office whether the discharge is directly attributable to military service or otherwise. In the former event, the matter is placed before the Ministry of Pensions for consideration so that the amount of pension or gratuity can be determined according to the Royal Warrant.

Throughout modern warfare there is a general absence of that static condition brought into being by the trench system of 1914-18, with two powerful bodies of highly trained men facing one another across the narrow strip of territory known picturesquely as no-man's-land. In the Second World War the speed of military movement, the employment of aerial attack and defence, and mechanization in general, added tenfold to the difficulties of the R.A.M.C. in the field of action. The distances for evacuation through a chain of organized posts, each more fully equipped than the last as one approaches the base, have been extended to an extraordinary degree and the area over which casualties have to be picked up widened immeasurably.

GALLANTRY IN THE FIELD

There have been many instances of doctors ignoring a fixed point of duty and going far forward into the battle-zone to seek out wounded men instead of waiting for casualties to be brought to them.

The case of Lieutenant (temporary Captain) Thomas Victor Somerville, O.B.E., M.C., R.A.M.C., awarded the Distinguished Service Order, brings home this point and the story is told officially as follows: "On December 11, 1940, at Ras El Saida a squadron of tanks were bogged within 400 yards of a strong enemy position and under heavy and accurate fire from more than twenty guns and many machine guns at that range. Captain Somerville went out among the tanks, attending to the wounded regardless of the heavy fire and with no consideration for his personal safety. He continued to attend to and bring in the wounded until all were under cover from the main enemy position, and thereafter he dressed them in a position where they were still unavoidably under fire from snipers. His cool gallantry was an inspiration to others who assisted him, and the means of saving many lives. In view of the shattering fire of the enemy, the bravery displayed by Captain Somerville was of the very highest order."

With a view to imparting a clear outline of what may be termed the history of a casualty, let it be supposed for a moment that the soldier whose fortunes as a recruit we have followed has been wounded. His initial action, if he is in a condition to undertake some measure of first aid, is to go to a small pocket in the trousers of his battle-dress uniform and extract the field dressing he has always carried since he joined up, applying it as he has been directed. If he is incapable of giving self-treatment there may be a comrade near at hand who can perform this service, for a working knowledge of the uses of iodine and dressings is part of the curriculum of every soldier's training.

It may well prove, however, that the wound is one of considerable magnitude and severity, so that a much larger dressing is required. In this case, it can be assumed that stretcher-bearers hurry forward, producing from their haversacks what is known as a shell dressing. This can instantly be set in place over the injury and the flow of blood assuaged.

Among casualties within the extended battle-area of modern warfare there is a limitless range of possibilities in the nature of wounds. Many types of lethal weapons and missiles are used, and the monotonous G.S.W. (gunshot wound) of the war of 1914-18 has given way to a much broader list of potential injuries. Whatever the character of the damage he has sustained, our non-effective soldier must now make his appearance at the regimental aid post (R.A.P.). He may walk, hobble or even crawl there, according to the exigencies of the situation and whether there are large numbers of other stricken men claiming their share of urgent attention. He may be assisted on his way—probably still well within the zone of fire—by the stretcher-bearers; but, if neither of these methods is within his capabilities, he may become a lying case and have to be carried on a stretcher.

In either event, our man will find available at the R.A.P. the hot sweetened tea that is almost invariably given to counteract shock. His dressings will certainly be looked over and reapplied or even renewed. Maybe our casualty has sustained a serious fracture of the bones of a limb, which must at once be set at rest in a splint. Almost assuredly there will be hæmorrhage to be arrested; and, if acute pain is present, his sufferings can be eased by the administration of morphia.

It is at this stage, whilst he is the recipient of attention from the R.A.P. staff, that there is set in motion some form of written history of the case. On a card, which is attached to the wounded soldier, is recorded briefly the nature of the injury, the date and time, treatment, dosage of medicine or sedative and so forth, according to the circumstances.

In trying to visualize the work of an aid post, one should bear in mind that in the majority of cases it is at this stage that a wounded man first comes under the care of a doctor. The trained eye can diagnose almost at a glance the precise nature of the injury incurred and prescribe without the slightest hesitation and in the form of military orders what steps are to be taken.

Diagnosis is indeed in most instances the one essential factor. The magnificent record of Lieutenant James Morton Muir, M.B., R.A.M.C., is an outstanding example of how service doctors face and dispose of a string of injured men passing before them. The words of the official citation, issued in connection with the award of the Distinguished Service Order to this gallant officer, are merely a bald narrative, but they call for no effort of imagination to picture the scene.

"During the battle of Sidi Barrani this medical officer was severely wounded in the shoulder and pelvis by splinters of a shell which hit the regimental aid post vehicle. In spite of his wounds he insisted on being propped up in a sitting position beside his vehicle, refusing an injection of morphia so that his senses might remain clear. Though suffering intense pain, he continued for approximately eight hours to give directions as to the care of the wounded as they were brought to the aid post until loss of blood made it impossible for him to remain in a sitting position. He was laid down, but nevertheless he continued to give directions and advice until the last wounded man had been evacuated and only then did he consent to be placed in the ambulance himself. This officer's devotion to duty undoubtedly saved many lives and was a tremendous inspiration to the personnel of the regimental aid post, and to the wounded lying around him."

The next link in the chain of evacuation is the advanced dressing station (A.D.S.), an outlying post of the field ambulance well up in the forward area. In some instances, more especially where the suitability of the roads is in doubt, a lying case casualty may be carried on a stretcher with relays of bearers, possibly under shellfire, through dive bombing or other aerial attack, or where the unmistakable whine of rifle and machine gun bullets is heard on every hand. Alternatively, the journey may be made by ambulance. The purpose of the A.D.S. in any event is to sustain the general condition of the casualty, ward off by medical means the onset of shock and give further morphia treatment if this is indicated. Generally speaking, a man's wounds are not touched at this stage unless the matter is one of the most pressing necessity.

MAIN DRESSING STATION

The A.D.S. may be regarded as an outpost of the field ambulance, gathering to it casualties from many regimental aid posts. The next move of our injured man must necessarily be to the main dressing station (M.D.S.) of the field ambulance and a well-found vehicle will be available for this portion of the journey. All the cars, indeed, are heated internally, some by the simple provision of hot pipes through which the exhaust gases from the engine pass and some by other means.

At the M.D.S. attention is bestowed upon the casualty himself rather than

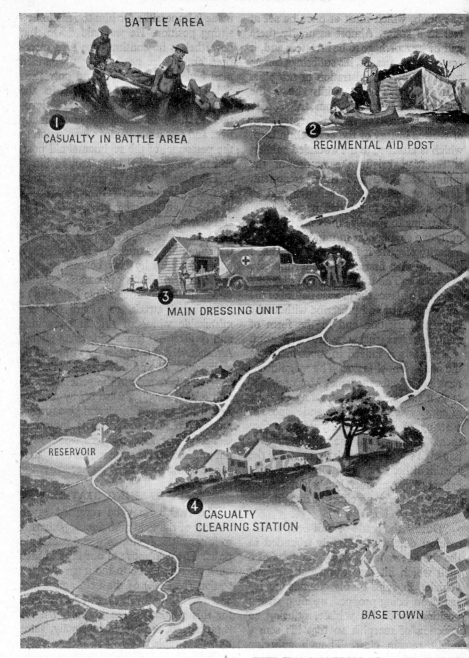

BATTLE AREA

① CASUALTY IN BATTLE AREA

② REGIMENTAL AID POST

③ MAIN DRESSING UNIT

RESERVOIR

④ CASUALTY CLEARING STATION

BASE TOWN

THE EVACUATION OF A CASUALTY

When a man is wounded he at once applies his field dressing. If unable to do so, a comrade or stretcher-bearer will do it for him. He will then go to the regimental aid post, where his wounds will be properly dressed. After a visit perhaps to an advanced dressing station, he is

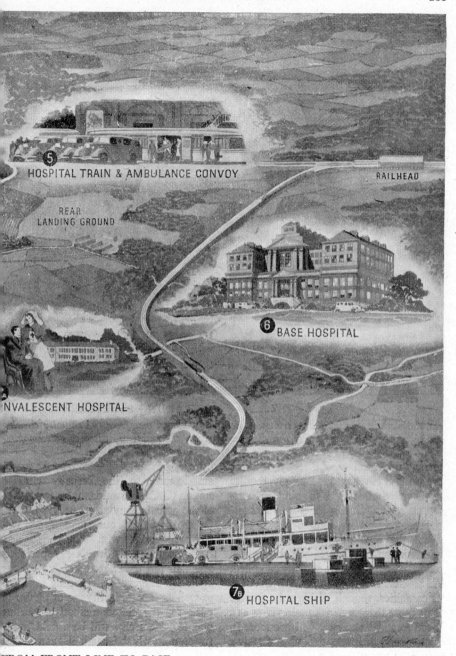

5 HOSPITAL TRAIN & AMBULANCE CONVOY

RAILHEAD

REAR LANDING GROUND

6 BASE HOSPITAL

NVALESCENT HOSPITAL

7B HOSPITAL SHIP

FROM FRONT LINE TO BASE

*hen taken by motor ambulance to the main dressing station. Thence a casualty proceeds
o the casualty clearing station. If not seriously wounded, he next goes to the convalescent
hospital. If his wounds are serious he will go to the base hospital and home by hospital ship*

ENTRAINING STRETCHER CASES ON

An ambulance train is used to transport sick and wounded men from the casualty clearing
station to the base hospital. If this distance is great, the trains are fitted to give complete

focusing medical care directly towards the wound. He may, for example, require to have administered to him an anti-tetanic serum. At this juncture his name, regimental number and other Service details find their way into the pages of an admission and discharge book, from which official casualty lists are actually compiled. All soldiers admitted to an M.D.S. count as casualties, though perhaps the trouble is no more than such a stunning blow as a piece of spent shrapnel will produce. In such a case, the patient requires merely a respite and some care and feeding before he can rejoin his unit in the field.

Continuing his journey, if this be necessary, the patient will now be taken by car, probably in a convoy of motor ambulances, to the casualty clearing station (C.C.S.) towards the rearward area of the actual Army zone. At the C.C.S. for the first time, our maimed man will come in touch with modern surgical equipment, anæsthetists, X-ray specialists and so forth. Thoroughly up-to-date operative surgery will here be available as well as experts in the use of plaster of paris for the closed method of healing wounds. Here also will be a field trans-fusion unit, which is stationed at a C.C.S. or may be moved forward in emergency to the main dressing station or rearwards to a general hospital according to the needs of the hour. Whole blood is often given to

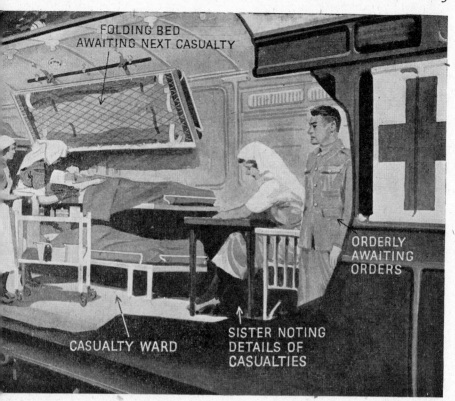

FOLDING BED
AWAITING NEXT CASUALTY

ORDERLY
AWAITING
ORDERS

CASUALTY WARD

SISTER NOTING
DETAILS OF
CASUALTIES

AN R.A.M.C. HOSPITAL TRAIN

medical attention. Medical treatment and, in cases of emergency, surgical operations are undertaken. There are also facilities for the preparation, if necessary, of food for the patients

a casualty either just prior to or immediately after a serious surgical operation.

We will imagine that our particular casualty has weathered the storm of a major surgical operation to the satisfaction of the doctors. He may spend a few days at the C.C.S., according to his condition and the number of other casualties expected or arriving. When sufficiently fit he will proceed by ambulance convoy or ambulance train to one of the general hospitals at the base. Here medical, surgical, eye, nerve and other specialists are available for those cases where the state of the injured man claims further investigation and treatment. The general hospital may keep the patient until he is in a satisfactory condition for transference to a convalescent depot. After a spell of hardening with special exercises, he may there prove himself ready to be returned direct to his unit.

If recovery and convalescence are, however, likely to be in the least protracted, it may result in what the old sweats of the last war termed a "Blighty" —a return to the Motherland in a hospital ship, a boat that has been pressed into the service of the R.A.M.C. Once at home there will be a further spell of hospital care or a period in a convalescent home. There may be complete and final discharge from the Army, with an attendant pension for life when the injury and its after effects justify such a course. On the other hand, our casualty may later return to his unit up the line, actually little or none the worse physically for the injuries that befell him.

All advanced R.A.M.C. units possess absolute mobility. If the forces to which they are attached sweep forward, the dressing stations, field hospitals and C.C.S.s must also go forwards, as well as

and comfortably to the field hospitals

The Director-General of Medical Services at the War Office is the head of the entire R.A.M.C. organization. He is represented at the headquarters of forces in the field, at army, command, corps, divisional, lines of communication area and base area headquarters. He has under him a medical directorate which attends to the administration of all medical units

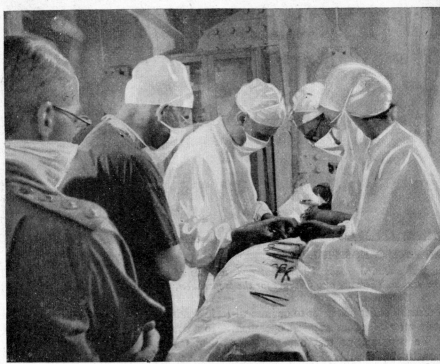

A SURGICAL OPERATION IN PROGRESS

This operation is being performed on a hospital ship at sea, staffed by doctors of the R.A.M.C

railheads for the ambulance trains. In times of retreat there must be the reverse movement, without the slightest dislocation or confusion. It is for this very reason that field ambulances have their advanced dressing stations and it may also be that special forms of transport have hurriedly to be made available. In the war of 1914-18, canals and tramways were in places utilized to convey wounded men smoothly

in the field, hospitals and other medical establishments and also the training schools. He is assisted by directors of hygiene, pathology and army dental services, and by the matron-in-chief of the Nursing Service.

So far as the average Tommy is concerned, he is scarcely likely to come into contact with members of the medical directorate. He will, nevertheless, very quickly meet his regimental medical officer. In peace time and during the quieter periods in war, the R.M.O. trains the men of his unit in the correct application of their field dressings and also gives them lectures on the subjects of first aid and hygiene. Under him are the stretcher-bearers of the unit and these are quite distinct from R.A.M.C. bearers, such as those attached to a field ambulance. Further, the R.M.O. is in the position of adviser to his own commanding officer on any matter that affects the health and bodily well-being of the men. He watches over sanitation and the general conditions under which the troops live. In action, the R.M.O. is at his regimental aid post.

STEPS TO THE BASE

From the regimental medical establishment, the next step is to the field ambulance. The duty of this particular unit is to collect the wounded from regimental aid posts, and for this purpose it is divided into a headquarters and two companies. Headquarters is divisible into a main dressing station and a section that may be detached to work individually in the field. As for the companies, each is divisible into three self-contained sections so that there may be seven individual units evacuating wounded men to the M.D.S.

As the vital link connecting the field ambulance with the casualty clearing station (C.C.S.) there is the motor ambulance convoy, referred to most frequently as the M.A.C. This is a medical transport unit for clearing sick and wounded from field ambulances to C.C.S.s and thence to ambulance trains. The staff of a M.A.C. is supplemented by officers and drivers of the Royal Army Service Corps, and the two branches of the Service work together admirably.

Ambulance trains are chiefly a means of transport for the sick and wounded, and their use must necessarily depend upon the distance from the C.C.S. to the base.

In emergency, medical or even surgical care can, however, be given during the journey and the trains are equipped with every facility for preparing food for the patients. Trains bear upon their sides the Red Cross and are manned by the R.A.M.C. under a medical officer.

The purpose of general hospitals at the base is obvious. They are invariably grouped together at a port where facilities are available for the speedy handling of hospital ships. The smallest type of general hospital has beds for two hundred patients. Other general hospitals may have 600 or 1,200 beds and they all carry what are termed surgical teams (each having a skilled operating surgeon) which can in emergency be sent either to field ambulances or to casualty clearing stations up the line.

Nothing has so far been written about stores, drugs, equipment and all the paraphernalia required in connection with the posts and stations, both large and small. This responsibility, as well as the duty of recharging gas cylinders for anæsthetics, is allocated to advanced and base depots of medical stores. The former carry for, and supply to, field units all the materials they require, while the latter feed the hospitals and also maintain the stocks of the advance depots.

BLOOD TRANSFUSION

Transfusion units, where the blood (often brought up from the base by aeroplane) is carried in mobile refrigerators, each unit in charge of a specially trained transfusion officer, mobile neuro-surgical units designed for use at a centre where head injuries are collected, and special teams of surgeons for maxillo-facial surgery and chest surgery all form part of the vast organization of the R.A.M.C.

It is undeniable, in fact, that no body of men the world over is better cared for in health and sickness than is the British Army by the Royal Army Medical Corps.

A BRITISH PARATROOP DROPS TO EARTH

Britain's paratroops are picked men, trained specially for surprise attack and sabotag

CHAPTER 16

Special Duty Units

Chaplain's department. Royal Army Veterinary Corps. Royal Army Pay Corps. Army Education Corps. Pioneer Corps. Parachute Units

THE modern Army is so complicated a machine that many of the smaller parts can be given but little space in a general description of the whole. It must be realized that these smaller corps, of which the duties are often not clearly known to all even within the Army itself, demand specialized ability of a high order. The Army cannot dispense with any of their services.

One of the oldest departments in the Army is the Chaplains' Department. As long ago as 1662 chaplains were appointed, one to each regiment of the Army. Their ideas of their duty were less strict than would meet with approval today. Moreover, few of them ever went on active service. In 1805 the Copenhagen Expedition had only one chaplain for 14,000 men. Wellington took this evil in hand. Henceforward every expedition that left Britain's shores for war had its chaplains with it, and chaplains were also attached to all our home and overseas garrisons. Many "padres," as they soon came to be called, distinguished themselves in the field by saving life and attending to wounded under fire. Several of them were awarded the Victoria Cross, the highest Service honour for valour.

CHAPLAINS TODAY

In peace time the upper age limit for chaplains was forty years but it was later raised to fifty. All denominations have their own chaplains in the usual proportion of one Church of England chaplain to each brigade. There are also Roman Catholic priests and ministers of other denominations in due proportions. Community of feeling and closer co-operation among them all is always excellent.

The chaplain's work begins as soon as a recruit joins the Army. It is his duty to get in touch with the newcomer at the first opportunity and to foster friendly relations with him on a purely natural and voluntary basis. These relations are quickly and easily established by visits to barrack rooms, playing fields and institutes. The men, as well as the non-commissioned officers and officers, come in most units to look upon the padre as at once a comrade and as guide, philosopher and friend when in difficulties.

Spiritual needs are catered for by the Sunday parade services and by voluntary early morning Holy Communion services which are usually well attended. Bible classes and debates on religious topics are also held on weekdays, as are classes and lectures for new recruits.

A full complement of Army chaplains of all denominations goes with the troops to overseas stations and also forms part of every British force in the field. On active service the chaplain's sphere of duty extends from the front lines along the lines of communication as far as the base. Anything that is for the benefit of his charges the good padre makes his personal and constant business.

Another corps with a long pedigree is the Royal Army Veterinary Corps. It can trace its descent back to Cromwell's time, but the Royal Army Veterinary Corps of today was formed only in 1881. All veterinary officers, except those in the Household Cavalry, were transferred to it from the establishment of the cavalry on which they had formerly been borne.

ANIMAL MANAGEMENT

For half a century the Corps did most admirable work in caring for the great numbers of animals of all kinds used by the Army. Its field of useful service, though diminished by the substitution of the mechanical vehicle for the horse as the standard means of military mobility, has by no means disappeared. So long as any animals are used, and wherever they are used, "animal management" must be carried on by skilled and practised hands. Management includes the prevention of disease, the care of sick and injured animals, arrangements for their collection and treatment, and control of contagious diseases, not only among Army animals but also among "civilian" ones in the areas occupied by the Army. The personnel of the Corps are trained in all these duties. As they have to be prepared to deal with any sort of draught animal from an elephant downwards, it will be realized that their work is varied. The scope of their knowledge must be similarly extensive.

The functions of the Royal Army Pay Corps are nearly as complicated as they are responsible. Although the very word "soldier" means "a paid man," the soldier's pay in the past—and not the very remote past either—seldom reached him promptly or in full. Even as late as the Waterloo campaign it was often months in arrears, and it had, before he pocketed it, to run the gauntlet of a bewildering variety of stoppages—some regulation, some highly irregular—which, in fact, accounted for a large proportion of it. It was never, and is not now, on a princely scale. The Royal Army Pay Corps is still responsible for many similar stoppages, but at least these are now all authorized. There is seldom any seriou and never any avoidable delay in the soldier's pay reaching him.

Paymasters have formed part of the Army ever since its institution as a standing force. At first they were known a "colonel's clerks" and then as "regimental agents" and were attached to units. Units were then the property of the colonel and a source of financial profit to him, to recoup him for the heavy purchase money he had spent for his firs commission and subsequent steps in promotion. The clerk or agent was appointed by the colonel. His primary duty was to see not that the soldier got his pay but that the colonel got his profit. This state of affairs gave rise to many serious scandals, not by any means all of which ever saw the light of day. The Army Pay Department was not set up until 1878 and after a quarter of a century it wa reorganized to form the Army Pay Department Corps. Its personnel, both officer and men, is not directly recruited but is transferred from other arms or branches of the Service. All the men must be in possession of first class education certificates, and the peace time training course extends over two years.

PROMPT PAYMENT

In wartime all the duties of the corps become far more complicated. Units overseas have often to be paid in foreign currency and personal accounts cannot be rendered for troops in the field as carefully, accurately and fully as in peace time. Frequent transfer of casualties and other accidents of war interfere with the smooth running of the pay machine. Precision, speed, adaptability and knowledge are its four vital words, and as a result of them the British Army of today is the most punctually paid in history.

The Army Education Corps is one of the youngest in the Service. It was instituted after the war of 1914-18 to help to fit the rank and file of the large Army then awaiting demobilization to take their places in civil life. Subsequently it took over the work formerly done by Army schoolmasters and schoolmistresses among the children of married soldiers in garrison and other schools. Later still a broad scheme of basic education in the Army was set up, with educational tests of varying degrees of proficiency.

EDUCATIONAL CERTIFICATES

All ranks had to qualify for these certificates as part of their normal syllabus of training. For promotion to non-commissioned or warrant rank the gaining of the higher certificates was made an essential preliminary. It fell to the new corps to administer this system.

On the outbreak of the Second World War, the normal peace time system of educational certificates disappeared. It was necessary to assist the great numbers of young soldiers conscripted into the National Army to begin or to complete the form of adult education which they would otherwise have undertaken for the purpose of their civil careers. Education thus became an important part of Army welfare work. The system adopted was to expand the Army Education Corps under a newly appointed civil director, and to work in close collaboration with recognized civil authorities, such as the Central Advisory Council, the local education officers and various professional bodies. By this means competent lecturers were provided, halls were secured where education could be carried on, and correspondence courses were arranged. Full use was also made of the many qualified lecturers and instructors who were to be found in many a unit where the services of the Army Education Corps were not available. The idea at the root of this scheme was, to adopt the official words, that while the soldier's first duty is to be a good soldier, he will be a better soldier if

M.A.—K

he has wider interests than the Army, and puts no part of his intelligence into cold storage just because he is wearing uniform. There is far more in the life of any community, including the Army, than technical perfection in the handling of the instruments which that community uses." This doctrine, it may be added, would have seemed revolutionary not so many years ago. The fact that it can now be embodied in an official pronouncement is a measure of the vast change that has come over the Army.

One of the newest corps in the modern Army is the Pioneer Corps. At one time, in certain units of the Victorian Army, there was a small establishment of pioneers who were distinguished by a special uniform, the carrying of axes on parade, and the privilege of being allowed to wear beards. Their exact duties were somewhat ill defined and their existence was not a long one. During the war of 1914-18 a pioneer battalion formed part of each division in the field. They were fighting troops, who specialized in trench digging and road construction and other work of a similar nature in the battle zone. In the autumn of 1939 the War Office issued a call for 15,000 men between the ages of thirty-five and fifty, directed specially to old soldiers and reservists who had passed the age of recall to first line units. The response was instant and full. As the companies were formed and sent out to France, they took over much constructional work on the lines of communication and at the bases.

ARMY'S HANDYMEN

Pioneers, it has been said, do for the Army what minesweepers do for the Navy—sweep away obstacles, smooth out the roads and the traffic routes, do running repairs to them and make free movement possible and continuous. Much hard work was called for, but it was work that could be done by men suffering from slight physical disabilities, such as bad eyesight, which would have debarred them from service in a fighting unit. In this way it was possible for the Corps to free these units for the job of fighting, or training for fighting, by undertaking vital duties with which they would otherwise have been burdened. Stores, ammunition and petrol in huge quantities had to be handled at the docks, railheads and dumps throughout the theatre of operations.

PIONEERS AS SOLDIERS

New roads were laid and existing ones repaired and kept in repair. Camps had to be erected; sites for new aerodromes had to be cleared and buildings and runways for them built. All these tasks called for hard work and skilled work. Some units of the Pioneer Corps were afforded, and avidly seized, opportunities for showing that they were good soldiers as well as good workmen. Tales are told of how little parties of veterans and young soldiers, discarding spade and pickaxe for rifle and bomb, accounted for German motor cyclists and tanks.

After the B.E.F. had been withdrawn from the Continent and invasion of Britain seemed probable, the Corps had to devote its energy to the erection of various defence works. These sprang up in a vast network all over the country to hem in, check and slow up the progress of any hostile force that might succeed in setting foot on British soil. During the period of heavy air attacks, the Corps were called upon to help clear streets, repair vital services, demolish shattered buildings and fill in craters in the various stricken cities up and down the land.

There is, by contrast, plenty of glamour and glory to be won by the members of another wartime creation of the British Army, the Parachute Units. The value of such troops was first shown by the Germans in Holland. Though their losses were heavy, they played a leading part in

disorganizing the Dutch defence and in bringing about the capitulation of the Army within a few days of the first attack being launched. Later, in the Middle East, they again led the way in the airborne attack on Crete and gave renewed evidence of the great potentialities of the new arm under favourable conditions.

Early in 1941 it was revealed that Britain, too, had her parachute troops. Wearing the badge of a white parachute between blue soaring wings, these men, chosen specially for their physical fitness, intelligence, character, initiative and "toughness," were a formidable force indeed. Once on the ground—and it costs much in the way of time, trouble and even petrol to get them there—they must show full value for their training and be able to give the best possible account of themselves. Only daring and clever men knowing exactly what they have to do and how to do it, specially equipped and armed, formidable in fighting, are capable of filling the bill. The *esprit de corps* and morale of the personnel of the "Special Air Service" troops, as they are officially termed, is as high as any in the Army.

PARATROOP EQUIPMENT

British parachute troops always wear uniform and have special boots and helmets designed to give protection when landing from aircraft. Their outer overalls are designed to minimize the possibility of any part of their equipment catching in any part of the aeroplane from which they have to jump. Their weapons also are specially designed for the job they have to do. Heavier weapons, stores and ammunition are, however, often thrown down with them in special containers also attached to parachutes. The actual jump from the machine is an act that requires much nerve, skill and practice, and much of the Corps' training is devoted to perfecting the personnel in it under all conditions. Jumping in quick succession is necessary if the men are not to land widely scattered and out of touch with each other. This is also a matter of careful drill as well as of skilful piloting and judgment on the part of the pilots of the aircraft carrying the parachutists.

Physical training, vigorous, systematic and continuous, is the first essential. Special emphasis is placed on exercises which need dash and boldness, to cultivate a confident attitude in a rough and tumble

do so from a dummy fuselage in a hangar. Here they learn to make their exit one after the other in rapid succession. Then they jump first from a balloon, and only then do they start on the real thing— jumping from an aeroplane in motion at various increasing heights until they have completely mastered the difficult art.

There are other lessons to be learned— the packing, fitting, adjusting and operation of parachute equipment and con-

INSTRUCTION FOR OFFICERS AT THE ARMY SCHOOL OF EDUCATION

The Army Education Corps strives to widen the interests of officers and men. These officers are being taught an easy method of instructing troops in the points of the compass for map work

fight. Then comes practice in jumping, working first up to a height of 10 feet from a wall. Great attention is paid to the art of falling correctly, which does not come naturally, and then of rolling backwards and forwards to break the shock. Jumps are made from increasing stationary heights until this part of the training is complete. Next the parachutists have to learn to jump from the air. At first they

tainers, the drill of entering and taking up positions in aircraft and then acting on signals. But these are less important and take up less time than training and practice in handling arms, in demolitions, and the use of explosives.

It may be taken as certain that this young and highly trained branch of the Army, which has yet to win its spurs in war, has a great and honourable future.

THE EYES OF THE GUNS

Members of the A.T.S. "spot" for the A.A. gunners. This girl scans the skies through her sun glasses. Close at hand is a range finder, which will be used as soon as the enemy is found

CHAPTER 17

The Auxiliary Territorial Service

Function. Reception depot. General duties available: orderly, cook, clerk, storewoman, driver. Special duties: Signals, A.A. work, Army proof and experimental ranges. Officers—their training and duties. Organization of the corps and its growth. Now part of the Army

THE function of the Auxiliary Territorial Service in relation to the Army is perfectly clear-cut. It is, to replace as many men as possible in those non-combatant duties which may reasonably be undertaken by women. This release of many thousands of able-bodied men for fighting duties helps considerably towards solving Britain's man-power problem. The records of the women's Service to date show a constantly widening scope for the abilities and activities of women.

THE RECEPTION DEPOT

The life of a girl as an auxiliary begins when she enters the reception depot, usually of the command in which she was recruited. These depots are vast training centres, improvised from country mansions or large hotels which have been taken over by the War Office, and, where necessary, enlarged by the addition of huts, messrooms, bathrooms and kitchens. Hundreds of girls pass through the depots in monthly batches. They are drafted while there into companies, their company commander, platoon officers and N.C.O.s being provided by the permanent staff of the depot. Each recruit goes through a rigorous medical examination, from head to toe, and any defects or ailments which might prevent her from being an efficient war worker and an agreeable barrack mate are at once carefully dealt with by the resident M.O.

Most recruits have little or no idea of Army methods and traditions. The depot starts their training to a soldier's regulated life. The essentials of squad drill: easy route marches: simple lectures on the organization of the A.T.S., and the duties of its members: anti-gas lectures, fire squad practices, and "fatigue" duties carried out in sections—all these develop that state of willing co-operation which is the real meaning of discipline. On the lighter side, team games organized and shared in by the officers, P.T. classes, country dancing, cinemas or dramatic and musical evenings give the recruits plenty of fun. Thus they are prepared for a community life in which they must obey the rules of the game and learn to suppress their own feelings and opinions in the interests of the Service.

SMARTENING UP

Recruits receive a generous issue at the depot stores of uniform, underwear, shoes, working clothes, "necessaries" for polishing up, etc. The uniforms are skilfully graded to the vagaries of the feminine figure. It is most encouraging to see how the novices smarten up after a few days of drill in uniform; slovenly hair is rolled up neatly into a net ; feet step out more purposefully in low-heeled shoes ; and an air of cleanliness and polish prevails.

At the depot, recruits are tested in the categories under which they have mustered—for example, A.A., clerk, typist, cook, etc. Those who are already efficient are posted to a unit; further training is arranged for those who need it. The A.T.S. runs special courses to train girls for every category of work required by the Army—stenography, signals, cooking, driving, pay, messing and A.A. gunnery.

Her training over, the new auxiliary packs up her new kit bag and joins her

Orderly work is within the reach of any willing worker, and is essential. A.T.S. quarters, whether in W.D. buildings, requisitioned houses, or huts—Army officers' quarters—military hospital wards —and every type of office, all these are subject to much wear and tear, and must be kept clean, tidy, warm and polished. Many Army sergeants' messes are served by A.T.S. orderlies. Duty in Army

MEMBERS OF THE A.T.S. COOKING FOR THE TROOPS

These girls have by their skill fully maintained the standard of Army feeding. The ovens are, in this instance, converted dustbins built into brickwork. The lid acts as a door for the oven

unit. Here, if she is to become a good "soldier," she will learn the pride of loyalty to a small group, and work to make her section and platoon the smartest and most efficient.

The duties of auxiliaries are varied and are becoming ever more so. There is scope for every kind of talent, and an abundance of work for every one to do.

officers' messes is very popular, and auxiliaries have shown themselves adept at this work. Medical orderlies who look after the sick in quarters are trained in first aid and home nursing.

Every woman should know how to cook; and the A.T.S. cooks with the Army have proved their worth. They have had to adapt themselves to all sorts of conditions — field kitchens in camps, reached at early morning hours by wading through mud and slush; old-fashioned, inadequate stoves and sinks in requisitioned houses; and sometimes up-to-date kitchens, with scientific and labour-saving equipment. Cooks must be prepared to go out with their parent unit on manœuvres, and feed the men from kitchens improvised in fields, woods, or perhaps on a windswept moor ; and to cut sandwiches and put up haversack rations for a unit suddenly ordered to move at any hour of the day or night.

Cooking for large numbers requires special training. Women who pass the course at the Army School of Cookery, where the most scientific methods are taught, are given sergeants' stripes, and paid sixpence extra per day for every day they cook. This training is invaluable.

EFFICIENT COOKING

A cook needs strength and patience to stand over hot stoves and steaming coppers, handling pots of soup and stew for a whole company. She needs a good head too, for rations must be carefully calculated when drawn, and the best use made of them. The standard of Army cooking has certainly risen and A.T.S. cooks can claim much of the credit. Meals are more varied, more attractive and quickly served, the diet is better balanced and there is undoubtedly much less waste when the A.T.S. are on the job.

The demand for good clerks of many kinds in the Army is increasing—clerical work is a sphere in which men can be most advantageously replaced by women.

Administration, both in the Army and in the A.T.S., depends upon efficient routine office work. In company and battalion or group offices, for instance, the business of registering correspondence, distributing papers through the correct channels, typing letters, forms, orders, etc., and filing all documents, goes on ceaselessly. This work can have much of human interest. The whole personal life of the unit is there, in these papers; every "casualty," with his individual problems, and the record of day-to-day activities. This work gives a real sense of working for, and with, the Army in a job that is essential to its smooth running.

PAY, RECORDS, STORES

There is also a very great number of A.T.S. clerks working in pay or records offices—girls who are quick at figures, methodical and accurate, are excellent in this type of work. It would take too long, however, to enumerate the many kinds of offices where A.T.S. clerks are at work. For those who need or want further training there are free courses at the A.T.S. Clerical School, where an all-round high efficiency is achieved.

A job for which women are particularly fitted is that of storewoman. In the clothing stores a woman can be very useful to the soldier in helping him to find just the right and sensible thing. In the department which issues rations, an auxiliary can gain experience of large scale catering and book-keeping.

Driving for the Army made a special appeal to women. Not only were there numbers of women qualified to drive efficiently; the driving itself attracted the energetic and the adventurous. Many joined in order to be trained as drivers. Map reading is a part of their training.

A.T.S. LORRY DRIVERS

Some driving work—at depots, Army and A.T.S. headquarters, etc.—is fairly light. Staff officers must be taken from one H.Q. to another, company officers must often cover miles to visit isolated platoons and detachments. But the majority of A.T.S. drivers work for the R.A.O.C. and the R.A.S.C. at their depots. A constant stream of supplies and army vehicles passes out from these depots to ports, to assembly points, to Army stores wherever required. Convoy driving is, for most women, extremely strenuous. The lorries are much heavier than the cars usually driven by women; and there is the added strain of keeping a set distance from the lorry in front and of keeping up a set speed, often very high. The distances driven are considerable. A convoy driven by auxiliaries, their sergeant in the leading lorry, may leave a depot in the Midlands early one morning and drive all day towards some Scottish port, covering only half the distance. At nightfall, they park their vehicles in some town on the way and go to emergency billets found for them by the police. An early start the following day and they reach the docks before night. They return to their unit, sometimes by a special bus, on the following day; and are quite prepared to go out in convoy again on the day after, this time to the south coast.

Wintry weather and the blackout increase the hardships of this work a hundred per cent, but on the whole the convoy driver really loves her work. For one thing, she knows it is of urgent importance; again, it demands great qualities of discretion, stamina and presence of mind; and it offers constant variety. The convoy driver can be proud of her job.

VEHICLE MAINTENANCE

A.T.S. drivers learn to service and maintain their vehicles. Other auxiliaries train as driver mechanics only and work for the R.A.S.C. and R.A.O.C. A venturesome spirit, combined with excellent physique and steady nerves, makes a good despatch rider, and a very large number of women have applied for this work.

The workshop duties carried out by auxiliaries attached to the R.A.O.C. are: servicing cars, cleaning plugs, vulcanizing tyres, repairing gas masks and raincoats, and attending to the numerous and varied drilling, sawing and power machines.

Women of the A.T.S. Signals companies work in their hundreds on the communications of the Army. A.T.S. telephonists operate switchboards in Army headquarters, from high to low. For instance, the main switchboard of a certain Army command is managed entirely by auxiliaries and the officer in charge is an A.T.S. officer, responsible directly to the C.S.O. (chief signals officer). At the other extreme, you will find, in a company H.Q., that two or three girls are responsible for the small switchboard, and relieve one another in shifts. A.T.S. telephonists sometimes have the thrill of accompanying their parent unit on manœuvres and working field telephones at emergency H.Q.s.

TELEPRINTER WORK

The A.T.S. telephonists who accompanied the B.E.F. to France did splendid work, one member winning the M.B.E.

The work of the teleprinter operator is highly confidential, as the teleprinter is the most secure means for "secret" communications in quantity. The clatter of machines in a large teleprinter office is nerve-racking, and the strain all round of this work is very great as it is carried on, night and day. These disadvantages are largely cancelled out by the interest of the work, and the pride of having a "secret" job. A still tongue in a wise head is essential for this work.

Communications count in this Second World War as in no other; and the women in signals work can feel sure that they are doing a very special job towards victory.

Duties on anti-aircraft gun sites are becoming so popular in the A.T.S., and the auxiliaries have proved themselves so efficient, as well as keen, at this work that a special training centre has been set up.

The jobs taken over by auxiliaries on A.A. work are: radiolocation; height and range-finding; predictor and telescope identification of enemy aircraft.

Auxiliaries who control the radio-location apparatus are known as operators fire control, and they actually control the aiming of A.A. guns. The radiolocator spots and locates the exact position of enemy aircraft. It consists of a generator, and aerials for transmitting and receiving, all housed in trailers. The women who work this vitally important apparatus

Teams of three or four trained women work on the height and range finders. These are optical instruments, consisting of long metal cylinders studded with dials. The operators work out the height and range for the gun position officer.

The predictor is a computing machine, and as a technical instrument it is most highly developed. It co-ordinates the

MEMBERS OF THE A.T.S. AT WORK IN A REGIMENTAL ARMOURY

There are always rifles and anti-tank rifles to be cleaned. Women do this work very well. These auxiliaries at a regimental depot release men for other important duties elsewhere

must have intelligence and presence of mind, good and quick eyes and hands, steady nerves—and absolute discretion.

Some auxiliaries work with the radio-maintenance companies of the R.A.O.C. on the repairing and maintenance of radio-location equipment. This work is skilled and requires a certain standard of scientific education. The Army has a training school for these workers.

information given by other instruments, height, range, location, wind velocity, speed and direction. At the same time the women at the telescopes keep up with the target and pass on their information rapidly to the predictor operators.

Thus, the men who actually man the guns have all their information and calculations given to them by the teams of A.T.S. women upon whom they rely.

A.T.S. GIRLS WORKING ALONGSIDE

The demand for personnel to operate modern scientific A.A. apparatus is growing. Many of
the delicate instruments are manned by members of the A.T.S. Here a team of girls is

MEN OF AN A.A. GUN POSITION
sharing the dangers of a gun pit with the A.A. men. They are operating a kine-theodolite, which by photography and mathematics relates the shell bursts in the sky to the target

The Royal Artillery, as well as A.A. Command, can replace men with women at certain tasks. Kine-theodolite operators have for long been helping to train gunners. The apparatus is a combination of camera and theodolite. Photographs are made of the shell bursts in relation to a target, and a knowledge of logarithms is necessary for the calculations made.

TESTING NEW AMMUNITION

A few highly qualified and picked women are at work on Army experimental ranges. They have been called "the girls *in front* of the guns" and their on-duty uniforms of blue reefer jackets and white skirts are designed to make them conspicuous at a distance. Their work is concerned with testing new types of ammunition; but, as they all have a knowledge of ballistics, and some of them have science degrees, they undertake other special work when required.

Good health, a fine sporting spirit, and stamina are necessary in all these special jobs with A.A. and R.A. Detachments, which are often isolated. But the absorption and excitement of the work, and the fact of working in a team with the men, make life very stimulating.

The complexities of modern warfare have created all sorts of "odd jobs" in the Army, many of which may be undertaken by women. Organization and running of emergency canteens; camouflaging cars and lorries, huts and other possible targets; projection of instructional films for the Army—these are some among many. In short, the variety of jobs open to women in the A.T.S. is very great. The wise officer will see to it that she has the right girl in the right job.

The most strenuous and concentrated training in the A.T.S. is the six weeks' course at the officer cadet training unit. No pains are spared to equip these women for their future responsibilities and complex duties as leaders of women.

The first essential in an officer is the capacity to take responsibility with all that that implies. In addition, she must know the technique of her job. She must have "power of command," initiative, tact and human understanding.

The officer's first duty is to see that her company or platoon is performing its service to the Army efficiently. That is why it is so important to put the right girls into the right jobs, to see that they are properly trained, and that there is no slackening-off. She must understand their work, and their special problems. Tact will play its part in the daily contacts with the parent unit (that is, the Army unit to which the auxiliaries in question are attached).

The officer is responsible for the discipline and good morale of her troops. Smartness on parade, courtesy in saluting and address, prompt and cheerful obedience of orders—these are the signs of a unit with a good officer. Squad drill is a most valuable means to this end.

OFFICER'S RESPONSIBILITY

The officer is, of course, responsible for the health and welfare of her troops. This "domestic" part of her duties may occupy the greater part of her time. Healthy living conditions must be ensured by constant checking up. Cleanliness and good ventilation of quarters, sufficient warmth, bathing facilities, airing of bedding, avoidance of overcrowding, nourishing food well served—these are the ultimate responsibility of the officer. If she has women on especially strenuous duties, all-night teleprinter operators, for instance, or convoy drivers, she is responsible that hot meals are ready for them and restful quarters when they come off duty. It is up to her to see that the girls have sufficient P.T. or other exercise to keep them fit, and sufficient recreation to keep them cheerful. The company officer has her office to run;

correspondence to deal with, daily orders to issue, duty posters to prepare, etc. She is responsible for the paying of her troops; for stores issued for messing; and for air raid precautions and training of P.A.D. (passive air defence) and fire squads.

DELEGATION OF AUTHORITY

It would not be humanly possible for one officer to do all this herself. She must delegate her authority. In a company office, for instance, one subaltern will be in charge of pay, another of messing, another of "Q" (stores) and P.A.D., and so on. These junior officers in turn work through non-commissioned officers. A good officer constantly trains her N.C.O.s. By putting them in charge of sections for certain routine duties, or practices of something new, she develops their ability to shoulder responsibility. The more mutual respect and trust there is between officer and N.C.O. the better able is the officer to deal with the problems which invariably arise among her other ranks.

The A.T.S. aims at turning out better citizens for peace time, as well as more efficient workers for the war effort. A wise officer sees to it that interspersed with E.N.S.A. concerts and cinema shows the ranks have classes in current affairs, first aid and home nursing, anti-gas and fire squad practices, etc. Such classes can be fun, when enlivened by debate or illustrated by team demonstrations. Just as the Army does much for the all-round development and welfare of its men, so does the A.T.S. for the numerous women who serve in its ranks.

The Auxiliary Territorial Service as a whole constitutes a *Corps* under the command of a "chief controller" (major-general), whose appointment is entitled Director of the A.T.S.

This corps is organized geographically in *commands*, which are subordinate to Army commands; their officers command-ing are senior controllers (brigadier) or controllers (colonel). Detached units form the various Pay and Records, R.A.O.C., R.A.S.C., and A.A. companies. There is an A.T.S. staff officer at each Army Command Headquarters. Her job is advisory, and she acts as liaison between War Office, command and the various A.T.S. *groups*. A recent innovation is the appointment of an A.T.S. officer as A.D.C. to the G.O.C.-in-C. Scottish Command, for all matters concerning the A.T.S. groups in his area.

The administrative unit of the A.T.S. is the *group*, which is based on *battalion* organization. The officer commanding a group is usually a chief commander (lieutenant-colonel), but may hold controller (colonel), or senior commander (major), rank depending on the size of the group under her command.

The working units subordinate to group are *companies*, under junior commanders (captains), or subalterns (lieutenants). The companies sub-divide into two or more *platoons*, under second subalterns (second lieutenants).

The non-commissioned ranks in the A.T.S. are now the same as in Army infantry units: a sergeant being responsible for a section, and a corporal for a sub-section, composed of lance-corporals and privates. There are now staff sergeants and warrant officers in the A.T.S.

A soldier's book (A.B.64) is held by each auxiliary and an Army number allotted to her, as with the men.

A.T.S. PAY

The Army pay and allowances system is unique, and those administering it must be trained for the job. A.T.S. pay is run on the same lines as the men's, the amounts being—both for officers and other ranks—approximately two-thirds of a man's pay in the same rank and grade. Special qualifications and training, of course, are rewarded by extra pay.

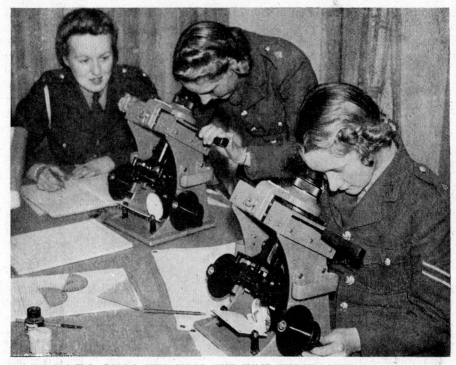

A.T.S. GIRLS STUDYING THE KINE-THEODOLITE FILMS
These girls are passing the films from the kine-theodolite through an instrument called an evaluator. This gives an accurate reading of the shell bursts, including the angle of the shoot

Health and hygiene in the A.T.S. are supervised by women doctors attached to depots and group headquarters. They hold the rank of lieutenant in the R.A.M.C.

The Auxiliary Territorial Service is young in years, and is now building its tradition. Its development during the Second World War has been remarkable. In 1935 Dame Helen Gwynne-Vaughan —already famous for her services in the war of 1914-18—organized an "Emergency Service," to create a nucleus of potential officers. A school of instruction gave weekly courses in Army discipline, drill, "Q," etc. The crisis of September, 1938, brought official recognition and many volunteers. The following summer saw A.T.S. officers at the War Office.

The pre-war "Women's Auxiliary Territorial Service" was organized on a county basis, as part of the Territorial Army. Civilian influence was strong, and only that small minority of women who had sufficient leisure, or some strong personal impulse, could or would give service. Local service was in order, as well as general service, and the former was popular, for few women really like to leave their homes. A most useful beginning was made, however, in the creation and training of three types of company: General Duties, Clerical and Motor Transport. There are many women in the A.T.S. today who are intensely proud to have been in this pre-war service, and to have coped with the discomforts and helped with the improvisations of those early pioneering days.

War meant whole-time service. Seventeen thousand women were called up in

September, 1939 and both Territorial Army and Women's Service were merged with the vast new Army in building. Local service came to an end, a War Office order brought the group organization into being, and volunteers signed on for a period of four years—or "the duration."

Reception depots were set up in each command (except Aldershot) and the newly opened recruiting offices all over the country passed to them a flow of recruits for training. It is interesting that the numbers of volunteers shot up after Dunkirk. In the winter of 1939 the cadet wing for the training of officers was opened. Its democratic principle is: promotion only through the ranks (with the exception of veterans of the war of 1914-18 and specialists for new jobs which are now open to women in the Service).

In April, 1941, the A.T.S. became by War Office order an integral part of the Army. Like the Army it now rests on the solid basis provided by Act of Parliament. Its ranks and other ranks are all equally subject to military discipline. Its officers hold the King's Commission. The Auxiliary Territorial is now permanently one of the Services of the Army.

The A.T.S. is a most progressive corps. Administration and welfare have improved markedly. The extremely high standards set at the officers' training unit, and the ideals and resolve which are instilled into every junior officer, point to a continuous raising of standards in every small unit, in every isolated platoon. For any woman who wishes to devote her full energies to serving Britain in this world crisis, there is no more fruitful field of activity than that provided by the A.T.S.

A.T.S. GIRLS LEARNING MORSE CODE

The need for wireless operators in modern warfare is urgent. Girls are more suited to this work than men. Here they are seen undergoing training in sending and receiving morse messages

REINFORCING A TRENCH

These Home Guards are being instructed in methods of reinforcing, or reveting, a trench.
If not efficiently done, bad weather makes the sides crumble and the floor waterlogged

CHAPTER 18

The Home Guard

Formation. German Army characteristics. Home Guard counter-measures. Speed and mobility. Irregulars and guerrillas. Local knowledge. Fieldcraft and streetcraft. Guerrilla training. Weapons. Anti-tank work. Signalling at night. Aircraft. Defence works. Booby traps

IN May, 1940, an entirely new Force was formed, to help to deal with the invasion which seemed imminent as the Germans swept across Belgium and Northern France. Allied to the Regular Army yet not actually part of it, poorly equipped, with only a shadowy organization and with no background of tradition to stiffen morale, its chief assets were the fighting spirit of untrained civilians, backed by that knack of improvisation which is one of this country's virtues. The new army was born of sheer necessity—to make the last stand—*to fight.*

Progress from L.D.V. arm-band and sporting gun to battle-dress and modern weapons will not be traced here. We need only note that the civilian volunteer has become a recognized unit of the British Army, anxious to fight.

TYPE OF RESISTANCE

With personnel who are only part-time soldiers, this force cannot be measured by ordinary Army standards. The small amount of training possible each week limits the effectiveness of the units in straight fighting. This is a primary factor in the use of the Home Guard. Each volunteer needs all the attributes of a good soldier without undergoing long hours of training as in the Regular Army. He is largely self-trained, and self-disciplined.

The other predominant factor is the enemy. Any invading force landed in this country would be the pick of Hitler's command. The German Army is unquestionably the best trained and best equipped army in the world at the present time, so these invaders will be the finest fighting units in the world. How then is the Home Guard to resist such a force?

First consider the enemy in more detail. Every German soldier is well trained. His weapons are good and he knows how to use them. The standard of fieldcraft and patrol work is very high. He is encouraged to use initiative and to co-operate with units of other branches of the Army. Mutual support is an axiom based on good communications (signals), the use of motorized transport (motor cycles, lorries, armoured fighting vehicles and aircraft) and concentrated fire power (light automatics, mortars and heavy machine guns). In advanced forces the place of artillery is taken by the dive bomber, other aircraft act as reconnaissance units, all using wireless communication. Tactics involve outflanking movements and infiltration and are marked by extreme ruthlessness. These characteristics apply to both parachute troops and infantry, and even the engineer and signal units are fully trained as fighting soldiers.

Now turn to the defence. The Home Guard aims at complete dispersal of its strength over the whole country. Every village and town has a fighting force drawn from the inhabitants. Here is an initial advantage to the defenders in their knowledge of the locality, and this must be exploited fully. Constant training over the actual defence area is necessary. Because of their dispersal, such units must be the first to contact the enemy. An excellent system of communications is needed so that signals may be sent back to area commanders, giving details of enemy positions, strength and movements.

THE FOUR ESSENTIALS

Since Home Guard training can never equal that of the regular army invaders, the opposition must be more a contest of wit than strength. If the enemy moves fast, the defence must be faster; if he is mobile, it must be more so. Local knowledge must outmatch fieldcraft, and its weapon power must destroy the enemy by sharp and accurate fire, avoiding a "stand up" fight unless in undoubted superiority.

Speed, mobility, fieldcraft (streetcraft in towns) and fire power, are then the four essentials of Home Guard warfare. The proper role will be reconnaissance

and patrol work followed by harassing and delaying tactics, always aiming to destroy the enemy whenever possible.

Home Guard tactics must be fluid to deal with any confusion in the initial stages of the invasion, the period when the force will prove most valuable. During organized resistance to the enemy, units will work under the orders of the local army commander, acting as irregular soldiers on the fringe of the main defence by the regular army. If, however, the area is overrun, cutting off the defenders from the main force, they will become purely guerrillas. On no account should resistance to the enemy cease. The invaders must be forced to fight not only for every inch of ground, but for every minute of the occupation of it.

It may be well to define here the two terms "Irregular" and "Guerrilla." The first refers to organized units acting in front of a regular army and in full co-operation with that command. "Guerrillas," on the other hand, are small separate units acting entirely on their own initiative, improvising attack and ambush wherever possible. They have no reserves, no bases, and no responsibilities other than the destruction of the enemy and the preservation of their own lives.

As Home Guard tactics are either irregular or guerrilla, the individual counts as of even more importance than in regular forces. Initiative, physical fitness and a skill in improvisation are vitally

THE PROPER WAY TO TAKE COVER

Fig. 1. *The correct use of cover is a simple but often vital matter. The lower a man can get on the right hand of the cover the better. In this firing position much less of him is exposed to enemy fire*

important. Every unit, be it an individual or a section, platoon or company, must be self-contained and self-supporting. But the larger formations, battalion, zone or area, need an elastic co-ordination only possible by the development of a first-class system of signal communications.

The primary advantage of the Home Guard is *local knowledge*. Too much stress cannot be laid on this point. In rural districts it is not sufficient to know all the roads and footpaths. Each man has to comb his section area and note the folds of the ground which give cover from view and fire. Especially must he note "dead" ground around each defence position : that is, ground which by reason of banks or other cover cannot be swept by fire and so gives an enemy a route of approach

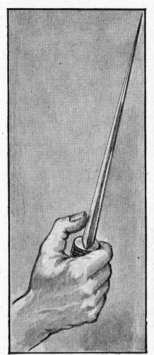

HUNTING KNIFE FOR ATTACKING SENTRIES

Fig. 2. *A hunting knife is an excellent weapon against enemy sentries. An attack from behind, one hand covering the mouth to prevent noise while the other uses the knife below the lower ribs, is a very effective method of attack*

to the post. Hedgerows giving cover from view must be memorized, also the gaps which are difficult to cross. Trees suitable for observation posts and which may be easily climbed without attracting attention are chosen.

In towns and villages intimate knowledge of the buildings is necessary. Which houses give commanding fire positions; and are their walls bullet proof? Is it possible to cross the gaps between them without being seen?

Consider the first condition as fieldcraft and the second as streetcraft. The rural defender must know something of the latter if he intends to fight around villages. An immediate warning is necessary not to use isolated houses, which are more likely to prove traps than fortresses.

Avoid such buildings, but fit them with plenty of booby traps for the benefit of the enemy who will take possession.

FIELDCRAFT AND STREETCRAFT

Fieldcraft may be defined as that use of ground which gives freedom of movement to obtain maximum power from the weapons at hand. Note the two points: (*a*) freedom of movement, (*b*) effective use of weapons. The ground is used not only to get cover from view and fire, but also to get into effective positions.

In choosing cover from view the Home Guardsman avoids skylines, for example, looking over walls and hedgerows which have only the sky as a background, unless the top of the cover is a broken line. In this case the head is moved very slowly into position and the sharp outline of the steel helmet camouflaged to suit the detail of the covering around the point of observation. During the war of 1914-18 the Germans showed great cunning in the construction of trenches for this purpose. The parapets were made untidy by throwing all sorts of objects and debris out of the trench so that sentries could look over the top without attracting attention.

front of an exposed tree, but keeping a little to one side in the shade of its branches; taking care to cover face and hands which always show up plainly; when looking from behind cover getting down to ground level, preferably on the right side so that he is in the firing position (Fig. 1). Avoiding roads which are always easily ranged by the enemy's fire, he will also keep away from isolated or

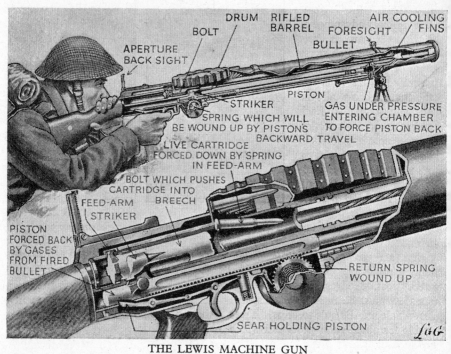

APERTURE BACK SIGHT — BOLT — DRUM — RIFLED BARREL — FORESIGHT — BULLET — AIR COOLING FINS

STRIKER — PISTON — GAS UNDER PRESSURE ENTERING CHAMBER TO FORCE PISTON BACK

SPRING WHICH WILL BE WOUND UP BY PISTON'S BACKWARD TRAVEL

LIVE CARTRIDGE FORCED DOWN BY SPRING IN FEED-ARM

BOLT WHICH PUSHES CARTRIDGE INTO BREECH — FEED-ARM — STRIKER

PISTON FORCED BACK BY GASES FROM FIRED BULLET

RETURN SPRING WOUND UP

SEAR HOLDING PISTON

THE LEWIS MACHINE GUN

Fig. 3. *This ·303 light automatic gun is air cooled and gas operated. With its mounting it weighs 30 lb.; the magazine holds 47 rounds. Lewis guns are mounted in pairs for A.A. work*

Scouts will advance cautiously, looking back more often than forward to allow the route to be checked, and to prevent surprise from outflanking enemy attacks.

Track discipline calls for much practice, returning by alternative routes to avoid an ambush and avoiding the wearing of tracks which show up plainly to air observation. The Home Guardsman is trained to make use of shadow and background, for example, never standing in

predominant features such as single trees. The scope of fieldcraft is inexhaustible and only constant training on the defence area will give the necessary efficiency.

Streetcraft requires the same perfect knowledge of the locality as does fieldcraft, and in towns it is useful to know the position and run of sewers to be used as communications if the road is under fire.

Tanks are unlikely to join in street fighting because of the loss of their power of movement, and the excellent scope for attack from the upper windows of buildings. In Madrid the Germans and Italians learnt a bitter lesson. Where streets were completely barricaded the tanks halted while the leading vehicles attempted to break down the obstacles with gunfire. In this helpless position they were attacked from doorways with showers of bombs and from first-floor windows with blazing petrol-soaked blankets which set fire to the rubber tyres of the bogie wheels.

TOWN DEFENCE

The strongest houses will be chosen for defence posts, walls and small buildings in the line of fire demolished and the debris levelled so that it does not afford cover for an enemy. A heap of brick rubble is not the best cover because of the danger of flying chips when a bullet strikes the pile, and of ricochetting bullets. Gaps between houses must be wired and blocked. If these gaps are out of view of the defenders, tins or booby traps are hung to give warning of any attack. Cellars suitable for storage and gas proofing must not be near water mains or sewers which could flood the room.

All glass should be removed from the windows of several houses around the fire position. If only one house is so treated it will attract attention. Lace curtains at the windows give good cover from view and do not obstruct observation of the street. Fish netting will serve the same purpose. Defenders should stand well back in the shadows of the room, never holding a rifle with the barrel projecting through the window as this will disclose the position; keep the muzzle just level with the frame is the rule, also when firing from a loophole.

Guerrilla training is carried out in case any area is captured by the enemy. Working in parties of from two to six men, equipped with knives, revolvers, grenades, explosives, and iron rations, the guerrillas aim to wreak as much destruction as possible. Absolute secrecy is necessary to avoid accidental betrayal. Only the men in the unit know the plans, each being fully informed so that he will not take individual action to upset the scheme. Enemy communications and small detached units are their special charge. They must be crack shots, quick witted and good at improvisation. A wide repertoire of schemes is essential as it is dangerous to play a trick twice at the same spot. For instance, grenades may be used by lobbing them from ditches or dropping them from overhanging trees.

The surprise factor must be carried to the point of mystery. A guerrilla will not burn petrol stores and so attract attention. Surface tanks might be drained and buried tanks treated with vinegar, say about a pint to 100 gallons. Water will be poured into motor tanks, as puncturing them would arouse suspicions. If there is time, a sparking plug may be removed, a nut dropped into the cylinder and the sparking plug replaced.

The guerrilla must use materials at hand. A stationary train, for example, can be fixed by putting grit and dust from the track into as many axle boxes as possible.

RIFLES AND GUNS

Rifles are the main infantry weapon, and fortunately practice with these does not call for much firing on the range. By using the aiming disc a high standard of proficiency is reached, after which a few rounds fired at a target is sufficient to give experience of actual shooting.

Sporting guns can be very effective if the cartridges are treated in this way: Remove the top disc and take out the pellets. Pour in melted candlegrease and replace the shot. Top up with more grease as the first charge cools, so that the solid block is flush with the end of the case. Nick the case with a sharp knife round the cartridge, level with the wad.

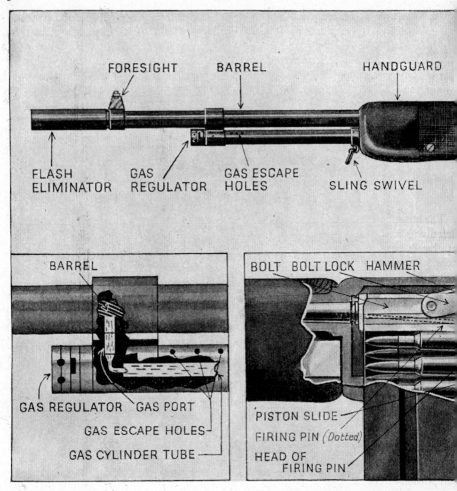

THE .300 BROWNING AUTOMATIC

Fig. 4. *Weighing about 16 lb., this automatic rifle is gas operated. Single rounds or continuous "bursts" may be fired by altering a lever. The magazine holds twenty rounds. The*

without cutting through the side. This bullet will kill at 100 yards, but it must not be used in a choked barrel.

Grenades and bombs are designed for a variety of purposes. As they are very short-range weapons the thrower needs cover and a low position to avoid the explosion. The "Tommy Gun," particularly good for "all in" fighting, is also a Home Guard issue. Bursts of fire from this gun are devastating, but care is

required to counteract its tendency to rise to the right in rapid fire. The correct aim is at the waist of the enemy.

A hunting knife with a blade between nine and twelve inches long is excellent against sentries and outposts. Attack is always made from behind, covering the enemy's mouth with the left hand while thrusting the knife upwards between the hip and bottom rib. Knives may be improvised from any good steel and a plain

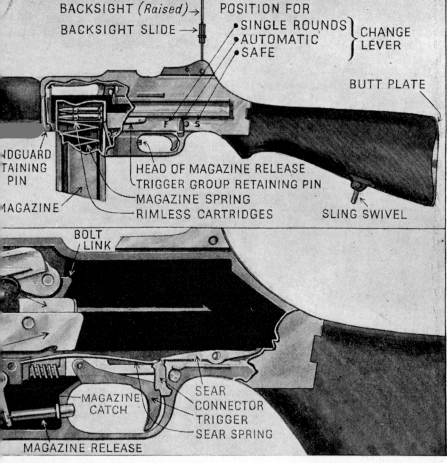

BACKSIGHT (Raised)→
BACKSIGHT SLIDE →

POSITION FOR
• SINGLE ROUNDS
• AUTOMATIC
• SAFE
} CHANGE LEVER

BUTT PLATE

NDGUARD
TAINING
PIN

MAGAZINE

HEAD OF MAGAZINE RELEASE
TRIGGER GROUP RETAINING PIN
MAGAZINE SPRING
RIMLESS CARTRIDGES

SLING SWIVEL

BOLT
LINK

MAGAZINE
CATCH

SEAR
CONNECTOR
TRIGGER
SEAR SPRING

MAGAZINE RELEASE

RIFLE USED BY THE HOME GUARD

gas regulator controls the escape of the gases. Too little pressure causes faulty ejection; too great pressure gives a severe recoil. Stoppages occur if the regulator is not properly adjusted

handle made from two pieces of half-round wood riveted to the blade. When striking, the knife should be held with the thumb along the blade, as shown in Fig. 2, to get good directional control.

Automatic guns of Lewis (Fig. 3) and Browning (Figs. 4 and 5) types give concentrated fire power. They are the foundation of strong post and platoon actions and anti-aircraft work. Single shot firing, except in emergency, conceals the presence of an automatic. Bursts are best fired when the enemy is at close range.

Anti-tank work forms a large part of Home Guard duties. Tanks will probably be supported by infantry in motor lorries, and these must be attacked first in open country; the tanks are allowed through and the supporting troops then broken up. Road blocks sited where no alternative route is available, as in a deep cutting, are not used as impregnable barriers. Their purpose is to slow down the tanks so that attack is more certain. Bombing pits at the roadside protect the troops and are sited in good cover well forward of the block. All-round defence is necessary. The tactics for anti-tank action include the destruction of motor cycle scouts in front of the armoured column before they can warn the tanks, withholding fire until the column slows down, then attacking the rear vehicles first. This action bottles up the front of the column and gives advantage to the defence. Bombing parties concentrate on the tracks of the tanks to dislodge them from the sprockets while Molotoff cocktails or incendiary bombs are used against the rubber tyres of the bogie wheels. When a tank is stationary the safest place for an attacker is close to it, as the main armament has such a limited vertical travel. If there are loopholes in the armour to permit the use of small arms by the crew, shots may be fired into the tank. A single bullet has been

THE .300 WATER-COOLED

Fig. 5. *This automatic gun is an effective weapon. The gun is mounted on a tripod. Elevating and traversing mechanisms are incorporated in the tripod mounting. The normal rate of fire is*

known to kill an entire crew by ricochetting off the walls. A heavy link chain or iron bar pushed between the sprocket and track has frequently disabled the vehicle by dislodging the track.

The most formidable weapons now in use are various flame throwers. They need no special equipment and can be sited wherever a tank is able to travel.

Drivers' visors are fitted with bulletproof glass. This becomes opaque when hit. Spares are carried, but when all are used up the open slot allows a crack shot to kill the driver. Anti-tank units play on these vulnerable points. In the Spanish Civil War it was noted that if fire was concentrated on one point of the armour, flakes broke away inside and wounded the crew. The anti-tank guns now issued are ideal for the purpose.

At night, tank columns camp in laagers protected by their supporting infantry, and Home Guard units will keep them on the alert to deny the crews rest.

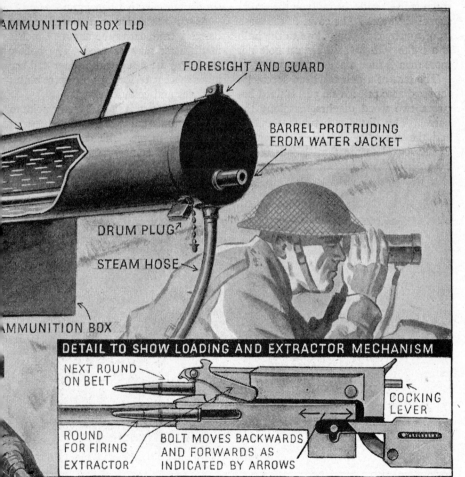

AMMUNITION BOX LID

FORESIGHT AND GUARD

BARREL PROTRUDING FROM WATER JACKET

DRUM PLUG

STEAM HOSE

AMMUNITION BOX

DETAIL TO SHOW LOADING AND EXTRACTOR MECHANISM

NEXT ROUND ON BELT

COCKING LEVER

ROUND FOR FIRING

EXTRACTOR

BOLT MOVES BACKWARDS AND FORWARDS AS INDICATED BY ARROWS

BROWNING HEAVY MACHINE GUN

125 rounds per minute. The weight of the gun, empty, is 30 lb.; the water jacket holds 7½ pints. An ammunition belt holds 250 rounds and the maximum effective range is about 2,500 yards

During any night actions, dispersed sections of a unit need good inter-communication. Wireless telegraphy is not in general use for the Home Guard and the normal morse lamp is apt to disclose a defence position owing to the width of the beam, even when shielded. A simple lamp may be improvised from the details shown in Fig. 6.

This is a "box section" gun of proportions similar to a Tommy gun. Just forward of the stock, an ordinary pocket torch is fixed with the bulb on the centre line of the barrel. The cover of the torch is, of course, removed. Close to the bulb is a baffle with a small central hole not more than $\frac{3}{16}$ inch diameter.

The lens of a pair of cheap spectacles (approximate price is 1s. 3d.) is fixed between two wood diaphragms along the barrel. The distance between the lens and the centre of the lamp element is exactly equal to the focal length of the lens. This dimension in inches is usually quoted as a number on a small label stuck to the lens. Choose lenses with a focal length between 10 inches and 18 inches. Another diaphragm is fitted at the muzzle end to stiffen the barrel and to support the fore sight. The hole in this should be about $\frac{3}{4}$ inch diameter. If this diaphragm is inset a short distance from the end of the barrel, different coloured screens may be pressed into the recess for identification between various sections using this simple but effective signal gun.

As an alternative to the box section barrel a cardboard tube about $1\frac{1}{2}$ inches in diameter may be used. The hollow stock may be fitted with a door and the inner space used for carrying spare bulbs, batteries and coloured screens.

In use the gun is sighted on the point to be communicated with, and the messages flashed in morse. The dispersal of the beam will be so narrow that interception

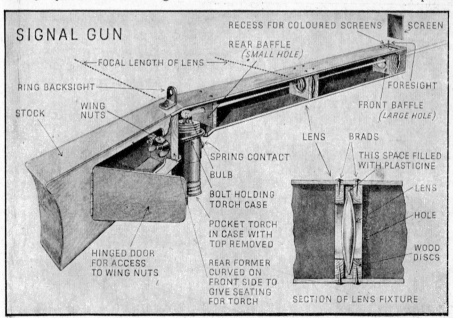

SIGNAL GUN

RECESS FOR COLOURED SCREENS   SCREEN

REAR BAFFLE (SMALL HOLE)

FOCAL LENGTH OF LENS

RING BACKSIGHT

FORESIGHT

STOCK

WING NUTS

FRONT BAFFLE (LARGE HOLE)

SPRING CONTACT

BULB

BOLT HOLDING TORCH CASE

POCKET TORCH IN CASE WITH TOP REMOVED

HINGED DOOR FOR ACCESS TO WING NUTS

REAR FORMER CURVED ON FRONT SIDE TO GIVE SEATING FOR TORCH

LENS   BRADS

THIS SPACE FILLED WITH PLASTICINE

LENS

HOLE

WOOD DISCS

SECTION OF LENS FIXTURE

AN INGENIOUS BOX SECTION SIGNAL GUN

Fig. 6. *Wireless telegraphy is not in general use among guerrilla units, and morse lamps are liable to give away a position. This lamp is specially designed to overcome this difficulty*

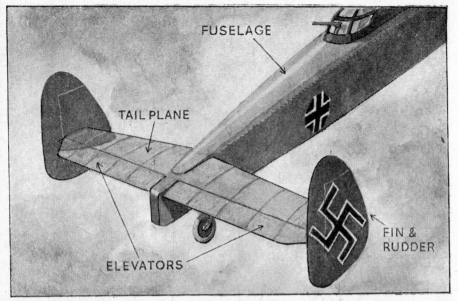

FUSELAGE

TAIL PLANE

FIN &
RUDDER

ELEVATORS

THE TAIL PLANE AND ELEVATORS OF AN AEROPLANE

Fig. 7. *The simplest and quickest way to prevent an aeroplane on the ground being put to immediate use is to destroy the fragile elevator with a sharp blow from the butt of a rifle*

by the enemy is extremely unlikely. The gun may be sighted along a fixed line during the day, ready for use at night.

Aircraft take a leading part in reconnaissance, bombing, and carrying troops and supplies. Firing on the first two unless they are definitely attacking only discloses a defence position. However, when, for instance, a dive bomber is steering for a target, the troops there will put up heavy rifle or machine gun fire, strictly controlled to give a dense barrage ahead of the machine's flight path. If the troops are in weapon pits or behind low cover there is little danger from bombs.

Where an enemy machine has landed for any reason, the simplest and quickest way to prevent its immediate use is to destroy the elevator. This is a fragile structure. It is shown in Fig. 7, and may be smashed easily with the butt of a rifle.

Parachute landings are beaten if the large containers carrying supplies and arms are destroyed. By keeping them away from the containers with sustained fire, the groups can be rapidly rounded up.

The only *defence works* the Home Guard will probably need are weapon pits and crawl trenches with an occasional deep shelter for stores and headquarters. Camouflage is carried out as the work progresses, not left to the end.

In soft earth the sides of pits have to be revetted; in fact, it is always advisable to carry this out to ensure permanence. Typical methods are shown in Fig. 8. Where the depth of soil is too shallow for the dimensions given, the sides are built up by breastworks. The extra soil is taken from borrow pits in front of the fire pits. These are made irregular in shape and filled with water, tangled coils of barbed wire being thrown in as an additional obstacle to attackers.

Dummy pits made as decoys are not dug full depth. Brushwood is laid in the bottom to accentuate shadows for the purpose of misleading air observers.

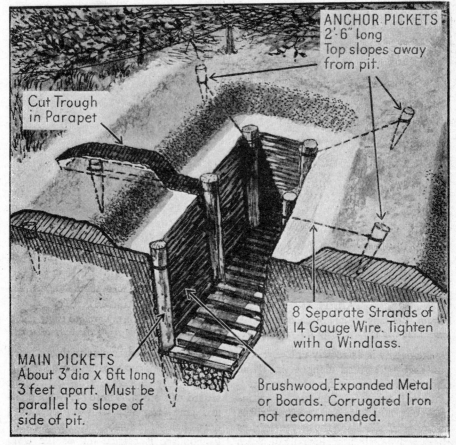

CUT TROUGH in Parapet

ANCHOR PICKETS 2'·6" long Top slopes away from pit.

8 Separate Strands of 14 Gauge Wire. Tighten with a Windlass.

MAIN PICKETS About 3" dia x 6ft long 3 feet apart. Must be parallel to slope of side of pit.

Brushwood, Expanded Metal or Boards. Corrugated Iron not recommended.

THE REVETTED SIDES OF A WEAPON PIT

Fig. 8. *In soft soil the sides of weapon pits have to be revetted as above. If the soil is too shallow for these dimensions, the sides are built up. Pits should be camouflaged and wired*

All defence works need protective wiring about 40 yards away. This is too far for enemy bomb throwing, yet within hearing to prevent wire cutting at night or in fog. Wiring is arranged to lead the enemy into pockets which are under fire from the defence position.

For street fighting the Home Guard will choose houses with the thickest walls. When cellars are used, emergency exits are made. First floors are shored up against mortar fire or bombing. Alternative fire posts are built in various rooms and quick access to these gained by cut-

ting holes in the party walls. Floors and joists in undefended rooms will be torn up to give timber for barricades and for ladders in case the stairs are destroyed. Wardrobes and chests of drawers will be used as protection around fire posts, filled with stones or gravel to make them as bullet proof as possible.

Few loopholes are cut as these weaken the walls. When a ground floor room is fortified a complete blockhouse will be built inside, with two of its walls reinforcing those of the room and with a strong roof in case the house is perhaps shelled.

Doors and windows not required for defence will be barricaded with timber from the undefended rooms. For these, boards are fixed inside and outside the openings and the space filled with rubble.

Ample stores of water for drinking, and fire precautions and sanitary arrangements exclusive of those in the house are required.

For windows suitable as bombing posts, a trap as shown in Fig. 9 prevents grenades being thrown back.

Most Home Guards action will be at close quarters and the handiest weapon for this is the *bomb* or *grenade*. These may be easily improvised.

The art of *booby trapping* is absorbing in its scope for improvisation. These traps are used to give warning of enemy approach, to supplement the strength of obstacles or as purely lethal weapons.

Any standard bomb or grenade which has a split pin safety device may be converted into a booby trap. The bomb must be firmly located, the safety pin tied to a trip cord and drawn almost to its full extent. When the trip cord is disturbed the bomb will be fired.

Home Guard training and discipline need special consideration. Difficulties there must be, when two important jobs have to be done at the same time. The claims of daily work and of training call for sacrifices, willingly accepted. H.G.s know defeat to mean the end of everything, while victory means—Freedom.

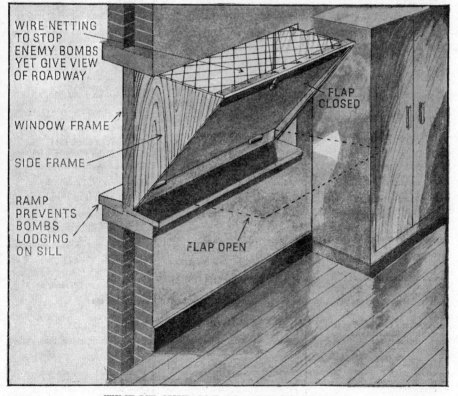

WINDOW SUITABLE AS A BOMBING POST

Fig. 9. *In street fighting, the ability to drop bombs on the enemy and not be open to counter bombing is important. The netting on the window gives protection and a view of the road*

S.642. Made and Printed in Great Britain by Odhams (Watford) Ltd., Watford.